Never Leave Your Wingman

Dionne and Graham Warner's Story of Hope

by Deana J. Driver

DriverWorks
Ink

Library and Archives Canada Cataloguing in Publication

Driver, Deana, 1956-
Never leave your wingman : Dionne and Graham Warner's story of hope /
Deana J. Driver.

ISBN 978-0-9810394-6-6

1. Warner, Dionne--Health. 2. Cancer--Patients--Canada--Biography.
3. Warner, Graham. I. Title.

RC265.6.W37A3 2011   362.196'9940092   C2011-903397-6

The story on these pages is a recollection of the events in the lives of Dionne and Graham Warner. Attempts have been made to accurately record and depict these stories based on the memories of those involved.

Editing and book design – Al and Deana Driver
Front cover and author photos – Deana Driver
Back cover and inside photos – courtesy of Dionne and Graham Warner
DVD produced by Stephen Folnovic

Thank you to our panel of proofreaders – Dionne and Graham Warner,
Barb Robinson, Dani Driver and Lisa Driver.

Printed and bound in Canada by Friesens.

DriverWorks Ink
110 McCarthy Blvd. N., Regina, Saskatchewan, Canada S4R 6A4
www.driverworks.ca   (306) 545-5293

Dedication

I dedicate this book to my loving and supportive husband Graham, who continues to show me every day what true love really is. You are the wind beneath my wings, babe.

I look forward to creating more beautiful memories with you, my love.

– Your 'D'

Believe

Believe in yourself, the beautiful person you are
Every challenge life has put before you
Has been met with fierce determination and grace
That only you possess.
Believe in yourself, look deep in your soul
For that never-ending courage still within.

Believe in love, as the saying goes, love can move
mountains,
The power of positive thought from those around you
Is a power second to none.
Believe in love, like the rays of a tropical sun
Let the love shine on you, warm you
And fill you with peace and strength.

Believe in angels, you have taught me this so well,
They're around you, beside you every step of the way
Endlessly, tirelessly, unconditionally.
Believe in angels, let them wrap their wings around you,
Comfort you and carry you through this difficult time.

I believe in you.

– by Karen Drysdale, for Dionne
  December 2009

CONTENTS

Prologue

The waiting room of the Allan Blair Cancer Clinic in Regina, Saskatchewan is quiet on this sunny August day. It's almost noon and a handful of people are sitting in comfortable chairs, wondering what their doctor will tell them or what their latest test results will show.

Is the tumour still there?

Has it grown?

How am I going to tell my family?

How long do I have?

Suddenly, there is a commotion around the corner in front of the admissions desk. A song is playing very loudly – a country song – and into view comes a strikingly beautiful woman in a cowboy outfit, riding on a man's back, shouting "Woo Hoo! Yee Ha!" at the top of her lungs.

She's swinging a lasso and yelling, "Save A Horse, Ride A Cowboy!"

What the heck is going on? This is a cancer clinic. The patients who come here are very ill. They seldom smile and they NEVER cheer.

Obviously, no one told that to Dionne Warner.

Dionne – Growing Up

'I don't care how stupid I look or what people may say.
*I just enjoy the laughter." - **Dionne***

Dionne Warner has been fighting battles for most of her life. Growing up in Mississauga, Ontario, Canada in the 1970s did not always make for happy memories. Although there were many moments of fun and celebration, her private, day-to-day life with her parents and two younger brothers was often a roller coaster ride of jubilant highs and excruciatingly painful lows.

Those behind-closed-doors experiences helped shape Dionne as a person and provided her with markers by which to set her course in life. Through these struggles, she became stronger, smarter and more independent as she grew.

Dionne was born on October 7, 1965 to parents of Jamaican ancestry in Toronto, Canada's most recognized city, set along the shores of Lake Ontario. She was smaller than average at six pounds, seven ounces and would keep a slight frame throughout her life. Her parents, Rupert and Pam Walford, named their daughter after the Ontario-born Dionne quintuplets, who in 1934 were the first quintuplets born in the world.

Rupert and Pam met in Kingston, Jamaica in 1961 and moved to Canada in 1964. Dionne came into the world the following year. Her brothers' births were two and four years later. Rupert was an auto mechanic and Pam was employed at different office jobs as well as being a stay-at-home mom during various times of Dionne's childhood. Dionne was in Grade 1 when the family moved to Mississauga, which was then a southwestern suburb of Toronto.

Young Dionne was a 'girlie girl' who loved to dress up and participate in stereotypically female activities. She loved music and from age six on, was involved in tap, jazz and ballet classes. At age eight, she loved to draw, write poetry and collect poetry.

Dionne was also a 'mama's girl' who clung to her mother for everything and was doted on in return. While her brothers were involved in hockey, soccer, baseball and other sports, Dionne developed a love of fashion at an early age. "Every Saturday, after the boys played hockey, we went to the mall and I got a new outfit. So I've grown up that way," Dionne explains. "I was never the sports girl. I played soccer for two years when I was 12 but I never felt confident enough in doing that. I was the only girl in our family, so those trips to the mall with my mother spoiling me were my treats."

Dionne's father remembers his daughter as being quiet and reserved as a child. "She made friends easily and loved to have her little girlfriends come over to set up doll houses and play with Barbies."

Sylvia Kavanagh was eight when she met Dionne. The two have been friends ever since. "D was my first friend in my new world order. We had moved to a completely new community. My mom told me a girl my age was across the street, and that was that." Kavanagh adds, "It was the '70s and striped socks and Adidas were all the rage. I remember spending a lot of time on our bikes, whether it was to go get milk and Popsicles from Mac's Milk or riding down the street singing the song *Car Wash* by Rose Royce as loud as we could while clapping our hands to the beat. I remember watching *Roots* in her family room, her giving me sugar cane for the first time, and learning to play Mille Bourne on green shag carpet with her family."

Kavanaugh adds that Dionne has always laughed loudly and often. "She speaks her mind, she's generous and curious. She's more private than people would think, she can keep a secret and when she's made up her mind, good luck changing it."

Dionne's cousin David Ballantine recalls her as a pre-teenager being "probably one of the most spirited family members. She loved to laugh, joke and have a good time. I don't remember her ever being particularly shy around the cousins. Once she got comfortable and you got to know her, she always had that excitable big personality."

Ballantine's late father and Dionne's mother were siblings. Most of the family events were the typical loud, Jamaican-style gatherings with everybody in the house having a lot of fun and being boisterous, says Ballantine, whose family lived in Guelph, Ontario about an hour west of Dionne's home. "We got together at least once a year at Thanksgiving or Christmas or to have a barbecue in the summer, in between whatever else would pop up. We always had pets. While we boys loved playing with the dogs, Dionne had a fear of dogs and most animals."

David's older brother Peter is the same age as Dionne. He also remembers her as being an independent child of strong character, "so much so that I looked at her as older. There were no other girls in our family; only her. She didn't play with us boys when we used to get together. We'd be there with the guys jumping off a roof and causing trouble and she'd be hanging out with the parents. She'd always be there looking all dolled up. She always looked attractive, even when she was young."

Dionne was quiet around her boy cousins as a young child but now "when she's in her element, when she is challenged, when she is inspired by a situation, then she's not quiet. But she's not loudmouthed by any stretch. Some people will speak without a reason to speak. Dionne will not."

Rupert says his daughter was helpful around the house as a child and a fairly good student, considering there were issues with her being the first black student in her school. "I was aware there was a problem with kids at school, but whatever racism we experienced when we went out as a family was very subtle and we sort of treated that as the norm," he says.

Today, Mississauga's population is split almost evenly between Caucasians and non-Caucasians. This was far from the case in the 1970s. The Walfords were the first black family to move into the area, recalls Dionne. "When I was about 11 years old, being the only black family in the neighbourhood, I remember girls chasing me at school and calling me nigger this and nigger that. I'd run into the bathroom and hide on top of the toilet seat. I shed a lot of tears."

Tattling to the teachers didn't do much good. Teachers had no control over students after they left school property.

"They also called me 'Potscrubber' because my hair was that kind of curly frizzy hair. I remember asking my dad one time if he was sure I was his because I was so different from my two brothers. They have kinky Afro hair whereas I didn't have that. My brothers are also darker skinned. Somewhere along the line, I lost that darker complexion. I am a lot lighter now."

In Jamaica, Dionne's father is known as a 'yellow man' because he has freckles, she says. "It's a nickname. He's got the fair skin, not the black black. It was kind of that yellow-man look. There's German in the background of my family. They say I get my fair skin from a great great grandmother of mine."

By the time Dionne was in Grade 8, attitudes had evolved somewhat and a few of her earlier tormentors had become her friends. Still, some prejudice persisted and Dionne lived with taunting about her ancestry for years. "When I was an adult, I was at a community fair one day and a gentleman came up to me and apologized. He said he felt really bad for all that he had done and said back when we were in grade school. I accepted his apology."

To the outside world in the mid-1970s, Dionne's family seemed like a typical collection of father, mother and children who were involved in all the right activities and were enjoying their weekends and holidays with relatives and friends. Behind closed doors, however, the scene was much different.

"You have the family act. When people come into your home, you look like that happy family. And then when the door closes, reality comes back."

Dionne's mother suffered badly from depression. As the years went on, her illness deepened into bipolar disorder and relationships collapsed.

"As a child, I watched my mother trying to commit suicide eight times," says Dionne matter-of-factly. "She didn't really want to do it but she set up the scene. I was probably about 10 years old the first time that I noticed something wasn't right. My mother wasn't at home and everybody was wondering where she was. She'd just disappeared."

Dionne's mother, who didn't drive, had somehow made it as far as London, Ontario, about 150 kilometres away from Mississauga, and then she called for help.

"Other times, there were notes. There were boxes packed. She would disappear. One time, she set my youngest brother up to find her in time. He was able to go spend the night at a friend's house but he was told he had to be back by a certain time the next day. You take pills, but they can pump your stomach as long as someone gets to you in time."

Dionne's parents were sleeping in separate bedrooms off and on by the time she was 11. Dionne snuck into her mother's room one day to see if she could find out anything about what was happening. Under her mother's pillow, she found a suicide note that blamed her father for a multitude of problems. "I tucked the note back under the pillow because I couldn't take it out of the room. I wanted to show my dad, but I couldn't let Mom catch me with it. I remember saying to my dad one time, 'Why hasn't she succeeded? She's tried to do it seven or eight times. If she really wanted to die, she would have done it by now.' Obviously, all she wanted was the attention. My father had to put her in the psychiatric ward one time and she was livid. 'But you keep trying to kill yourself; what else are we going to do? If you took your medication, there wouldn't be an issue.' My mother was mad at everybody. She was in denial of the problem."

The Walford family was living in turmoil. They attended family counselling sessions, but it did not help. While Dionne's mother had initially wanted them to see a counsellor, Dionne discovered that her mother did not actually want the counsellor to hear the truth about their situation at home.

"I told the counsellor I was tired of my parents fighting and I didn't think they should be together. I remember coming home and getting the whooping of my life from my mother for opening my mouth. 'Why are we going then if I can't say the truth and how I feel?' " Dionne asked her mother at the time. There was no reasonable answer.

Shortly after that, Dionne made some life-changing decisions. "I decided I would never be like her. I would be stronger. From that point on, I knew I should not be afraid to speak my mind."

Did Dionne ever worry that she herself would suffer the same sort of depression? "I made sure I didn't get there," she says.

The pre-teen Dionne tried to intervene often to protect her younger siblings from the friction in the household. If someone was going to get a spanking, she would try to take it for them. She tried to protect them as much as possible. "I was the older one and I felt sad they had to go through this. I felt that someone had to slip in and just protect and try to save them from as much of it as possible. To do that, you have to grow a tougher skin."

In February 1981, when Dionne was 15, her father announced that he was moving out of the family home into an apartment nearby and that any of the children who wanted to come with him were welcome to do so. Dionne said that she would go live with her father while the boys stayed with their mom. "I was the only child who could legally make a decision as to who I wanted to live with; my brothers were too young. I believed each parent should have somebody with them."

It was the last thing Rupert expected. "The boys also said they wanted to come with me. After some conversation trying to convince Dionne to stay, to no avail, the boys were left to live with their mom."

Dionne's relationship with her mother became a seesaw of acceptance and rejection from that point on. The boys were told not to acknowledge Dionne or her father if they saw them at school or anywhere else. "If they saw us in the mall, they were to walk past us. My mother wouldn't look at me. This was her punishment."

Dionne remembers a discussion with her father where he told her that he had stayed in the marriage so long because of the children. She responded, "that's probably the biggest mistake you ever made, Dad, because having us live through all of that was probably harder."

Dionne tested her independence more after she moved in with her father. He gave her space to do as she pleased within guidelines and, most of the time, they enjoyed living with each other. While Rupert continued to pay the bills for the entire family, Dionne had a part-time job at a pancake house so she would have spending money. Rupert says his daughter became very independent and outspoken "and almost wanted to control her dad's life. She was not really outspoken until she was in her mid-teenage years. I think this trait must have been from my dad, who was just as strong willed," he muses.

"If he could have had his choice, he would have preferred his boys," Dionne laughed. "Looking after a teenage girl was ... well, we had our times. My dad has always known I speak my mind. He may not like it all the time, but I tell it like it is."

Over the following years, there were times when Dionne was welcomed back into her mother's arms after she'd had a disagreement with her father. "There's that kind of thing when children bounce back and forth from house to house, depending on who is treating them better. Children are not stupid. We figured out what we could get away with and what we could do. And when you have an argument with Dad, if Mom would talk to you, then you went back there for a bit. There was a time when I was maybe 16 or 17, I was getting along good with Mom. Then it just broke again. It always had to do with my dad somehow. She never wanted me to talk about my father, which I found very hard to do. My father always wondered how Mom was doing. It just didn't work out between the two of them. I will always believe it was this disease that she wasn't willing to accept which destroyed that marriage."

The stress of her parents' separation and ensuing divorce soon became too much for Dionne to bear. "I couldn't handle school and the family problems so I left school after Grade 10 and worked for a year, stringing pearls at a downtown jewellery shop that my friend's father owned. My dad was very clear. He told me, 'If you're going to quit school, you're going to pay me rent.' " Dionne then set her own clear terms – if she was going to pay rent, then he could not ask her what time she was coming home at night or if she was coming home.

Wanting desperately to be the opposite of her mother, Dionne couldn't wait to get her driver's licence, which would give her more freedom. "My mother depended on my dad to drive her everywhere until finally when they got divorced, she had to figure life out on her own. I didn't want to have to depend on anybody for anything. I wanted to do my own thing, be able to move around wherever I wanted to. At age 16, Dad taught me to drive."

The following year, Dionne went back to school, but not in Mississauga. A girlfriend attended school in downtown Toronto, so Dionne enrolled in the same school and began getting up at 5 a.m. to make the two-hour journey downtown by subway and bus. "I didn't want to go back to the same school where everybody knew our family business. I needed to focus on my schooling. It was like starting fresh. It was the best thing I did."

She completed Grade 12 downtown as well. At age 17, Dionne worked at three different jobs – at the pancake house, in the men's wear department at a Woolco store and at a condo sales office. She was determined to make her own way in the world.

When Dionne was 18, she talked with Judith Kobin, whose sister Margaret was dating Dionne's father at the time. Kobin was working at Freightliner of Canada Ltd., a leading manufacturer of medium, heavy-duty diesel trucks and specialized chassis in North America, with dealers across Canada and the United States. Kobin suggested that Dionne apply for a job at Freightliner. So Dionne filled out an application and was hired in 1983 to work on the reception desk of Freightliner Trucks' corporate office in Mississauga. Within a short time, Dionne's father co-signed for her to buy a new vehicle of her own with her now full-time pay cheque.

Dionne would work with Freightliner, in the reception area and then the service department, for the next 22 years.

Dionne happily embraced her 20s and had grown into an extraordinarily beautiful young woman with an exuberant, infectious laugh. She had decided she would not get married until she was 30 and she was determined to live every day with an enthusiasm that few others could manage.

"I decided to enjoy life to the fullest with no regrets. A lot of that came from when I watched my parents staying together and faking it in this horrible marriage. I realized I didn't want to live that way. Never. I started thinking about what I would not take, what I would take, what I would embrace, what was and was not important, how far I was willing to stretch, when 'no' means 'no,' and when enough is enough."

She'd greet co-workers with a cheery 'Good morning!' and if no greeting was returned, she'd ask what was wrong or, if there was a continued reluctance to respond, Dionne would inquire why it was so difficult to simply wish others a good day. Her outgoing personality and forthrightness sometimes irritated people, but those people were in the minority.

"Dionne's dad has a dry sense of humour and, as a child, she had a sense of humour," said Kobin, who had known Dionne for three years before convincing her to apply at Freightliner. "From the get-go, Dionne had a mind of her own. She was high-strung, high-spirited, happy all the time. She had such good energy and a great personality. She got along with everybody at work, was always such a positive person and I just loved her energy."

Kim (Kimmie) Robulack-Mendes was applying for a job at Freightliner of Canada in Mississauga in the early 1990s when she met Dionne. "I was quite nervous as I entered the building and there was a beautiful girl sitting behind the reception desk. She had big hair and a big attitude, and I knew that if I got the job, we would be friends! I got the job and the friend!"

Robulack-Mendes is two years younger than Dionne. She worked in the marketing department on the second floor while Dionne worked on the first floor. "Dionne had been working at Freightliner awhile and had her network of friends and she was very much the leader in that network," says Robulack-Mendes. "She was the first one who asked me out for lunch and took me under her wing. She's like the popular kid at school who would take the new person in and say, 'Come sit with me.' There was a group of five of us who would do lunch and it was usually Burger King because Dionne loved Burger King. We became like a family."

Dionne is the type of person where "what you see is what you get," adds Robulack-Mendes. "She would never back down from a superior at work if she believed in something. She would stand up for herself or any of her colleagues if she felt there was an injustice. She's not afraid of confrontation. While expressing her opinion and beliefs, she would never disrespect anyone, though. Dionne never stepped on toes. She wasn't the one trying to climb the social ladder. She always wanted to improve herself and do a better job."

When Robulack-Mendes first learned that Dionne was the fill-in receptionist and the assistant to the service managers, she was surprised. "I thought she ran the office and the company. She seemed to be in full control of the service managers and the service department. She was so organized and meticulous. She did everything for those service managers.

When it was their wives' birthdays, Dionne was the one reminding them. Plus she took on full responsibility for all social events for the entire office. If it was someone's birthday, Dionne ordered the cake. If someone was getting married or having a baby, Dionne co-ordinated an office collection. Dionne made everyone feel special. She's always just celebrated every day. At work, she dressed up for Halloween. She has always had the greatest attitude."

Dionne laughs when she thinks back to some of the events she organized at Freightliner's corporate office in the 1980s and 1990s. "I enjoy getting people together and having fun. Any way you can get people together and get the right music, pull out a theme or do something like that, I enjoy that so much. I've always been that way. I'm a games person all the way."

The objective of the games was always to have some fun while building camaraderie within the workplace. When participants have to put an object down their top or bring it up through their pant or skirt, "even the shyest person gets pulled into this," she says. "You've got to come out of your shell and get to know the other people." The game of Musical Chairs can be especially amusing when participants are in formal attire at the office Christmas party. "It doesn't matter if you're in an evening gown – when you want that chair, you're going to flip the other woman off!" laughs Dionne.

Another memorable game was a wheelbarrow race in which Dionne, in her mid-20s, was partnered with the man who was her boss at the time. "He was the one walking and I was pushing him. I was in a hurry, man! I wanted to win! We ended up popping his shoulder out. I can't remember if we won, but I remember seeing his face turning colour from the pain."

Her boss did not hold his injury against Dionne after he returned from the hospital. "We were all competitive back then! We had a lot of fun doing all sorts of games!"

Freightliner Trucks also raised funds for charities at the request of Dionne and others. After a hurricane hit Jamaica in 1988, Dionne asked the president of the company if she could start a fundraiser for that cause. "He was the first person to put a donation in and we raised $5,000 which was sent to Jamaica for their relief fund."

Robulack-Mendes recalls a special trip that she and Dionne took in 1994 to a Vancouver trade show. "It was the first time Dionne was able to travel for the company. I was doing the marketing and co-ordinating for this trade show. We convinced the company that she should come and help there, too." One of Freightliner's suppliers decided to get on the good side of the company and he upgraded the rooms for Freightliner staff attending the trade show.

"So Dionne and I walked into this room and we were amazed. It was just a huge suite with two huge king-size beds and couches. The curtains were open and all we could see was Stanley Park. We just started hugging each other and laughing. We were so excited. We had never stayed in anything like this before."

There were robes laying on the bed and a huge basket of goodies was sitting on the coffee table. The women thought they'd hit the jackpot! "Oh my gosh, they gave us this gift!" It was filled with jars of cashews and pistachios. There were cookies and other treats as well, recalls Robulack-Mendes. "This basket had to be two feet by two feet. It was just stuffed. We thought this room is so luxurious ... you know the kind where there are robes on the beds. And we started eating. We're both skinny but Dionne and I could eat. We were just shovelling it in!"

Then Dionne got thirsty and looked in the small fridge for water. That's when she found the menu price list for the food they'd eaten from the beautiful basket. 'Oh my God! Put it back! We don't have the money!'

"We'd spent all our money on clothes," laughs Robulack-Mendes. "We didn't have the frickin' $20 for the cashews! So we were putting the lid back on the cashews and trying to manoeuvre it in the basket to hide that we'd eaten from it. We laughed so hard! It was unbelievable! Both of us are loud. It's a wonder we didn't get kicked out because we were screaming at each other. 'Put it back! Put it back!' "

The women's repacking job must have worked because the hotel never charged for the missing food.

It wasn't all fun and games in the workplace, adds Robulack-Mendes. There were times of stress, often created by some of the other women who worked in this male-dominated office. "Dionne is not only a fun, smart girl. She's also extremely attractive and other women, who were maybe a little bit older, found that intimidating. If she came in wearing a mini skirt, it was an issue. I would love to recall with Dionne how many times she and I were reprimanded because we didn't have nylons on or our skirts were too short. It was always a male boss who reprimanded us – because some female had complained. It was women cattiness."

Both she and Dionne found it easier to work with men than women for that reason and because neither of them were interested in viewing the other women as competition for the few jobs there were for females in that workplace. "For Dionne and I, that was never an issue. We both loved our jobs."

When work was done for the day, the 20-something Dionne was busy with an active social life. She was a bona fide 'party girl' and could almost always be found in the evenings and early mornings at a popular Toronto nightclub or bar, dancing the night away on the floor, the stage or speakers.

"She was the party girl who didn't drink, didn't smoke," says Robulack-Mendes. "All of us were having cocktails – she would drive. I don't really recall her ever having more than two drinks. She would be dancing on the speakers and most of the other girls dancing on the speakers probably had 10 vodka paralyzers. She'd nurse one all night and she loved to talk and dance – with anybody."

Natalie Akoon has known Dionne since they were both 15. "We used to go dancing a lot with two other friends. We took a trip to Montreal once where Dionne got a bit antsy waiting for us to get ready, so she left for the club and told us to meet her there. We kind of joked about it ... the three of us whom she left behind started singing *All By Myself.* It was hilarious to us at the time," says Akoon, who describes her friend Dionne as being "vivacious, fun loving and tenacious. She cannot or will not quit. She can also be stubborn."

Punctuality has always been important to Dionne, but it was especially crucial in those days if one wanted to get through the nightclub line-ups and avoid standing out in the cold. Dionne would phone Natalie ahead of time to tell her what time to be ready for Dionne to pick her up. "Natalie always knew and she was ready, man!" laughs Dionne. "I'd tease her that if she wasn't ready, 'I'll be through the line and you'll be on the outside!' "

Akoon laughs that Dionne always attracted the most attention of all the women in their group. "Most of the time when we entered a club and started to dance, Dionne was the one getting noticed. She never had a problem finding the guys to dance with ... but the guy had better know how to dance!"

Music was Dionne's escape and it was true that those who didn't have the dance moves might get a shorter shift on the dance floor. "Dancing lets your spirit be free," says Dionne.

"The right music makes me feel so good and sometimes takes me to another place. Back in the day, I was the speaker chick. I loved to be on the speaker and dancing and having fun and feeling free. Those were great times, great days."

She would often be out every night of the week at a different club. "You'd never think I had a full-time job," Dionne laughs. "Wednesday night was Richards. Thursday, Friday and Saturday, I still partied. Sunday was for rest until they opened up another bar. I was up until three o'clock in the morning. My body never felt anything. I got up at five and got ready for work.

Dionne's cousin Peter Ballantine recalls turning on the television in the late 1980s to watch the weekly Canadian dance show *The Electric Circus*, and often seeing his cousin on the show. "That wouldn't be a surprise. Basically you just go on there and they film you while you're doing your dance moves.

"When Dionne went to the bars, if there was a stage, she was dancing on the stage. It's part of her make-up – very confident and outgoing. She liked the bar scene. She didn't have a ton of formal boyfriends. She had fun."

His brother David Ballantine fondly recalls joining Dionne and her friends for many of those nights of dancing. "Dionne always knew which bars were the hottest. If we went to Toronto, she always knew the doorman to get you into bars. She loved to go and party and have a good time."

While dancing was important, the proper clothing for the occasion was also essential. Dionne has made some of her girlfriends change their clothes before going out with her if they were wearing anything inappropriate or ill-fitting. "I've told them, 'I am not going out with you looking like that. Go change.' And I've always expected them to tell me the same thing. That's why you're my friend. I have to take the good, the bad, the ugly, so I know. Don't sugar-coat it for me. Tell me the truth.

"We can go out to a club and see a girl and I'll think, 'She must not have any friends to tell her how horrible or how slutty she looks.' We joke about it. I'm the person that if I saw someone and we had the same dress on, I'd just say, 'We have great taste!'

"I'm an honest person. I'm not afraid to say what's on my mind. It will always come from the heart if I'm saying it to somebody I care about. You may not like to hear it but somebody's gotta tell you. I do it because I love you and I care about you. I'm not going to keep my mouth shut if I think something is not right. I want you to hear it from me because nobody else is going to tell you. I will take the consequences. You may not want to talk to me. It may take you months afterwards to realize, 'Wow, she really did care and she meant well.' I'll still be there, but you need to figure this out. There have been friends who have come into my life and for different reasons, I didn't like what was happening and we went our separate ways. There are some friends who have come around and realized I spoke the truth. I am not a person to hide things. I don't think that's right. Live life to the fullest with no regrets. That's very important."

Dionne describes herself as a very spirited person. "I can be stubborn. I'm very strong-willed. Is that the same as stubborn? I'm very passionate and very protective when it comes to my family and my friends. If you hurt them, you hurt me and I'm coming after you!" she says with a laugh.

Natalie Akoon recalls a time when Dionne did some research to make sure Natalie was safe. "While working at an ad agency, I started getting to know the studio manager and we would hang out together. I found out that his wife was murdered and I was not 100% sure he was telling me the truth about his innocence. I told Dionne the complete story and she had detective skills I did not know about. She found out where, when, others involved, newspaper clippings of the murder and the person who was charged. She could have been an amazing detective!"

Dionne has also been known to ask friends' boyfriends or partners whom she feels might become short-term to step away after the first group photo so that she can take a second photo of just the friends or family. "I've said to them, 'You have to step out because if you two break up, it will ruin this picture.' Do you know how hard it is to crop people out of a group photo?" she asks with a giggle.

"I love to laugh. I've always felt laughter heals so much. It's good for you and it makes you feel good inside. I don't care how stupid I look or what people may say. I just enjoy the laughter."

Dionne has always loved to travel. The sand between her toes and saltwater on her skin have always been among her favourite experiences. By her late 20s, she had been to Italy, Barbados, Bermuda, Cuba, Mexico and Canada's East Coast with girlfriends, boyfriends or family members.

On long weekends, she often travelled with her father to visit his mother in New York. 'Gramma Jamma' had her own unique style and sense of humour, often trying to set up her granddaughter at various house parties. Dionne laughingly recalls the day she learned a unique lesson about life's temptations.

"Gramma Jamma would have a little glass of 150-proof white rum by her bed and a smoke. I remember saying to her, Gramma, how come you smoke and how come you drink?' She said, 'Gramma does a lot of bad things.' To teach me about the smoking, she lit one up for me and I choked to death. 'See, now you'll never smoke,' she said; and I never did. I was probably 13. She also said, 'It's okay to like boys. Just don't get pregnant too young 'cause that's not good.'"

When Dionne's grandmother died in February 2005, Dionne felt she had lost a significant source of support and love.

In 1985, Dionne's half-sister Shayna was born in Toronto to Dionne's father Rupert and his second wife. Dionne was 20. In 1987, Rupert decided he had had enough of Canada's cold winters so he sold his business and joined his wife, who had already moved back to Jamaica. When Shayna was 16 years old, she and her mother moved back to Toronto, separating from Dionne's father. Shayna and Dionne remain close despite their 20-year age difference.

After her father left for Jamaica, Dionne moved into an apartment with a boyfriend but that relationship soon went awry and Dionne called Rupert back to Canada to help her retrieve some possessions that her ex-boyfriend had refused to give back to her. "It was the biggest mistake of my life but I learned my lessons along the way. He was very controlling, but these are life lessons. I didn't know then that you should have an apartment under both your names."

Dionne's relationship with her mother and her middle brother remained rocky but her youngest brother lived with her in a basement apartment for awhile, without their mother's knowledge. "We were very close back then. If Mom knew we were living together, my fear was she wouldn't even speak to him and I didn't want to destroy that relationship. It was the best-kept secret."

In her late 20s, things were going well for Dionne. She was working in the clerical staff in the service department at Freightliner Canada and enjoying every minute of it. "I did administration and co-ordinating the training for the dealers all across Canada and their technicians. At one point I looked after the eight to 10 men in the office and I was so happy."

"At the time, our group could have been classified as 'Service Gunslingers,' " says Craig Smith, who later became Dionne's boss at Freightliner Canada. "That is, we rode into town, fixed the dealer's warranty and technical problems, threw our white scarves over our shoulders, and rode off into the sunset."

He recalls watching with awe as Dionne typed Technical Product Reports on an ancient machine called a typewriter. "They looked like a modern-day keyboard attached to a file cabinet, and Dionne could make it sound like a machine gun. To this day, I have never met anyone who could type as fast as Dionne. I always thought she typed like a pissed-off woodpecker – 'Get it over with fast, this is giving me a headache!' "

Smith adds that "Dionne was always dependable, accurate, timely, and never very timid in the office environment." She organized programs like 'Technician of the Year,' which involved a year-long ordeal of technical testing and tracking of numerous results. "If Dionne ever screwed up any of the results, we never knew, and everyone was happy. When I took over control of this program, Dionne had to come along to keep everything straight."

She also went on a couple of the Technician Of The Year award trips with her work colleagues, including a NASCAR event in North Carolina. "I was the only female with 12 or 13 men invited on this trip. Craig was very kind and said, 'You organized it so you should be coming with us,' " recalls Dionne.

She took part in the Richard Petty NASCAR training school, racing a fully functional NASCAR race car by herself for six laps and then she went on to complete an additional three more laps as a passenger with a professional driver at 188 miles per hour at the Charlotte Motor Speedway.

"I was afraid but I was crying tears of joy. Whoa, it was lots of fun! The next year, I got to go on a fishing trip to the Queen Charlotte Islands with the men."

Dionne admits that her years with Freightliner's corporate office were not all rosy. She recalls making waves with her unique approach to performance reviews. "My ex-boss would call me stubborn or just determined. They had a score out of 5 with 5 being the best and we had to score ourselves first. I would circle 5, 5, 5. 'Perfect in everything?' he asked and I said, 'You never complained about anything I did.' Then he would try to say something and I would say, 'To the best of my knowledge, my work was a 5. If you had an issue with me, you should have told me and I could have corrected it instead of waiting for a review.' He got the message.

"I knew I'd worked hard," adds Dionne. "I tried to quit Freightliner three different times for different reasons or different opportunities with more pay. It's fascinating that people always admire you more and respect you more when you're ready to walk out the door. Then they're going to offer you more money or a different position but as long as you sit there and keep doing what you're doing and you don't want to go any further, that's where you'll sit in life. I've never been that type of person. I've always been the person to say, 'Give me more.' "

The May 1995 issue of *Today's Trucking Magazine* ran a Freightliner truck parts advertisement that featured a photo of Dionne wearing a service advisor's uniform. Her co-workers joked that they sold a lot of parts that year because of the beautiful young woman pictured behind the parts counter in that ad.

While things were going so well at Freightliner, Dionne started dating a Mississauga policeman and when he proposed two years later, Dionne said yes. In September 1995, one week before their wedding and three weeks before her 30th birthday, Dionne felt a lump in her right breast.

She mentioned it to some girlfriends. They told her it was probably nothing. They all assumed she was too young for it to be anything serious.

Dionne – The First Two Cancers

*"If I cry and cry and cry every day, I'm not gonna get anywhere." - **Dionne***

By 1995, Dionne had been estranged from her mother and brothers for several years. However, she had become particularly close with one of her mother's sisters and she adopted this aunt as her mother figure.

This made sense given the family dynamics, says Dionne's cousin David Ballantine. "Most of my dad's sisters have tended to struggle with mental health issues. That's certainly a challenge the family has suffered. Dionne replaced her existing family with more of an ideal, or what she perceived as more of an ideal, so she reached out to her favourite aunt and some new brothers."

Relationships on her mother's side of the family had always been tenuous and the children rarely knew who they were allowed to speak to at any given time, says Dionne. "It was off and then it was on. My mom would say, 'You can talk to this person now but you can't talk to this person.' Then two years later, we'd be having a Christmas party and my mom would say, 'Go talk to that person.' It was a roller coaster."

Dionne's Aunt Janet was the exception to the rule. She kept the children in touch with each other against all odds. Thus, Aunt Janet became Dionne's close friend and surrogate mother for many years until eventually that relationship also disintegrated. "I could talk to her about anything and everything. She was the spirit, full of life. I would do anything for her in a heartbeat. No matter how much trouble there was between her brothers and sisters – including all this not talking to one another – we would all come to her house because she loved all of us and made sure we would all get together."

Through the efforts of this aunt, Dionne and her male cousins Yuri Collesso and David and Peter Ballantine became especially close. "Dionne is the sister I always wanted," says Collesso, who is a year younger than Dionne.

Dionne's mother did not come to her wedding – because she wasn't invited. "I wanted my father there. I didn't want the negativity around me and I didn't want to have to worry about what would happen that evening. I knew my father could be civil if my mother was there. With my mother, though, I had no guarantee what would happen. I had to make choices."

So it was to her Aunt Janet that Dionne confided about her breast lump in September 1995.

"When I was getting dressed on my wedding day, I had my aunt feel this lump. I guess because it was my wedding day, she didn't panic."

Instead, Aunt Janet told Dionne to enjoy her two-week honeymoon and to get the lump checked out after she returned. So Dionne went to Jamaica with her new husband and visited her family doctor a couple of weeks later. "He almost killed me with the biopsy he did. Personally, I think he had the wrong-sized needle. I screamed so loud in that room that the people in the waiting room must have all flinched when they heard me. I was never in so much pain … He came back and told me it was nothing to worry about."

When Dionne told her aunt what the doctor had said, Aunt Janet wasn't persuaded. She insisted that Dionne get a second opinion, so Dionne made an appointment to see a surgeon on Friday, November 10, 1995.

"That female surgeon also thought it was nothing, but she did a biopsy and I could see it in her face when she came in to tell me what she'd found. The first thing she said was, 'I shouldn't have told you it was nothing. I'm so sorry. It is something and we need to operate as soon as possible.' "

Dionne had gone to the surgeon's office alone that day, thinking that there was no reason for concern. "I was by myself in her office. The surgeon had a very compassionate way of telling me it was breast cancer without actually using the word cancer."

Although shocked by the surgeon's news, Dionne was thankful that the surgeon had been so caring. She asked if Dionne had come to the clinic alone. When she found out the answer, she further asked Dionne if there was anyone she would like to phone.

"I said, 'I'd like to call my aunt but she lives in Guelph and it's long distance.' The doctor handed me the phone and said, 'You call anywhere in the world you want to, my dear.' "

Dionne had just turned 30 years old and she had only been married for a couple of months. For her at that moment, her Aunt Janet was the logical person to call. "I needed a female voice to call and cry with first.

I knew she would say the right things to me. Then on my drive home, I pulled over and called my co-worker friend Alsie Jones and gave her the news. She is a very spiritual lady in my life. Although we were both crying, her caring and compassion helped me get home safe and sound. My landlady was upstairs awaiting the news. She knew I was going for the appointment. She heard me come in and she came downstairs, and she and I cried and cried. Then I called my husband and let him know, and he came home from work right away."

The news of the possible breast cancer was quite a blow to Dionne's husband. "He was five years younger than me and, of course, we were newlyweds. Then the next phone call was to my father in Jamaica, who was just devastated by the news. The hardest part was calling my father and telling him I had breast cancer, then hearing him cry. It was so painful because he was far away ... especially after we had just spent time together. We were in Jamaica on our honeymoon. I looked fine. I felt fine. I felt fabulous.

"I never contacted my mother. We were so distant by then and if I could only have one parent in my life, I chose my dad. I couldn't be involved with all of that struggle and her negativity and look after myself as well. Choices had to be made."

Dionne then stopped in at her workplace to let her boss and girlfriends know about the diagnosis. "I remember her coming into the office and saying she had to tell us something," says Robulack-Mendes. "I can still see it in my mind. To this day, it's kind of slow motion. I was 28. I didn't know anybody who had cancer at that stage. We were all crying and she was consoling us. She said, 'Okay, don't worry. We've scheduled a lumpectomy and it's all going to be taken care of ... no problem.' She was young, invincible. We didn't really understand what breast cancer was and we didn't know about chemotherapy either."

The surgeon worked quickly to arrange treatment for Dionne. Diagnosed on a Friday, Dionne had all her bloodwork and other tests done on the following Monday. On Tuesday, November 14, 1995 at Credit Valley Hospital in Mississauga, Dionne had a lumpectomy to remove the tumour. "Everything moved really, really fast to try to get as much of this cancer as possible."

Dionne found out after the lumpectomy that it was a Stage II-III breast cancer. Breast cancer is diagnosed in Stages 0 to IV based on three factors: the size of tumour or presence of cancer cells, whether it has affected the lymph nodes, and metastasis (spread of the tumour). A Stage II-III diagnosis means there is an invasive tumour and/or cancer cells in the breast and/or lymph nodes. Stage IV is the highest designation for when the cancer has spread to other organs of the body – usually the lungs, liver, bone or brain.[1]

The days after the lumpectomy were surreal and strange for Dionne. She was still confused and overwhelmed by the diagnosis and the immediate removal of the tumour.

"I cried my heart out at first. It was the first diagnosis I'd gotten with cancer. I asked, 'Why me?' for awhile and then I thought, 'Why not me? I've gotta suck this up. I've gotta fight back now. Stop the crying and start to fight and hang on. If I cry and cry and cry every day, I'm not going to get anywhere.' Friends would come visit me and they'd start to cry and I'd say, 'No more tears; I'm taking the high road.' "

It was easier some days than others.

Shortly after her diagnosis, Aunt Janet said to her, 'Didn't you see the fear on my face on your wedding day?' It turned out that Aunt Janet had been diagnosed with breast cancer shortly before Dionne's wedding and was scheduled to have her own lumpectomy while Dionne was away on her honeymoon. "She figured I would never have left if I had known, and she went in by herself." This news caused Dionne's heart to ache even more, but Aunt Janet, Dionne's hero, recovered well from her surgery and few people knew about her operation at that time.

Dionne's treatment plan called for the lumpectomy and then one chemotherapy treatment every two weeks for six months at Credit Valley Hospital in Mississauga. She also went to Princess Margaret Hospital in downtown Toronto every day in that first month to have a radiation treatment as well, on top of chemotherapy.

She began chemotherapy on January 2, 1996 and is forever thankful for the advice she received on that first day in the clinic. "When I walked in for my first treatment of chemo, there was Mrs. MacDonald, a nurse who was the mother of Julie, one of the girls I went to school with in Grade 6. Mrs. MacDonald recognized me and was totally surprised. The one thing she said to me was, 'Do not read everything or you'll drive yourself crazy. Just take it one day at a time.' That's what I've always done. That was so important and I'm glad she was the one I saw first when I walked into that chemo room."

Dionne's dark wavy hair hung down past her shoulders at that point, and the effect of chemotherapy on her hair was difficult to accept. "That was the most horrific thing. For many women, their hair is everything. You never realize how your hair is so important until you lose it. I was the girl born with the curly hair that I couldn't stand and I wanted to be that

[1] www.info.cancer.ca; www.about.com; www.breastcancer.org

white girl with the straight hair. I spent two hours straightening my black curly hair one time because I hated it. And now here I was losing my long, beautiful hair."

Dionne hated watching it fall out and she cringed when she woke in the morning and saw black hair all over her pillow. "It was just devastating. I remember going down into the basement in my house one day, sitting there and crying. I was pulling it off of me in strands during the day and it was on my face. I couldn't dust myself off enough and I didn't want to wear white because it showed up. I was just in denial and hoping that maybe not all of it was going to fall out. I had it trimmed but it was all uneven and by my third chemo treatment, that was enough. I knew I had to have chemo for six months, so I went to a hair salon and had it shaved off after about one and a half months. I felt naked without my hair and I shed many tears over it."

The loss of hair wasn't the only stumbling block in her treatment plan. On the way down to Princess Margaret Hospital after her first chemo treatment to discuss radiation treatments, Dionne noticed that her face didn't feel quite right. "I was starting to lisp. I was trying to fight it. I wasn't saying anything to my husband and we were walking through the mall to the car. Then I said, "Something's not right." They had given us an emergency number to call, so we called the hospital and they told us I was having an allergic reaction to one of the chemo drugs. My jaw was starting to lock up and they told him to get me to an emergency hospital. We weren't far from a hospital. One shot of a needle and I was okay, but it was very painful and very scary because I didn't know what was happening."

Throughout her chemotherapy, Dionne did not have to face the treatments alone. "Family and friends were just amazing during that time frame. I always had somebody coming with me. My husband was a police officer, so it was hard for him to get the time to sit with me. Either two or three friends would sit with me as I was going through treatment. I was surrounded by so many people all the time. They helped to give me that strength. They believed in me that I could beat this, so how could I not believe in myself? I then told myself, 'Get through these treatments. There is an end to this. Just get through these six months of chemo and the one month of radiation. My hair will grow back. I'm going to be okay.'"

On one of her father's trips to visit, she asked him to come in and sit through one of her chemo treatments. "He wasn't keen on being there, but he made it through. The nurses said to him, 'See you did it! It wasn't so bad.' He would tell you, 'My daughter doesn't take 'no' for an answer very well.' I'm okay with that. It was important for me to have my dad there."

At one point, Dionne wondered what would happen if for some reason no one was able to come to her treatment with her. She wanted to feel strong and confident enough to go through a chemo treatment by herself and she wanted to be able to say that she could do it, "so I told everybody a little white lie one day that I already had family and friends coming to stay with me. It ended up that two girlfriends showed up anyway. They said they didn't care who else was coming, they were coming anyway." Once they realized that Dionne had lied to them, they scolded her. "I really tried to pull it off on my own and they caught me. I was in trouble then," she laughs. "I was busted!"

Kimmie Robulack-Mendes recalls that all of Dionne's Freightliner colleagues could not initially believe that she had been diagnosed with cancer. "Cancer happened to 'old' people. Dionne was too young," they thought. "There must have been a mistake." But it was not a mistake and as Dionne went through her treatments, she benefited as much from the strength of her friends, family and work colleagues as they sometimes did from her. "I remember her being so brave, so young, and in love with the person we all thought was the man of her dreams," says Robulack-Mendes of Dionne's battle with breast cancer. "But cancer was an unknown to us all. It was scary. Dionne seemed to take care of all of her friends while she was fighting. That's who she is ... brave face, bold face. She can do anything. And she did! She beat it!"

In February 1996, Dionne began radiation treatments at Princess Margaret Hospital in downtown Toronto. It took considerably longer for her to get downtown by subway than it did for the 10-minute treatments in the radiation room. Still, it was an important part of her treatment protocol and she never complained as she went through the procedures designed to keep her cancer at bay.

If nothing else, Dionne's breast cancer was an important lesson for her 30-year-old girlfriends. "A lot of my young girlfriends realized you have to check yourself because at that age, it's still possible. It happened to me."

One of the blessings in her life at that time was the excellent employee benefits program of Freightliner of Canada. Dionne was able to take one year off work and receive 100% of her pay during that period. "I was very lucky with the program they had. I didn't have to stress about money. If I had been off for more than a year, it would have gone down to 70%. That was one thing I didn't have to worry about and that was an important part of my survival, knowing I would be okay financially."

She also received moral support from her co-workers. "Everybody at work from the president down was so supportive. All they kept saying was, 'Do not worry about it. You will have a job here.' The only thing they didn't tell me was that I might not have the same job when I came back. Unfortunately, the different job I was placed in did not make me very happy."

Seven months after going back to work, Dionne was celebrating the night away as the matron of honour at a girlfriend's wedding. She was her typical self, dancing up a storm, feeling great, laughing, giggling and regularly shouting 'Woo Hoo!' from her spot on the dance floor.

The next day, on June 30, 1997 Dionne was sitting on her living room sofa and talking on the telephone with a girlfriend who lived in Brampton, Ontario, half an hour away. All of a sudden, the right side of Dionne's body began to shake. She told her friend, "Something's wrong. Something's wrong," and when she wasn't able to explain what was happening other than by muttering a confused, "I don't know," her girlfriend told her to hang up the phone so she could call 9-1-1 to get help for Dionne.

Dionne hung up her phone and then wondered what would happen if her friend wasn't able to convince anyone to send help. By now, she was feeling excruciating pain on her entire right side and her right arm was cranked back in a painful uncontrollable twist.

"I rolled onto the floor and dragged myself on my left side to the front door. I managed to unclick the latch and prop the door open a little bit and I lay there and prayed that somebody would come by and see me. I was able to call for help a couple times. Some neighbours were walking their dog and they heard me. He was a firefighter and he asked me what was wrong. I had no clue. I had never experienced anything like this before. He knew I was having a seizure."

The ambulance and fire truck arrived within a few minutes, and Dionne still finds it strange that the first thing the attendants asked for before providing her with any assistance was her Ontario Health Insurance Plan card. Her firefighter neighbour insisted that the attendants forget about the OHIP card and get Dionne to the hospital. Now!

And that was where Dionne woke up awhile later to see the face of her distraught husband. "He was there and then he disappeared for a little bit. He came back and I could see he had been crying. I said, 'What's wrong? What's wrong?' and he told me I had brain cancer. It just blew my mind and I thought to myself, "Thank God it happened today and not the day of my girlfriend's wedding. That would have been awful for her."

It took a week before the doctors decided to do a craniotomy to try to remove Dionne's brain tumour. The procedure was arranged for July 11, 1997 at Toronto Western Hospital in downtown Toronto. After the surgery, she was scheduled to have five radiation treatments.

Until then, Dionne could only stay in her hospital room and wait.

She spent the first day in distress, worrying about a girlfriend whom she was supposed to drive to the hospital for her own cancer surgery the day before. "I was supposed to pick her up at the airport and then take her to the hospital so they could admit her. The night before, I had the seizure and I was diagnosed with brain cancer. All I could think about was who is going to get her? She was depending on me and now I'm sick. It was an awful, awful feeling that I wasn't there for my friend. When I finally got to see her, it was tears, tears and more tears. She was okay but she had to get to the hospital for her surgery on her own."

Dionne herself was rarely alone during her brain cancer battle. Her father had flown in from Jamaica and he, Aunt Janet and one of Dionne's girlfriends were taking turns at Dionne's bedside, along with Dionne's husband when he was not at work.

Upon waking one morning shortly before her surgery, Dionne was shocked to see her own mother sitting there watching her. "I actually closed my eyes again because I thought I was having a horrible nightmare and I looked back again and there she was." Dionne was not speaking to her mother or her brothers at that point in her life, and she was surprised and annoyed that her mother had come to the hospital. "Somebody, and to this day I don't know who, took it upon themselves to tell her I was sick. I was so angry because somebody had set me up and didn't have the guts to be there when she was in the room with me."

Dionne's mother immediately began crying and complaining. She was upset and angry that Dionne had not told her about her brain cancer diagnosis. "It was a very tough situation. I had a brain tumour. I didn't need this upsetting time right now. I was just trying to stay as calm as I could and not to set this thing off any worse than it was. She was carrying on and I had to look at her and say, 'Mother, stop crying. I'm sick with brain cancer and you're in here upsetting me even more. If you have nothing good to say, then leave this room now.'

"Then my brothers came in, too. They had become untrustworthy people. One of them said, 'We're sorry for what we've done. We need to say this just in case you die.' Nobody had said to me at that point, 'You're going to die.' Nobody. All of this was going on with this family of mine."

A few minutes later, Dionne's husband arrived with her father and aunt to find this uncomfortable situation, knowing it was about to get worse. He had never met Dionne's mother. Aunt Janet and Dionne's mother were not speaking to each other then, and Dionne's father was unsure of the reaction he would receive from his ex-wife. Dionne herself was nervous and agitated.

"I was so scared that my aunt was going to leave because my mother was there, but she stood there on the other side of my bed and said, 'I'm not going unless you want me to leave.' I begged her to stay. My dad was good. My mother was still carrying on and my dad finally got her out of the room."

Dionne was nervous about her mother popping in during the remainder of her stay in hospital. "She knew where I was and I couldn't leave the hospital. She could show up at any time whenever she felt like it. Everybody was nervous around her." Dionne's brothers did show up occasionally and at one point, Dionne's girlfriend actually ushered the brothers out of the room because she could see they were upsetting Dionne. "She said, 'You come with me,' and took them out."

Dionne had decided to avoid negativity so she could heal, a mantra she has practised ever since. "I need to be around good healthy people. I need to be around positive people. I need to take care of myself."

One of her happier moments in hospital occurred on the evening before her brain cancer surgery. "I hate hospital food and I said I would really like a treat, because you just don't know what's going to happen. Would this be my last supper? My dad, aunt, husband and a girlfriend were there and I said I would just love a Burger King Whopper and french fries and a strawberry shake for my dinner before I have my surgery. Everybody said, 'I don't think you should have that.' Unbeknownst to me, my dad and aunt disappeared for a little bit. My husband was with me and he had held off the girls from bringing in the dinner tray from the hospital. I was wondering how come they weren't bringing in my dinner yet because I could see that other people were getting served. Then my dad and aunt showed up with a bag from Burger King and I was so happy to have my Whopper and fries!

"If that was my last supper, it was the best supper ever! We all had Burger King that evening. It was wonderful. It's a good thing I had a room of my own. That was very special."

For quite a few years after that, Dionne and her girlfriend went to a Burger King on June 30, the date that she was diagnosed with brain cancer, and ordered a Whopper and fries in celebration. "She always remembered," smiles Dionne.

"Another moment that was cute with the brain cancer was on one of the evenings before the surgery when my girlfriend and my aunt were outside my room. I was wearing these boxer shorts that had hearts on them and a tank top, and I woke up. Usually my room was filled with people whenever I woke up. This time, nobody. I wondered, 'Where is everybody?' I was hooked up to an IV, but I got out of my bed. I pulled my IV pole and walked out of my room and started walking down the hall. There was my aunt and girlfriend and they looked at me and said, 'Where are you going?'

"I said, 'I don't know. There's nobody in my room. You left me.' They just started laughing. They couldn't believe I did that. They said, 'Thank God we were out here! You would have walked forever in your hearts boxer shorts!' It didn't matter to me. I was looking for a friend."

Two Freightliner girlfriends, Kimmie Robulack-Mendes and Jeannie Bachmann, came every day to visit Dionne in hospital. Robulack-Mendes brought Dionne a small ceramic angel statue as a gift one day.

Dionne named the angel Emma and embraced the gift as a source of strength and courage as well as a constant reminder of her friend's love. Neither the gift giver nor the recipient knew then what significance angels would play in Dionne's future.

"Dionne and I would always give each other little gifts," says Robulack-Mendes. "Maybe that's why we were so close. You do those things for girlfriends. You see something and it reminds you of that person and you buy it for them. It's just natural."

Dionne has always been generous with her possessions and her time," adds Robulack-Mendes. "If I was going out or had a function to attend, she would say, 'Do you want to borrow my jewellery?' She'd often buy us lunch. There was often a birthday gift and there was always a birthday card or a little note. I always knew she had my back, that she loved me. I feel blessed that she is my friend. I've always felt she's had more of an impact on my life. I never would have thought I would have had an impact on her life."

On the day before Dionne's brain tumour surgery, Robulack-Mendes and Jeannie Bachmann brought two shades of nail polish to the hospital and painted Dionne's toenails "so I looked good going into surgery. I think it was pink and green," says Dionne, who would later adopt many different colours and costumes in her battle against this disease called cancer.

Without question, Dionne says the surgery to remove her brain tumour was the most horrific that she had ever or would ever experience. This was mostly because she was terrified of the unknown.

"I knew nothing and my whole family had gathered downtown. My cousin David worked downtown. He came to the hospital that morning and said, 'I can't work. I need to be here so Dionne knows I'm here and waiting for her on the other side when she comes out.' My girlfriend Dawn, whom I went to school with in Toronto, came with her husband David. My father was there. My aunt was there."

Dionne and her family and friends went to the hospital chapel and said a beautiful prayer before the surgery. "The nurse was so kind and fell in love with my family. She let them come down even further than most people can go as they're prepping patients for the surgery. My family was waiting in a hallway and the doctor and nurse took me into this room.

"Dr. Mark Bernstein sat me down in this chair. He said to me, 'I have to poke – I think it was four needles – to freeze your head.'

"I said, 'Okay, what are you going to give me before that for freezing?'

"He said, 'This is the tough part. I can't give you anything. So you're going to have to sit there. We're going to hold your head and we're going to do it.'

"When he poked, I screamed loud. Then I said, 'my poor father's out there. He must have heard me scream bloody hell.' The doctor went into another room and came back with what looked like a bird cage."

They placed the contraption over Dionne's head, then asked her to lay down on the hospital gurney so they could strap her to it. "I said, 'You can't move me out in front of my family like this. This is not something they need to see. There was only one way out." Dionne asked the nurse to go out and tell her family what they would see when she came out of the room.

"I was still crying from the hurt when they rolled me out. Everybody was still there and I saw my father drop towards the ground."

Rupert Walford, Dionne's father, cries easily and freely. He remembers being completely devastated when he heard the news of

Dionne's brain cancer, then further distressed when he heard her screaming inside the hospital room. "I started crying. I cry very easily and there is a joke in my family that I am a professional crier. When they wheeled her out, I almost fainted when I saw the contraption they had put on her head and the bleeding where the screws were inserted. I remember being supported by other members as I kept saying, 'Why not me instead of my precious daughter?' "

Dionne's cousin Yuri Collesso walked over to her and asked if he could wipe some of the blood off her head. This was allowed and after a few minutes of talking with Dionne, her family walked down the long hallway beside her gurney on the way to the operating room. "They reached for me and said, 'You're going to be okay and we're going to be here when you come out,' " she recalls.

Dionne went into the operating room without them, still terrified. She thought she would be anaesthetized and was surprised to learn that she had to remain conscious during the surgery so the surgeons could ensure they were not damaging anything while taking out the tumour. "It was the most bizarre surgery because I heard everything they did from the opening of the saw to them going in and talking while they worked. I couldn't feel anything. It was wild. The anaesthetic nurse would say, 'Okay, move your left foot. Now move your toes.' I was just amazed. Wow."

The doctors and nurses told Dionne they had managed, during the five-hour operation, to get what they felt was the entire tumour. When she was moved back up to her room after the surgery, Dionne surprised everyone by asking to speak to the surgeon. "I wanted to tell him 'thank you' because I knew he was going on holiday but he had postponed leaving to do my surgery. They managed to get hold of him. He was the most surprised man that a patient was calling to say, 'Thank you.' This man helped save my life. I wanted to say, 'Thank you.' I needed to say, 'Thank you.' "

Only 24 hours after her surgery, Dionne was getting ready to be released from hospital and sent home to recuperate. Her head was wrapped in gauze and she joked that she looked like a Q-tip. A nurse came into her room and removed the bandage. "I could actually see staples on the left side of my head. The nurse handed my dad this package which had a staple remover, bandages and tape in it. My dad said, 'Oh my God, you don't expect us to take those staples out ourselves, do you?'

"The nurse laughed and said, 'No, no, she has to go to her family doctor to do that.'

"My family already thought sending me home in 24 hours was crazy, but that's how they do it – boom, boom, you're out of here. Then the nurse put this gauze pad on across my staples. When I looked in the mirror, it looked to me like I had caught an Always maxi-wing pad in the wind. I said, 'This sure is pretty, isn't it?' Everybody started laughing. It was nice to hear some laughter through all of this. To see Dad's relief on his face that he didn't have to pull those things out of my head was great, too."

Unfortunately, when Dionne got home that night, she had an allergic reaction to one of the medications they had given her. She was having trouble breathing, so after a 2 a.m. trip to the emergency ward, she was on her way home again to recover.

"Dealing with this brain cancer was very, very hard on me. I became very frail, very shaky. I had to learn walking and movement again. My husband had to help me to stretch and walk. I went to Princess Margaret Hospital every day for five days of radiation as well.

"I would not have recovered so well if it had not been for the people around me. So many people brought so much food to our house. We had trouble closing the fridge. People would come and I would lie on my couch or on my bed and they would say, 'Can I say a prayer for you?' Friends and parents of friends, whom I'd never really met, were coming and cooking and wanted to sit with me. It was … Wow, it was amazing, incredible, never overwhelming because we just felt the love and we knew we weren't alone. This was family and friends. I thought, 'They believe in me. I can get through this. I have to get through this again.' I gathered their strength and took their strength they gave me."

After the brain surgery, Dionne was placed on seizure medication. She decided to take this medication for the rest of her life, even against the wishes of some doctors she met later on. "If I get behind the wheel of my vehicle and I have a seizure and I kill somebody, I would probably go home and kill myself. If I take this medication, I know I'm okay," she says. "My car is my wings. If somebody told me I couldn't drive, that would mean I'm grounded. That would be hard."

Less than two months after the brain surgery, Dionne returned for a follow-up visit. The doctor looked at her brain scan and saw something that concerned him. He thought it was another tumour. Dionne was devastated.

"My husband was with me and I said, 'I can't do another surgery.' I survived the first one and I was so afraid of what could happen coming out of that. I looked at the doctor and I said, 'How long will I have?' It was late August. He said, 'You won't see Christmas.'

"I looked at him and said, 'That's okay. I have enough time to do everything I want to do.' I was really scared because now I knew what the surgery involved and that's a whole different ball game to go through all of that again. I was just feeling better and now, oh no, you're going to put me back in this again."

The doctor left Dionne and her husband alone for a few moments so they could talk about her decision. "First, he said, 'I want you to really think about this.' I thought, 'I can't. I'm petrified. I now know everything that's involved. At least this time, I could speak and I could walk. What happens if I can't the next time?' "

Dionne's husband told her what he was thinking. "He said, 'You've hung on for so long, you can't give up now.' I believed in him, then I started to believe in myself. His strength pulled me out from under."

When the doctor came back in the room, he looked at Dionne and gently said, 'Give me one more chance. Let me go in. I will never ask you this again if this happens. Trust me and give me one more chance.'

Dionne was moved. "It's rare that I had ever seen something like that in a doctor, that compassion. And I said, 'Okay.' So he went in on September 4, 1997 and I ended up having another brain cancer surgery."

Fortunately, what the surgeon had seen was only extra fluid that had built up from the first surgery. Although Dionne still had to go through the whole procedure again, she was thankful that it wasn't another tumour. The second brain surgery extended the scar all the way down the back of her head but recovery was not as difficult this time. Having been through it before, she managed to get her strength back a lot quicker. She still had the same wonderful support as before, including a weekly visit from a nurse who not only helped her with her recovery but also with some housework tasks. Dionne was back to work one year after her initial brain cancer diagnosis.

Again, she had managed to collect her full pay for the time that she was off. Under Freightliner's policy, she had to be working for six months before she could collect full pay for another time off. "I got sick in the seventh month with the brain cancer. If I had been sick with that brain tumour one month before, I would have received 70% of my pay. Once again, not having to worry about money was a very big key to surviving. It's one of those things you do not want to have to worry about, to know that you're still going to be okay and you're going to be able to keep your home and this and that. It was also a good feeling knowing I was holding up my part of the marriage financially."

Dionne often thinks back to the moment that she trusted Dr. Bernstein to go into her brain a second time, and she is overwhelmingly thankful to the medical profession.

"I've been blessed to have the doctors I've had along this journey. I may have had two bad doctors out of all the doctors I've been through. When I was diagnosed with the brain cancer, one female doctor asked to sit and pray with me at my bedside. She was a phenomenal lady.

"When I go back to Toronto to visit and I have enough time, I try to go back and find those doctors and nurses and say, 'Hey, I'm still alive!' Now, they can't wait to see me when I come back. I try to track them down and find them. 'Remember me?'

"There were three male doctors who looked after me with the breast cancer diagnosis. I try to go back to the clinic and see them. I thank them and remember how I used to tease them when I would come in for a breast examination and ask, 'Okay, which one of you won the coin toss to examine me this time?!' "

Peter Ballantine says in an understatement that his cousin is a very strong woman. "If she had been born in an earlier time, she would have been the type of woman who would have sat at the front of the bus. We don't know what defines a person's character – nature or nurture. Ultimately, the mix of nature and nurture in Dionne has resulted in a very unique character that wherever she is put, she's going to make some kind of mark, some kind of statement."

While Dionne had to watch her hair fall out over a matter of weeks during her breast cancer chemotherapy treatments, the same situation did not occur with her brain cancer diagnosis. The hair had to be shaved to make way for the surgery, and it became the least of Dionne's worries. She made the appointment with a salon and grew to accept and learn to dress up her beautifully round, bald head.

In October 1997, a little more than a month after her second brain cancer surgery, Dionne attended a half-day workshop with the *Look Good ... Feel Better* program, an initiative of the cosmetic, toiletry and fragrance association to help cancer patients feel better about themselves. She was also interviewed and photographed for a story in the Summer 1998 issue of *Images Magazine*, which was available through the Shoppers Drug Mart stores. In the photos, the beautiful bald-headed Dionne showed how to wear hats and scarves to feel more comfortable as a woman undergoing cancer therapy. Her husband was beside her in one of the photos and the headline read: *'The Power of love – Dionne faced cancer twice in two years and beat it both times.'*

Dionne spoke about her struggle to feel attractive after her initial hair loss with the breast cancer chemotherapy and how she gave up all attempts to try to improve her appearance. "I felt so unattractive. I thought, 'Why bother with makeup?' So, if I had to go out, I'd just put on a hat and that was about it.'

The support and love from her husband, family and friends helped her to overcome her own insecurities as she healed from her surgeries, she said in the article. "Dionne decided to attend a *Look Good...Feel Better* workshop because she knew she needed something to make herself feel better. And, in October 1997, actually on the day before she was photographed for the *Look Good...Feel Better* magazine, she went," said the magazine article. "At the workshop, I put on one of my hats because my head was cold and everyone commented on it! It's a real thrill that I was asked to be the hat model for the magazine, because I'm a hat collector – I have about 30 different types of hats," she says. "I feel so much better about myself, the workshop really made a difference to me."

Dionne had learned about the *Look Good ... Feel Better* program through the cancer clinic. In the article, she encouraged all other cancer patients to attend a workshop, use the products in the gift box provided for participants and start feeling better about themselves. "Thanks to *Look Good ... Feel Better*, my skin is incredible, I feel great and everyone tells me I look good, too. It's a wonderful program, and I know that anyone who participates will feel the same way!"

Dionne was now concentrating on taking care of herself and getting healthy again. She and her husband had joined a gym together, she was watching what she ate and was taking vitamins. She organized a get-fit program in her office and went on to win a fitness challenge between Freightliner employees. "It makes a difference in your work environment if you can feel better about yourself," she says.

Looking back on how she felt when crying over her first bout of hair loss compared to accepting hair loss as a right of passage in her subsequent cancer treatments, Dionne admits, "I've come a long way. After the brain cancer, I realized that if you take control, you're 10 times better off."

Dionne – Cause and Effect

"I wasn't that same young vibrant person. I was going through hell." - Dionne

During her breast and brain cancer diagnoses and treatments, Dionne wanted answers to many questions, including 'Why did I get cancer?' and 'Could I do anything to make sure I don't get it again?'

The answers she received were specific, yet vague. Hormones and genetics were the largest factors to come into play for Dionne. She also might be a victim of circumstance, being born female instead of male.

"The doctors were pretty adamant that my cancer was hormonal – it's estrogen-related – and it could come back," says Dionne about her breast cancer diagnosis. "Everything I take, including anything I try that's new, they make sure there is no estrogen in it because that can cause my cancer to kick into full gear."

Dionne's family also has a long history of cancer illnesses, with three of her mother's four sisters having had at least one type of cancer. The males in the family have not been affected. At age 30, Dionne was the youngest person in her family to receive a cancer diagnosis.

Most women who develop breast cancer have no risk factors other than simply being a woman and getting older, especially being over 50. Other risk factors for breast cancer include:

- having had breast cancer before;
- a family history of breast cancer (especially in a mother, sister or daughter diagnosed before menopause or if mutations on the BRCA1 or BRCA2 genes are present);
- a family history of ovarian cancer;
- an above-average exposure to the hormone estrogen, which a woman's body naturally produces. Above-average exposure could exist because a woman: has never given birth or gave birth for the first time after age 30, began menstruating at a young age, reached menopause later than average, have taken hormone replacement therapy (estrogen plus

progestin), have dense breast tissue (as shown on a mammogram), have a history of breast biopsies showing certain breast changes such as an increased number of abnormal cells that are not cancerous (atypical hyperplasia), had radiation treatment to the chest area (for example, to treat Hodgkin's lymphoma), especially before age 30.[2]

The Canadian Cancer Society adds that some factors which can only slightly increase one's risk of breast cancer are obesity (especially after menopause), drinking alcohol, and taking birth control pills. 'Some women develop breast cancer without having any of these risk factors. Most women with breast cancer do not have a family history of the disease.'

Other risk factors for breast cancer include being of Ashkenazi Jewish ancestry, taking hormone replacement therapy (HRT) and being of high socio-economic status.[3]

When Dionne was a young adult, she ate junk food all the time, teases Judith Kobin, a self-described health-conscious person who worked with Dionne at Freightliner's corporate office. "I used to take carrot juice over to her and try to get her to drink it. She didn't enjoy it," laughs Kobin.

Dionne defends herself against the charge, saying she was working on the switchboard at the reception desk at the time "and the coffee truck kept coming by. I always had Cheezies and a slice of pizza, so I figured I was getting my four food groups," she laughs. "And I was 18, I never worried about my diet."

Although consumption of junk food could possibly be included in the breast cancer risk factor 'high socio-economic status,' that was not a significant factor for Dionne's cancers.

Research shows that up to 10% of breast cancers are thought to be hereditary, caused by abnormal genes passed from parent to child. Dionne's mother Pam and one of Pam's sisters are the only two of the five female siblings who have not had any type of cancer as far as Dionne knows. Aunt Janet, for example, has had Hodgkin's disease, thyroid cancer and breast cancer. Another sister had lung cancer. No one is sure what type of cancer a third sister had, but they know she did have the disease.

"Dionne's first illness with breast cancer was shocking," says her cousin David Ballantine. "At that point, the family history of cancer was more of an afterthought. All of the aunts had dealt with it when they were younger and it hadn't been discussed. A few years after Dionne's diagnosis, one of our other female cousins got it and the whole history came back and started to be discussed. It was shocking, but not shocking

---

[2] Canadian Cancer Society - www.cancer.ca

[3] Canadian Breast Cancer Foundation - www.info.cancer.ca

once you thought about it in terms of the family history. It was sad that it had come back. That was probably one of the first times you saw the family pull back together, racing down to the hospital in Mississauga to console Dionne and be there to support her."

Ballantine says the family history of cancer in females is "of great concern" to him because he has two daughters. The males who are Dionne's age have escaped the disease so far, but no one knows yet whether their female offspring will get the disease.

Ballantine remembers that Dionne was terrified with her first diagnosis, but she quickly adopted a different perspective. "Dionne is one who loves life and fears death, but she will fight against that until the end. Whatever options are available, she will try and take them on. She is frightened but is trying to be strong and brave, trying to laugh through adversity. It's very real to her, the situation she is in, especially with the family history. She can't help but feel this ominous cloud that 'you're next.'"

In hindsight, Dionne should never have taken birth control pills because of the estrogen in them. Unfortunately, she did not know the potentially deadly long-term effects of the pill on her body until it was too late.

"I was taking birth control when I was 17 or 18 years old, before I got sick with the breast cancer, and I was playing around with it because it was giving me migraines," she says. About twice a month, a migraine would put her out of commission for three or four days. "I'd just want to sit in the dark with a cold cloth on my head. I'd almost be in a stroke-like state. It would numb me. My eyes would get all blurry and then the numbness would come up my arm and I'd think, 'Okay, gotta stop taking this birth control pill because the migraines are getting worse.'"

But she did not stop taking the pills altogether. If one doctor wanted to take her off the pill because of the migraines, she found a different physician who would prescribe a different brand. "I thought I had to take something else because the birth control pill was the only thing I trusted. Popping a pill is easy. I didn't trust condoms. I was young and stupid."

When she was diagnosed with breast cancer, Dionne was officially cut off of birth control pills forever. While her husband was unhappy about having to wear a condom, she prayed she would not get pregnant.

Dionne's oncologists told her that she should not have children because her cancer was so affected by hormones. "My husband wanted his own children. He wasn't into adopting. I had been told it was not a good idea because I could get sick again. I could die. It was a really tough choice for me to not have children but it was something I had to accept. I wanted to live, and the worst thing that could happen was I could be looking after a child when I was sick."

Two cancer diagnoses within two years of marriage and the tensions surrounding not getting pregnant added a huge strain to Dionne's relationship with her husband. Although he was helpful and caring during both her breast and brain cancer diagnoses and treatments and his family was supportive as well, Dionne could see it was starting to wear on him.

Dionne believes her husband's age contributed to their difficulties. "A lot of it had to do with him being five years younger than me. We'd just been married not even a month and I was diagnosed with breast cancer. That's one thing to get over. Then I was back to work and seven months later, I was diagnosed with a brain tumour. For him to try to deal with this so young, it was a lot to handle. His job was a stressful job. It felt at times that he was bringing that home. Being a police officer, you have to have a tough skin. When your wife is emotional, she doesn't want to see that tough skin."

After two bouts of cancer in two years, Dionne was no longer the woman he had married. "I wasn't that same young vibrant person. I was going through hell. I couldn't go out and party as much. I didn't feel as energetic. Travelling wasn't so easy then. I couldn't do that. What we did before was not happening any more. It was a big change for him."

After the brain cancer treatments were completed, Dionne's husband tried again to convince her to get pregnant. 'You're fine now, let's have kids,' was his theory. "He dragged me to four different hospitals to try to find a doctor who would tell us it was okay for me to get pregnant. Everybody said it would be risky. I remember my aunt and dad talking to me one evening and saying that if I chose to have kids for him, knowing what these doctors were already saying, and if I got sick again, they would really hate him because he was too pushy about having his own children. It was just too risky."

She and her husband grew further and further apart.

On July 4, 1998 Dionne gave it one last try. "I surprised him with renewing our vows before our three-year anniversary. I just felt like, 'Let's try to celebrate here and bring things back to normal as much as we could. With the breast cancer, the brain cancer, I'm still here. Let's celebrate and try to figure it out.' I tried to keep things on the positive side."

Her husband had been staying out later and later after the end of his shifts and Dionne began to wonder whether he was involved in another relationship. She found a pile of his nightclub clothes in the back of his car one day, ready for when he went out after work. "There was probably some infidelity. One day, I got tired of the worrying. I decided nobody should have to live through this – asking the questions and not getting the answers."

Just before Christmas 1999, Dionne decided enough was enough. "We did our best as much as we could. That wasn't easy. My life changed quite a bit. He didn't really want it to change. He didn't feel it should change."

It was a long, painful break-up that involved many tears. Although separated in mind and body since December, they lived under the same roof until April 2000 when the house was sold. In the process of moving out, words were exchanged that will never be forgotten and can never be taken back.

"Upon me packing up and leaving when it was finally over, he told me that nobody would ever want me because I was damaged goods. That's his famous quote. I was 'damaged goods.' " Although he later apologized for his behaviour and pleaded for Dionne to take him back, it was too late for Dionne.

"I've kind of grown up with this idea – it's weird and I don't know why – this 'three strikes and you're out.' You hurt me once. You hurt me again – twice – and you still don't get it. And then the third time? Enough is enough. I belong with good people, surrounded by love, not people who continue to hurt and hurt and hurt. Life is too short for that. There are so many wonderful people out there. I don't need any more of that in my life. I treat people with 100% of my love and compassion and friendship. When you feel like you are on the end of the stick getting beaten all the time, it's not worth it. You have to move on."

Dionne knew that she would be okay on her own. Aunt Janet left a bad marriage and raised two boys on her own. "I thought if she could do it, how could I not? Probably watching her and how independent she was made me realize that women don't have to rely on men."

A few days before the house was to be occupied by its new owners, Dionne stopped by to make sure it was still in good shape. She and a girlfriend had gone to a movie and Dionne decided to stop by the house on their way home. She was surprised to find two cars in front of the house, including that of her soon-to-be ex-husband. Her friend stayed in the car while Dionne used the key she still had and entered the house, surprising her husband in the process. She noticed two pairs of shoes in the entrance area and watched him as he nervously followed her throughout the house while she checked every room to make sure the house was clean for the new owners moving in the next day.

In the master bedroom, Dionne saw a young woman sitting on the floor on top of a blanket. "She was dressed. They had blankets. There was a boom box playing. I walked up to her and said, 'Hi. I'm the soon to be ex-wife, but you're welcome to him. He's all yours. Good luck.'

"I came out of the house laughing and I got back into the car. My girlfriend said, 'What happened?' I told her, 'You should have come in.' She said, 'I wanted to come in but someone had to be on the outside in case you never came back!' It was so funny. I felt so much strength. He was not my problem any more. I could sleep through my nights.

"It's stuff like that which has made me stronger. I learned what I would accept if I was to get married again, if I was to look for a man. If I was to be single and on my own, that was okay. I have great friends. I have an awesome family."

They officially divorced in October 2001. "Yahoo!"

In the spring of 2000, one of Dionne's doctors asked her if she wanted to have genetic testing done to see if they could determine anything more about her cancers. She decided to have the tests. Other members of her family were invited to be tested as well. Aunt Janet accepted the offer and had testing done alongside Dionne.

It took several months to get the test results back and the women were told that they could decide whether they wanted to hear their results or not. Dionne chose to hear her results. "That's when I was told I did have the mutated BRCA1 gene. It's the gene that can activate the breast cancer full throttle."

Everyone has BRCA1 (BReast CAncer gene one) and BRCA2 (BReast CAncer gene two) genes, but most of the inherited cases of breast cancer are associated with abnormalities in these genes. 'The function of the BRCA genes is to repair cell damage and keep breast cells growing normally. But when these genes contain abnormalities or mutations that are passed from generation to generation, the genes don't function normally and breast cancer risk increases.'[4]

Aunt Janet, upon hearing Dionne's genetic testing results, decided she did not want to hear what her own tests revealed. "She has a granddaughter and was afraid of knowing that she had passed it down," believes Dionne, who understood her aunt's decision.

Dionne also had moments of sadness as she thought of what she

[4] www.breastcancer.org

could have changed about her life if she had known about her genetic make-up sooner. "Number one, I wouldn't have gone near birth control. The different things I could have done possibly wouldn't even have activated this cancer. Birth control was something that was totally wrong back in the day and here I was taking it 24-7."

Dionne has become a proponent for genetic testing and urges young girls and woman to take whatever steps they can to keep cancer away. She was not given the option of a double mastectomy when she was first diagnosed at 30 years old but in hindsight, it would have been a smart choice. "If people did this genetic testing sooner, it would be so good. Girls, if you find out you have this gene, you will know there are things you can stay away from right away. Christina Applegate, who discovered she had the gene, had a double mastectomy because she saw what her mother went through.

"We told everybody in my family that I have the gene and there have been sisters who passed away with cancer. I'm the only one to this day who has had the results of testing. Nobody else has ever gone to check."

Dionne is pleased that ongoing research and new therapies are helping to reduce the risk of cancer, leading to earlier diagnosis and improving the prognosis and quality of life for cancer patients. She hopes that some of the trials and therapies she has used will some day lead to a further improvement in cancer knowledge so that others do not have to suffer what she has endured.

One of the frustrations she has had in being a cancer patient has been the large amount of information available that is not always consistent between physicians and/or other therapists. For example, the female surgeon who diagnosed Dionne's breast cancer in 1995 told her to stop wearing wire brassieres because they can cause strain on the lymphatic system. Dionne has since heeded that advice and, after much searching, has found comfortable wireless brassieres through Victoria's Secret.

She has wondered, however, why no other oncologist or therapist has ever echoed this caution about wire bras. A recent article in Scientific American notes that this notion of brassieres affecting cancer first came to light in a book published in 1995 (the year in which Dionne was first diagnosed), but it has since been proven to be an 'urban legend' that is not supported by scientific evidence.[5]

Dionne has also since heard conflicting doctors' opinions on the value of nutritional supplements and alternative diet and various therapies as well. The multitude of information can at times be confusing "and it feels like none of it comes together at any point. It's totally frustrating ...

[5] Scientific American - http://www.scientificamerican.com/article.cfm?id=fact-or-fiction-underwire-bras-cause-cancer

everybody has their own opinion. You get dizzy. So we all have to take a little bit of this, a little bit of that. We've gotta put our own story together to make it work and keep doing what we're doing. It will ruffle some feathers, we know that. We have to have no regrets."

Graham – Early Years

*"As a teenager, I would stay in the construction camp by myself
and run the gravel semi truck on weekends, offering to do it without pay
just because I loved trucks so much." - Graham*

Graham Warner was born on August 3, 1962 in Kipling, Saskatchewan, a small town about two hours southeast of Regina that decades later would become well known as the town that traded a house for what started as a red paperclip.

Graham was the second of four children and the first son born to Everett Godfrey, known to all as Goff, and Audrey Warner. Graham's parents named him after Toronto native Ivan Graeme Ferguson, a co-founder of IMAX film technology, who was a cousin of Graham's father, born to Grace Warner and Frank Ferguson.

Although Graham grew up with one older and one younger sister, he would always remain closest to his brother Brent, who is six years younger than Graham.

Goff Warner was a pioneer in Saskatchewan's road building industry with his company Warner Construction. Goff was not only dedicated to his work, but he was a character as well. "My dad became a legend in this province for building roads and highways," says Graham with a smile. "We can go into any town in Saskatchewan today and somebody will know Godfrey Warner very well or mention that they worked for him. His crews hired so many people from each town when they were working nearby. He was a colourful character."

Goff was totally committed to his construction business, was always in a hurry and didn't have much time for other things when he was at work, says Graham. "He was actually digging an outhouse hole with a backhoe for the newly-moved construction camp when my mom phoned him and said she'd gone into labour. He asked if she could drive herself to the Kipling Hospital because he was busy – they had to get this camp put in. She did drive herself but she didn't want to go into the hospital and have all the nurses know what her business was, so she sat in the car in the parking lot for 15 minutes or so, waiting for the shift to change and then went in and had me 15 minutes later. I was born at 4 o'clock in the afternoon."

After Goff and Audrey married, Audrey first taught school while her husband used one old bulldozer to build his business of oilfield site clearing. When Goff moved into building grid roads two years later, Audrey cooked meals for the crews and did the bookkeeping for Warner Construction until their children were born. She then became the main caregiver for the children as Goff was often away building roads all across the province.

The Warner family moved into the city of Regina when Graham was four years old. Graham was an energetic and independent child. When he was about five, he tried to run away from home, but he didn't get far. The Warners lived on a crescent and young Graham wasn't allowed to cross the street, so he went as far as he could down the block and sat on the sidewalk in front of a neighbour's house until it was time for supper. "I could only go that far without crossing the street and I couldn't be late for supper – but in my head, I was making a statement. I don't remember the issue. I actually may have done it a couple of times. It seemed adventurous at the time. I actually put a little bag on the end of a stick because I'd seen that on a cartoon."

Graham and his siblings were always busy throughout their young lives. While attending McNiven School and then Campbell Collegiate, Graham was involved in piano and trumpet lessons, hockey and the Regina Lions Junior Band. "The Lions Band came first before school, family or religion," he says with a laugh.

"I practised piano at 7 o'clock in the morning, went to school, took trumpet lessons at lunch from Lions Band director Bob Mossing at his home, went back to school, came home and either went to baseball or hockey. I would eat supper in the back of our car as I changed into or out of whatever uniform or equipment was required for the next event. I was also in Boy Scouts, Cubs, swimming lessons, whatever. My siblings were just as busy. My mom wore out four cars raising four children. Everybody was involved."

For a number of years, Graham bugled for the Royal Red Arabian horse show that was held in Regina. As a member of the Regina Lions Band from ages 6 to 18, he played in the marching band and went on some trips with the band, including one journey to Hawaii. Graham would come to respect and appreciate band director Bob Mossing for his leadership skills. "I believe the Lions Band was the next closest thing to the army for teaching discipline, morals, hard work and teamwork. It did all that. I had to have short hair in the '70s when the style was long hair. You got called a fag just for having short hair, so you took a lot of pressure."

Graham fell in love with trucks at an early age. He made trucks out of Lego, tried to figure out what was underneath the hood of every vehicle he saw, and couldn't wait to get on the big machines that his father worked with every day.

At age 10, Graham began working for his dad. "My first job was picking rocks out of the bottom of the ditch. I would walk in front of a Cat loader, throwing rocks into the bucket. When I was 11, I started running the heavy equipment like the packer."

On one memorable day about a week before his 11th birthday, Warner Construction's crew was building a road beside the main highway at Milestone, about 40 minutes south of Regina. Young Graham was driving the huge packer when an RCMP car drove up and stopped beside him. "I thought, 'Oh oh, I'm in trouble.' I hadn't turned 11 yet. One of the RCMP officers came right up to the machine and said, 'How old are you, son?' I lied. I said I was 11. I was so scared. I figured, 'I'm going to jail.' The foreman saw what was happening. I think it was lunchtime and he was coming to pick me up, so he went and talked to the cops. Then the cops drove away. I climbed off the machine and the foreman said, 'They just had a bet going between them. One thought you were over 16 and the other one didn't.' It was legal," says Graham with a smile. "I wasn't actually breaking the law."

Warner Construction had its shop in an industrial area near a steel mill on the northern outskirts of Regina. As a pre-teenager during the spring and autumn months, Graham often rode his bicycle from their home in the south end of the city all the way across town to get to the shop. "Even though my dad might not be there, the shop was still open. I would hang out with the mechanics after school. Almost every weekend, I'd work Friday night, Saturday and Sunday at the shop. Usually I would shut it down by 6 o'clock Sunday night and do my homework."

At age 12, Graham was running the world's largest bulldozer. He had taught himself how to operate the machine while it was being repaired in his father's shop over the winter. One day on the job site, the machine's operator failed to show up, so Goff turned to Graham and asked if he thought he could run the bulldozer. The confident young Graham looked at his father and said, "I know I can." Graham operated the machine for two or three years. He then set his sights on others pieces of equipment and pestered his father to let him try driving the earth movers.

"I was on the Cat at age 12. I kept trying to sneak on what's called buggies – the earth movers or scrapers. My mom thought those were too dangerous, so my dad and I had to keep that a secret from her that I was operating these buggies. I was on the buggies quite a bit. I tried to keep a low profile."

Although both of Graham's parents enjoyed the odd joke or two, no one in the family has ever taken humour as seriously as Graham. It was a personality trait that he honed while working with the road construction crews.

During the summer breaks from school, Graham would go out to the jobsites and stay there during the week. "I thought it was pretty cool living out in the construction camp. I missed a lot of the summer band trips. I chose work over the Lions Band."

Young Graham lived in the bunkhouse with the hired men and was thrilled to be getting paid $1 an hour. "Sometimes we were away for two weeks at a time. We'd stay out the whole week and come home for the weekend. We had a cottage at Kenosee Lake and Mom would be there with the other kids. Dad and I would drive to the lake for a day and a half, then go back to the road construction camp."

Graham loved the camaraderie of the men and they in turn treated him like one of the guys. Sometimes Graham was the butt of some jokes. Other times, he just sat back and enjoyed the games.

"There were always little pranks being pulled by the guys. They'd grease the underside of the door handles or steering wheels of the earth-moving machines. Sometimes your machine would be hidden while you were in camp having lunch or dinner and when you were dropped back off to go to work, you would have to go walking to find it hidden behind some clump of trees. Of course, there was always dirty jokes being told, and all this was absorbed like a sponge by a wide-eyed 10-to-17 year old!"

As Graham grew, he adopted this fun-loving behaviour and became well known for his use of humour and his over-and-above efforts to pull pranks.

"He was always a prankster," says Graham's brother Brent. "I remember one time when I was pretty young, my friends and I were playing hide and seek downstairs. Graham stood at the top of the stairs with a light behind him, holding a big butcher knife. He was just scaring us."

Graham learned other lessons at the construction site, including how to eat his meals in record time. The daily routine for Warner Construction workers was to wake at 5 a.m., eat breakfast and be in the back of the pickup truck at 5:45 to be driven out to the job site, "because at 6, you'd be moving dirt until noon. The pickup would come get you and you'd ride back to the camp. You'd get into camp by 12:10 and you'd have to eat your lunch – hamburger steak, mashed potatoes, vegetables, and a piece of pie – and be back in the pickup truck at 12:30. So you learned to just inhale your food. Then you would work until 6 p.m. The pickup truck would come and pick you up again. You'd eat T-bone steak, mashed potatoes, vegetables and then cake. Then we'd be back in the truck by 6:30 and then we'd quit at 9 o'clock at night. I didn't get paid overtime."

Working on road construction was not an easy or clean job. "One time, my mom came out to visit on the job site. She didn't recognize me because I was literally covered in dirt. I remember sometimes you'd bend over to eat your food and it looked like you'd put pepper on the food because the silt would fall off your face."

Some of the roads that Warner Construction built were several hours away from Regina, and Graham's father would travel back and forth to the sites on his own airplane. "He was quite a character flying," says Graham, who has had fond memories and some unnerving experiences with his dad as the pilot.

When they'd fly to visit Goff's parents at their farm near Kennedy, Saskatchewan Goff would first buzz the farmhouse to let his parents know to come pick them up at the nearby airstrip at Carlyle. Graham's eyes mist up with emotion as he recalls how his grandmother always came outside waving a white handkerchief to indicate she'd seen them. Then his grandfather would pick them up at Carlyle and drive them to the farm. "When we'd get to the farmhouse, there would always be warm cookies and milk."

When Graham was about 12, he went with his father to one particular job site. "Lots of times, my dad didn't land on a runway. The grader would have made a landing strip on a side road near the construction site and he'd land there. Sometimes he would land in farmers' fields. It wasn't meant to be disrespectful. He wasn't arrogant. He was just sort of in his own world. It was a field – just land in it. You're not hurting anything."

On this occasion, Goff landed in the field and he and Graham were picked up by one of the crew to go spend the day at the nearby road construction site. At about 4 o'clock, when they were driven back to the field to fly back home, they found a surprise. The farmer had obviously been offended by the airplane landing in his field and he had cultivated all around the airplane, "row after row after row," so it would not be able to leave the scene as easily as it had arrived.

Graham remembers that his father looked a little bit guilty, but it didn't slow Goff down for long. "He said, 'Get in. We'll see if we can get out of here.' We got in and the nose wheel of the airplane went into the first furrow and we couldn't get through. Then I looked and saw the RCMP coming down the road with their lights on, so I was thinking, 'We're going to jail!' To a 12-year-old, when the cops turn the lights on, you're going to jail."

With the plane stuck, Goff turned to Graham and said, 'Get out and push.' So Graham got out of the plane and grabbed the wing strut – the bar that connects the wing to the fuselage – and started pushing.

"Now, we didn't discuss a plan about when I would get in or what happens next. I don't even know what good I did ... So I pushed and the airplane started to move across these furrows. And I was thinking, 'When do I get in?'

"My old man was a big burly guy. He was flying the airplane and he reached over, grabbed me by the back of the belt, and just yarded me in. I went in underneath the instrument panel sort of head first. The airplane was literally smashing over these furrows. I was down underneath the instrument panel, which is like a dashboard, and it was so rough that the radios of the airplane broke out of their spots and they were falling on me and cutting me and we were smashing. And of course when you're taking off in an airplane, it's loud, and I knew the cops were chasing us.

"He got it airborne and I got out from underneath the panel and I was off the floor by then, and I looked down and saw a cop standing beside his car shaking his fist at us ... There was no big hubbub made about it. That was just kind of a typical day flying with my old man."

On another occasion, Goff had a grader level off a section of a ditch so he could use the ditch as a runway. "We were racing down the ditch, and at the end of the runway area was a power line," says Graham. "We were just about airborne and he turned to me and said, 'Should we go over it or under it?' I remember sitting there thinking, 'I'm 13 years old. I don't think I should be making these kinds of decisions.' And we were getting closer, and I didn't think we could make it over the power line, so I said, 'I think we should go under.' So that's what we did. We flew under the power line on takeoff."

For another job at Maymont, Saskatchewan Graham was working on the ground with the crew when the foreman came by and picked him up in the truck to take him to a nearby field, saying, 'I thought you might want to see this. Your old man is bringing some parts.' Graham thought this was all normal and fine until he learned that Goff was not planning on landing the plane to bring in the parts.

"My old man was always in a hurry – time is money in road construction. He had four or five Caterpillar roller bearings. They're probably 40 to 50 pounds each and rather than land and hand these to the guy, he circled over a field and threw them one at a time out the door. They're solid iron so it's not going to hurt them to drop them, but even though it was a summerfallow field, these things bounced four or five feet in the air when they hit the ground. It was pretty cool just to see this airplane circling and these roller bearings flying out of the plane."

Some weeks, Goff flew his plane three or four times and then there were other periods when he did not go up for 10 days at a time. Graham and his mother always fought for the front seat in the airplane because they both got airsick and the front seat was easier on the stomach, says Graham. "Some trips, she'd be in the back seat and some trips, I'd be in the back seat," Graham smiles. During road building season, Goff was away almost all the time.

Despite his airsickness, which continues to this day, Graham learned to love flying. He started working on obtaining his own pilot's licence when he was 15 years old. "When you're 15 and a half, you can actually solo an airplane. I'd either arrange my classes at Campbell Collegiate so I could have the afternoon off or I would skip out of gym class and I'd ride my bicycle to the airport. It was humiliating that I had to ride my bicycle because I wasn't old enough to drive, but I could climb into an airplane and solo fly with a student pilot licence. I always thought that was ironic."

Graham continued working part-time for his father's company throughout high school. "As a teenager, I would stay in the construction camp by myself and run the gravel semi truck on weekends, offering to do it without pay just because I loved trucks so much. I was about 14 and I would have done it for no pay, just so I could drive the big semi." By the time he was 16, Graham had saved $5,000 and bought a brand new Kenworth semi truck. His father co-signed the loan because Graham wasn't legally able to take out a $55,000 loan on his own. Graham hired a driver, because he wasn't old enough to legally drive the truck, and he leased the truck to different freight companies. "Mostly, it was Tri-Line Freightways, and they looked after dispatching the truck. It hauled freight all over North America. On weekends, I'd change the oil on it and wash it."

Brent says Graham was a good big brother. "He was always mechanical. As a mid-teenager, he had motorbikes and trucks and go-karts and stuff like that. He'd include me in his projects. He'd build a go-kart and then I would drive it. Every Sunday night during the summers, I remember my dad and my big brother leaving together to go to work. I was quite sad. After supper, they'd get in the truck and head out to the job site about 500 kilometres away or wherever, all over Saskatchewan. We'd all go out to the site for a few weeks every summer. When I was 10, I finally got to do the same thing. It was, 'Let me come out and work, too!' "

Brent also recalls that as a big brother, Graham could coax him to do just about anything. When Graham was about 17, they both got into a semi to drive it to a job site. "We left the shop and we got about 20 kilometres north of Regina and something happened to the semi trailer – can't remember if the wheels locked up or whatever. He decided that I should hitchhike back to the shop and he would wait in the truck. I was probably 10 or 11 years old. He was my big brother, so I did it."

At age 17, Graham got his pilot's licence and became "a lot different pilot" than his father. Graham was never as daring a pilot as Goff and he took his training further than his father ever had, gaining his instrument rating and night-flying credentials.

By late 1978, Graham had no doubt about what he would do with his life. "I loved trucks and I loved doing what I did, but I missed my dad terribly when I was a kid. He spent most of his life away from his family. I knew I wanted *not* to be in construction because of that. That's when I answered an ad in the *Regina Leader-Post* for a diesel truck franchise."

With his father's backing and using his father's shop as a base, 17-year-old Graham acquired the franchise for Japanese-made Hino trucks. He started selling them to anyone he thought might benefit from the better fuel mileage they provided over gasoline powered trucks. "That was when medium-duty diesel trucks really started to come into play. I would call on prospective customers and introduce myself as being with Regina Hino. They would say, 'What is that, a washing machine?' Some of those customers would eventually buy these three-ton trucks that were mostly sold as grain trucks, fuel trucks and van delivery trucks."

Graham travelled all over southern Saskatchewan to sell his new Hino diesel trucks. "I called on every fuel dealer, lumber store, any business that used a truck in every town." In its first year of business, Regina Hino was awarded the honour of being Top Canadian Hino Dealer Of The Year.

At age 18, Graham bought another semi. He leased it to the Hagan

Mayflower Moving company in Regina and bought a specialized trailer as well for moving furniture. Graham had mapped out the future of his own life by then. He would sell trucks until he was 40 years old and then semi-retire and become a charter pilot.

Things went well with the Hino dealership for the first few years and then another business opportunity presented itself. "In 1981, the manufacturer White Freightliner went broke. It was purchased by the Mercedes Benz company and Mercedes Benz hired the national sales manager from Hino, Jim Alden. The White-Freightliner dealer in Regina decided to retire at the same time as the manufacturer went broke, so that left Regina with no Freightliner dealer. Jim Alden, newly hired by Mercedes Benz, phoned me up one day and said, 'Graham, what do you think about selling Freightliner trucks instead of Hino?' I said, 'Let me think about that for a second, yes!!!' "

Within a few weeks, Graham Warner, again with his father's support, started the Regina franchise for Freightliner trucks. He did it because they were big trucks and he loved big trucks the most.

"Freightliners at the time were only available as big rigs and because they didn't offer a medium-duty truck line to us, we were able to continue selling the Hino medium-duty trucks. Eventually however, we had to let that Hino franchise go when Mercedes Benz offered us their own line of medium-duty trucks. I started selling Freightliners out of an Atco office trailer parked in front of my dad's shop."

The Freightliner dealership, now with a much wider product line to offer, still does what it did then – sells trucks, repairs them, sells parts and provides financing. An entire semi truck pulling a trailer can easily cost more than $200,000 and weigh 140,000 pounds. A medium-duty Freightliner truck could be custom built into a specialized ambulance designed to deliver neo-natal medical teams and their services between major hospitals. "It's such a fun and fascinating business to be in!" says Graham.

In 1982, the Warners erected a new building at 330 - 4th Avenue East in Regina to be shared for only a few years by Warner Construction and Freightliner Truck Sales Regina Ltd. Today, it is the present-day site of the renamed and expanded Warner Industries Group of Companies.

Graham – Working for Fun

"He doesn't stop at the first roadblock. He puts his head down and works through it." -
Graham's brother Brent Warner

In August 1984, Graham married a local Regina girl whom he had met a few years earlier. At age 22, Graham was a strong young man with dark hair and a ready smile. Graham and his wife seemed like the perfect couple.

Two months after his wedding, Graham travelled to Toronto to attend a Quality Service Plus workshop hosted by Freightliner Canada.

It was there that he first laid eyes on Dionne Walford.

"It was a three-day course in Toronto and there were probably 30 people in it," says Graham. "They had the tables set up in a U-shape and Dionne was sitting right across from me on the far side of the room and looking like an exact replica of a young Whitney Houston."

Dionne, a fairly new Freightliner employee at the time, was there with the corporate office's service department. Graham was the youngest dealer in all of Canada by 15 to 20 years and he and Dionne were close in age, so it was inevitable that they would end up talking throughout the three-day course.

"I remember being smitten with her. Absolutely love at first sight," says Graham. "The only other thing I remember about that was there was a coffee break on the third day and the hotel had a little bench set up in a courtyard. Dionne and I went out to sit on that bench and it started raining ever so softly. During our discussion, I said to her, 'I think I've married the wrong person.'

"I didn't know why I was experiencing the connection I had with Dionne and the feeling I had in talking with her. I was happily married. It was a universal connection I felt with Dionne. It felt spiritual. It felt like something bigger than me or her – bigger than both of us."

Graham still recalls having to calm the butterfly feelings in his stomach and being very confused about his emotions. "I was sitting there wondering how could I have feelings for Dionne when I had just married the love of my life? It was a struggle."

Dionne was young, attractive and single at the time and was used to men saying nice things to her. She has no memory of what Graham said that day. "I expect we were just chatting, like one does at these business meetings ... He was a happily married guy. I just thought he was a very nice, decent man, a good man, easy to talk to. I wasn't flirting with him. I'm nice to everybody. If I did respond to his comment, I probably said, 'Ah, you're funny.' "

The workshop ended, with no action taken by either of them, and both Graham and Dionne carried on with their own lives. They connected occasionally through phone and e-mail conversations about Freightliner service topics, and their relationship remained strictly professional.

The workshop proved to be a pivotal moment for Graham's business, though.

When Graham returned from that Quality Service Plus training, he considered how to improve his company's customer service and decided to renovate the front part of the shop to include an open parts counter. "People told me I would lose stock doing that, but why would I deny 97% of our customers better service to protect against the 3% who will steal?" Graham hired an unemployed man he met in a local donut shop to help him build the shop's mezzanine, because "even though he wasn't a skilled carpenter, he had the right attitude." When that mezzanine was completed, the results were more than worthwhile and helped the company reach out to customers in a new way. That newly minted carpenter with no heavy-duty parts experience was also retained and remains employed today as one of Warner's best parts employees.

Graham followed his father's example of hard work and long hours to build his company. He was determined to sell as many trucks as he could to create a foothold for Freightliner in Saskatchewan and security for his new wife.

"I would fly to Vancouver on Friday morning, climb into a new semi that had two more stacked on the back, drive back to Regina over the weekend, then Monday to Thursday I'd run the dealership and sell the trucks. I was the only salesman in those first few years. Then the next Friday, I'd do it again."

Graham and his father were very close in many respects, but when Goff and Graham worked together, "it was a little bit oil and water," says

Graham's brother Brent. "Dad was very methodical. Graham always wanted to take big steps."

Graham often learned lessons in the most difficult ways possible, adds Brent. "Everything came so hard to him. He'd go out to the shop yard to do something with the equipment when he was in his late teens. It was inevitable that something would go wrong. The backhoe rolled over on him one time and he would have been killed if it hadn't landed where the window popped out. Another time, he broke his ankle outside putting up the Freightliner sign and had to drag himself to the shop for help. He would go to haul a piece of equipment and something would go wrong … the truck would break down." What one would think should take four hours would then see Murphy's Law apply and add another eight hours to the task. "If something would make a job more difficult, it would always happen to Graham, but he learned to work through the hard times," says Brent.

"He doesn't give up. He'll get the job done ... he doesn't stop at the first roadblock. He puts his head down and works through it. He gets that from our parents."

Graham has always been a showman and will go out of his way to make a statement, says Brent. "He'd fix up an old Chevy half ton and it had to be a little bit different than everybody else's. It always had a different paint job or he'd lowered the truck. In his business, you can see that today. It's a little different than a regular truck dealership. Their motto is 'fun friendly people' and that's who they are. It's a different vibe than if you go into someone else's truck dealership. He's very meticulous. His vehicle is never dirty and his lawn is never unkempt. He's very detail-oriented."

In 1986, Goff bought another building for his road construction company and Graham's Freightliner Truck Sales business expanded into the entire shop space. Goff still kept regular tabs on Graham and his Freightliner dealership, though, and was involved in hiring Roger Pettigrew, who would later become a key member of Graham's Freightliner Truck Sales team.

The Pettigrew and Warner families lived next door to each other and Roger and Graham shared similar backgrounds. They both were involved in the Lions Band, Roger as a drummer, and both had a knack for motorized vehicles. Their parents were good friends who went on vacations together and their fathers were both hard-working entrepreneurs, with Pettigrew's dad selling industrial woodworking equipment and Bobcat skid steer loaders. Roger worked part-time for his father throughout high school, then in distribution and then for his father again until Pettigrew Sales closed in 1988.

Roger recalls, "My dad saw Goff one day and asked, 'Will you hire him?' Goff said, 'He's got fire in his eyes, we'll take him.' So I joined the company. In May 1988, I was employee #19. I was with the service department for a month working on the trucks, then I went into sales. It was extremely enjoyable. Graham's a good guy and we had a friendship, so that made it a lot easier."

Having known Goff and Graham for most of his life, Pettigrew is quick to compare the two Warner men. "Graham's always had an entrepreneurial spirit, a driven spirit. He is a principled man. That's what his dad was. His dad was very gruff. One of his fingers was the size of two of mine. He was a 'no bullshit' kind of guy. Hard, hard, hard working. Graham knew as a child that it was all about hard work. You work hard, you work honest and everything will work out. Goff always pushed Graham to be the best that he could be and made him work. If Goff expected an employee to work 16 hours, he expected Graham to work 18.

"Graham's mother Audrey always says Graham has his father's drive," adds Pettigrew. "Graham treats everybody with respect. With our staff here, if he won't do it, we won't ask you to do it. Customer service comes first."

Like most entrepreneurs, Graham has been known to throw himself completely into his work, at times leading to the confusion or chagrin of those around him. Glen Mason of St. Albert, Alberta, recalls attending Freightliner's Western Canadian Dealer Meeting at a ski hill near Kelowna, British Columbia in about 1989. "It was Saturday night and we had just finished the big wind-up dinner after a full day of skiing. Graham, Roger and I decided that we would go to the bar downstairs from the restaurant to enjoy some additional adult beverages. To our surprise, we were able to get a great table that was in a slightly raised area right next to the dance floor. Our focus was not on the dancing or the music. We were anxious to continue our conversation from dinner," says Mason.

"Beverages soon arrived and we became engrossed in our discussion. The place was rocking. The dance floor was full and the ambiance was at max. In the middle of all this emerged three attractive young ladies from the throng of people dancing in the bar. I remember that they had to work to get our attention. Only one of us, I forget who, was able to hear what they wanted over the music. These girls had come to ask us to dance. I remember us looking at each other and almost in unison shaking our heads, 'No.' One girl responded loud enough that we all heard it. She said, 'You guys are a bunch of duds!'

"With that, the bond was formed and the 'Dud Brothers' came into being. We toasted ourselves and laughed long and hard that night and on many other occasions over the last 25 years for being the Dud Brothers," laughs Mason.

In 1995, Roger Pettigrew was appointed general manager of Graham's company Freightliner Truck Sales Regina Ltd. "Graham is a great business partner from the perspective that he allows me the autonomy to look after the company's affairs," says Roger. "We go back 41 years. I'd never spend a dollar of his money that I wouldn't spend of mine. He is a very trustworthy man. He's principled."

In 1996, Freightliner Truck Sales Regina Ltd. doubled the size of its shop and added a 75-foot-long service pit. Graham proudly notes that his company has an excellent training program for its employees and is "the only place in southern Saskatchewan that's open seven days a week."

By this time, Graham Warner was a caring father of two who had established a reputation as a hard-working gentleman who prided himself on his sense of humour. He also became known as a generous man who shared his wealth with others, supported his community and was quick to show appreciation to his loyal customers, employees and friends.

A photo in Graham's office proudly displays a group of eight men with a smiling Graham at the centre of the group. It's a memento of the 'Graham and The Dogs Tour' to a NASCAR race in the mid-1990s when business was mixed with the pleasure of a fast-paced road trip.

Pettigrew teases Graham that he is a 'pretty boy' who is 'always about the ladies.' "He's a little socialite. He wants to be the centre of attention, talking to the ladies, but at the same time, he's a stable man committed to his wife."

Graham claims that he's only a ladies' man because the women 'migrate' to him. "Whatever," laughs Pettigrew, who cannot deny that "all eyes were on Pretty Boy" during the Graham and The Dogs Tour.

It is obvious that Graham is comfortable in the presence of large groups of men or women and he has hosted all combinations of the sexes for various trips over the years. In addition to the NASCAR trips, he treated friends, customers and work colleagues to ski trips, boating days and more. In 1998, Graham attended the funeral of a customer "and I realized all his dreams were being buried with him." It made Graham look at his own life more carefully and consider more seriously what he could do to help others achieve their dreams.

In gratitude for more than a decade of fun and learning through the Regina Lions Band, Graham surprised band leader Bob Mossing and his wife Wilma with a vacation invitation. "Bob Mossing really changed my life, and a lot of my best employees are Lions Band graduates," says Graham, who had already helped provide the band with a brand new Freightliner truck but still wanted to do something for Mossing personally.

The band leader had talked often about his lifelong dream of travelling to New Orleans to listen to real Dixieland music. Graham decided to grant him that wish. He videotaped the end of the *Blues Brothers* movie, where Aretha Franklin, James Brown and other blues singers belt out the song *Come On Down To New Orleans*. "Without technical help, I copied just the portion of the video with that song and delivered it to Bob and Wilma. I said, 'I'm just going to leave this with you. Watch it and then phone me and let me know.' At the end of the video, the mother of my children videotaped me inviting Bob and Wilma on an all-expenses-paid trip with us to New Orleans. They watched the video and saw my invitation and were just thrilled, so we took them to New Orleans and just had the best time."

The Mossings and Warners visited a huge all-black Baptist church located in the middle of one of the poorest sections of New Orleans. "There was a warm-up preacher and then the regular preacher," recalls Graham, who will never forget the message of the latter. "He talked about, 'You need to improve your lives and the only way you can do that is to improve your inner customer service.' He was all about self-motivation, self-talk. I really liked it. As a business leader, that's what you have to do with your employees. I thought, 'Oh my God, this is what church is about!' They had people fainting. It was a blast."

Anyone connected to Freightliner Truck Sales has at least one story of a prank that Graham has pulled on a friend, co-worker or associate over the years. "He has always been fun," says Roger Pettigrew. "Some people have an ability to have fun and some people make fun of other people. Graham is one of those guys who likes to have situational humour.

"On Halloween for four or five years, Graham used to wear this scary henchman costume and scare the bejeebers out of a receptionist we had here. One year, he'd be under her desk. The next year, he'd be in the women's washroom wearing that mask and cloak while holding an axe over his head. You'd hear her screaming."

Graham smiles as he recalls dressing up for Halloween and hiding on the nervous receptionist. "She never knew where I would be but she knew I'd be somewhere. I was like that little Chinese guy on the *Pink Panther*. I would hide. It started off that I'd be behind the door. So the next year, she figured she had me because she looked behind the door before she came in but I was underneath the desk with the chair pulled up, and when she pulled the chair out, I was laying there with a real axe and, of course, this scary henchman mask and a black robe. The next year, I hid in the ladies' bathroom. She checked her office – nothing. Her desk – nothing. So she thought, 'He must not be around.' She hung up her coat, walked down the hall, went into the ladies' bathroom and I was behind the door with the axe over my head. That was a good one. There was that delayed reaction. Her mouth was wide open. That's where I actually saw her tonsils, I think!"

"That is what Graham's like," laughs Pettigrew. "If he thinks he can get one over you, he's going to try, try, try. He's a socialite to a point. He is very crafty. Graham is a planner."

At one time, the company's controller Dennis Zohner lived across the street from Graham in White City, a bedroom community 18 kilometres east of Regina. Every morning, Zohner opened his garage door, started his car and then went back into his house for a few minutes before leaving for work. So on one April 1st morning, Graham utilized this time to run over and stick a sign on the back of Zohner's vehicle, then slip back into his own house before he was caught in the act.

Zohner's wife worked for the federal government in downtown Regina at the time, so Zohner had to drive her all the way downtown before coming back to work on the east side of the city. He noticed that everyone on the road during this 25-minute ride into work seemed particularly friendly that day, honking and waving at him like he'd never experienced before. When he got downtown, someone suggested he take a look at the back of his car – where he saw a neon yellow cardboard sign that said: 'Honk if you got some last night.'

One day shortly after Pettigrew joined the company, Graham asked him if he would drive downtown to drop off the bank deposit. The balding Pettigrew said yes, jumped into his truck and headed for a bank in the centre of the city during the busiest time of day. "All the way downtown, people were honking at me. I didn't go check the back of my truck until much later. There was this huge sign there – in fact it was the same size as my tailgate, so I couldn't see it in my mirror. It said: 'Bald Guys Need

Friends, Too. Honk If You Want To Be Mine.'"

Another trick played on Pettigrew was the Warner version of a 'bull in a china shop.' In a popular promotion with the local CKRM radio station called *A Meal In The Field*, Freightliner Truck Sales Regina Ltd. arrives at the field of a farmer during harvest time and provides a complete T-bone steak meal for 21 people. "We do this for all of the winning contestants. They get to talk on the air. It's a wonderful thing," says Pettigrew.

On this day, they were at a dairy farm not too far from Regina and Pettigrew, whom Graham says is the real 'pretty boy' – "he's a city slicker" – became infatuated with the farm's calf operation. "They had some sucking calves there. Roger asked the farmer's wife a question – something about when a cow gives birth to a baby. She looked at him with an amused look of disbelief and then corrected his terminology by clarifying, 'Do you mean when a cow calves?' That was funny!" says Graham. "Then the farmer's wife said to Roger, 'Come over here. Don't be so scared. Put your finger out there.' And gingerly Roger put his finger out and this calf started sucking on it. I think by the end of the night, he almost had his whole arm up there," laughs Graham.

After Pettigrew went home, Graham visited for awhile longer with the farm family and enjoyed a bonfire and a beautiful harvest night. "We all got joking behind Roger's back about how in love he fell with this bull calf, so I asked the farmer if I could come back at 4 or 5 o'clock in the morning and borrow this calf just to put in Roger's office. He was all for it, so that's what I did. I went out the next morning and picked up this calf and I put it in my pickup truck. I carried it in to the dealership cradled in my arms. Karen Drysdale, our receptionist, was already there.

"Karen asked, 'What do you say when your boss comes walking in the door carrying a bull calf?' I then set the calf down in the showroom and I was going to lead it into Roger's office, but it couldn't stand because the showroom floor was so slippery, so I had to pick it back up and carry it into his office. Then I had to go explain to Karen what I was doing and why I was doing it."

That was only the beginning of the gag.

"We made a sign and we hung it around this calf's neck that said, 'Thanks for last night, Roger.' Then we phoned Willy Cole at CKRM Radio and told him what I'd done and arranged for him to phone Roger live on air shortly after Roger came into his office. So, of course, Roger came blasting into his office at 100 miles an hour because that's the way Roger moves, and he said, 'What the hell?' Then, of course, he said, 'Oh, you're so cute. Poor little thing.' There's a picture of that somewhere. Roger's sitting at his desk patting this bull calf. Then Willy Cole called Roger and put him on the air to grill him about how his night went. That was funny," adds Graham.

"It was just because I could pick on him and it was something good to pick on him about. That's why we're called 'fun friendly people' in our company slogan."

Graham's biggest prank to date, though, occurred in December 1997 as an over-the-top payback for an alleged breach of good humour.

As a member of a business association in Regina, Graham and about 100 other top executives meet for lunch on Fridays and share business leads and camaraderie. "We have some very strict rules of conduct. This one Friday, the sergeant at arms fined me $1 for telling a bad joke and I didn't think that was appropriate," says Graham with a sly smile. "The next week, I arranged for a tow truck to tow the sergeant at arms' van from the rear parking lot of the hotel, while we were meeting inside, to the front of the hotel. I wanted to mess with his mind.

"I think it worked pretty well because at the following week's meeting, the sergeant at arms was grilling everyone about it but, because no one else knew about the joke except one of the hotel's owners, Don Urzada, who is a good friend of mine, I'm pretty sure the sergeant started questioning his own memory. However, during that next meeting, I arranged for a tow truck to tow the sergeant at arms' van to the hotel across the street, so now he knew somebody was screwing with it."

Christmas and New Years intervened and the next meeting of the business group occurred three weeks later. It was long enough for sergeant-at-arms Jerry Flegel to have a reprieve from the pranks and for Graham to enlist the aid of other business members to pull off the biggest prank yet. The plan was to move Flegel's van to a platform then hoist the platform past the hotel's glass-windowed two-storey restaurant and up onto its roof. An engineering firm within the group was enlisted and recommended that a plywood platform be built to hold the van's weight. A towing company moved the van onto the platform and a couple of cranes came into the tight quarters of the hotel's parking lot and carefully lifted the van past the glass windows and onto the roof while the meeting continued inside the hotel. Photographs were taken and the local media just happened to arrive to document the transporting of the van to its new rooftop viewpoint. A large sign was attached to the van: 'Jerry Flegel – Have You Found Your Van?'

It was 35 below Celsius with a howling wind, but the show must go on no matter what the weather. Graham's general manager Roger Pettigrew helped direct the task to its successful completion in less than 55 minutes, providing an excellent alibi for Graham as he sat in the lunch meeting.

Graham also arranged for two police officers to assist with the gig. They walked in and interrupted the room near the end of the meeting. When they called out Jerry Flegel's licence plate number and asked for the owner of that vehicle to step outside to talk to them, "Flegel put his head down and said, 'Now what?' " smiled Graham.

"They told him, 'It's against City bylaws to park your van on the roof of the hotel.' He said, 'What did you just say?' So he went with them and so did some of the rest of us. When he stepped out of the hotel, he stepped into a paparazzi of cameras."

Flegel was the good sport that they expected him to be and when asked how his van got up on the roof, he said he suspected that Don Urzada and Graham Warner were to blame. As the cameras rolled, Urzada was interviewed by a reporter and did his best Colin Thatcher impression in responding to allegations that he was involved by saying, 'Deny, deny, deny.' Graham just smiled as he quickly vanished from the crowd, wanting to avoid any unnecessary spotlight on himself.

The next morning, Graham received an inquisitive phone call from a Freightliner colleague in London, Ontario who had seen a clip of the prank on CTV's *National News* the previous night. "We had a lot of fun with that," laughs Graham. "I continued to deny any responsibility for many years."

Flegel did get even in a way. A short while after the event, he and Graham and Urzada were invited onto a local cable television show to see if the truth could be uncovered. Flegel sat on an armchair while Graham and Urzada sat on a couch. Graham maintained that he was only at the hotel to shovel snow. The only illuminating fact that came from Urzada was that it would have cost someone about $3,000 to hire those cranes to lift the vehicle. As the two men continued to avoid answering the interviewer's questions, two stagehands snuck up behind them and pied them each in the face while Flegel looked on and smiled.

So why did Graham go through so much trouble for that and other pranks? "Because I could. It's a lot of fun. It's living life. Roger came to work one day to find a bull in his office and here we are talking about it 10 to 15 years after it happened. To me, that seems like how you should live life. If you can do something that is funny and memorable and lightens up the day, why wouldn't you do it? Otherwise, you just become a cog in the workplace and you retire at 65 and what kind of a life is that?" Amid this fun atmosphere, Graham and his staff are very serious about their business. On a tour of the shop, Graham points out awards won by his staff and the cleanliness for which they have a passion. There is also a long open pit that was built especially for maintaining semi trucks and trailers and a special computerized machine that tests a vehicle for a multitude of safety and maintenance items. "We test for brake efficiency. We're the only people that have this machine in southern Saskatchewan." He also noted that although semi trucks are a lot more complicated these days with computers controlling the transmission, brakes and engines, there is still a need for the down-and-dirty work that only human hands can complete properly.

"When there's an accident with a semi, sometimes we see gruesome things in here. One time, when some employees were just too squeamish about a particularly bad wreck that came in, I had to go wash human remains off of a truck grill." Once again, it proves his philosophy that he would never ask his staff to do something that he himself would not do.

One Saturday night in 1997, Graham saw an ad in a flying magazine that announced an essay contest of the National Capital Air Show (NCAS), an annual non-profit family event held in Ontario. It invited readers to send in a 500 to 600-word essay on *How Winning A Cessna T337B Super Skymaster Will Change My Life*. The entry fee was $125 Canadian, with 900 applications having to be received to make the fundraiser worthwhile. The prize of a six-seater Cessna Skymaster aircraft would be awarded to the 'most original, interesting essay.'

Graham went to sleep thinking about the contest and considered ideas that would be creative enough to get attention. He had heard several news stories about the 60th anniversary of Amelia Earhart's ill-fated flight around the world and these were on his mind as he drifted off. When he woke, the idea was in his head.

"At 6:30 in the morning, I got up and went to my computer. In old English font, I wrote a letter as if I was Amelia Earhart's husband George Putnam. I was shipwrecked on a Bermuda island. All the men had been lost in a storm. I was writing her to come rescue me."

The letter is dated November 10, 1935 and tells dear Amelia how he and some of the crew 'drifted for days, half sunken, half afloat. With no water on board and all of us half gone from exhaustion, we didn't stand a chance when the second storm hit. Mercifully, it was quick for most of the men. We hit a reef and the rocks quickly finished the job the first storm had started out to do. I awoke on a white sandy beach tucked into a bay in what I have determined to be an island. I suppose under different circumstances most would call this place paradise. A search of two days has turned up no survivors.

'Fortunately, a trunk washed up from the shipwreck today. I think it came from the Captain's quarters and it contained a limited supply of paper on which I am now able to write to you. Being able to record my thoughts to you gives me such comfort, such peace of mind. It's almost as if I am speaking with you.'

Graham went on to describe a few other supplies that had washed up, which he modified to ensure his survival. 'They might even make my stay on this piece of earth bearable until we are together. One prized find is an axe. I have been using this to clear a landing strip. There seems to be no godforsaken ships in the area so I have placed my hopes on an airplane rescue. I lie and watch in the clear blue sky the big jumbos lumbering across the sky filled with people, civilization, comfort, yet here I am isolated, unseen, and unknown from them, the world ... and you.

'Remember the times we used to fly? The feeling of leaving the ground, the softness of the air during an early morning flight. Remember the deafening quietness, stillness, the slight numbing feeling we got throughout our bodies when the prop ticked over to a stop after completing a long flight?

'Amelia, if I do get off this island and back to you, that's what I would like to do with you again. Until then, I will toil away at my runway. I know that this will be my best chance at getting back to you. I have estimated that this island is too far from any mainland but within flying range of Bermuda. The only aircraft that could have the range and landing capability would be the Cessna Turbo Skymaster. So I have made sure this strip is long enough for that plane. Remember the red and white one we used to fly in? The T337B Super Skymaster. If I owned one of them right now, how my life would be different! I would be soaring off of this island right now and home to you. We could start that flying business we always dreamed about. We could be together for the rest of our lives, and we could be happy for the rest of our lives.

'Say, wait! I hear something! Dear, I think it's a plane! I must say adieu now and go signal it. I hope we find ourselves together long before the chance of this note reaching you.'

He signed the letter, 'Love, your devoted husband, G.'

Graham finished the letter, but he wasn't anywhere near done with it yet. "I printed that off, soaked it in lemon juice, then baked it in the oven one minute, watching it turn all brown and leathery, and then I burned and ripped the edges so it looked old. I then went to an antique shop and bought an old-looking bottle with a stopper on it. I rolled up the letter and put it inside the bottle and couriered it to the company."

Graham told the *Regina Leader-Post*, "Everybody is a better writer than I am, but presentation is everything."

About eight months later, he received a phone call at the office that told him he'd won the $100,000 airplane.

Graham didn't believe the phone call at first, since he had only recently played the prank with Flegel's van and he thought some of his business association friends might be playing a trick on him. "I asked the man on the phone a couple questions that only the people from the contest would know and then I put the phone down. My knees went weak and I thought, 'Holy cow, I just won a twin-engine turbo-charged Cessna aircraft!'"

Graham did not have his twin-engine rating as a pilot yet, so he had to take a friend with him who had that rating when he flew commercial to the Ottawa-Macdonald-Cartier International Airport in Ottawa to pick up the plane. It was June 1998, almost a year after the initial entry was sent because the contest had been extended to receive enough entries to cover the fundraiser.

Like his father, Graham had been using a single-engine airplane in his business until this point. Once he won the twin-engine Cessna and obtained his licence to fly it, he sold the single engine plane and began to use the twin.

Getting Together

*"And then the letter appeared. I read it and all of a sudden, that P.S. took on a whole new meaning." - **Graham***

In 1999, Graham's company expanded to a second location in Moose Jaw, about 45 minutes west of Regina. The company was now not only selling and providing parts and services for Freightliner semis, but was selling fire trucks and rescue equipment such as the Jaws of Life from the Moose Jaw location. At about the same time, Graham purchased a Thomas Built Buses school bus franchise.

"Graham has a visionary ability to see a business that would work," says Roger Pettigrew. After watching for opportunities and studying all angles of a possibility, Graham has made decisions to grow his company that might have seemed spur-of-the-moment but were actually well considered.

"He bought a property on 1st Avenue for our Thomas buses," says Pettigrew. "He phoned me and said, 'Hey, Rog, we're going to buy a building today.' His dad was the same way. He's got that same business savvy. If it seems right, it likely is. If it seems wrong, it likely is."

"I've always had that tendency to look for more options," explains Graham. "In business, I learned, 'Do you know how you make a good decision? You get good information. Do you know how to make a great decision? Get great information.'"

Things were going well in his business life, but his personal life, unbeknownst to him, was about to take a turn for the worst.

In early 2000, Graham returned home from a combination bus-driving/airplane-flying road trip in the northern part of the province, during which he had been introduced to all the potential customers of the Thomas Built Buses franchise. That evening, Graham's wife informed him that she had feelings for someone else. Graham was shocked. He wanted to salvage his 15-year-old marriage but he was later devastated to learn that she had been having other extramarital relationships for years. "I had no clue. My marriage went from what I thought was still in a honeymoon stage, even though it was in its 16th year, to separation within two to three weeks."

He and his family had been living in the elegant three-bedroom house he'd built with his own hands in White City, just outside of Regina. In April 2000, Graham moved out of the family home so his children and their mother could stay there.

He temporarily moved in with Sean Westerman, a friend who lived within bicycling distance for his kids to visit him. Sean later became an employee with Graham's company. During the seven months that he lived with Westerman, who had also just become single, Graham let loose when he wasn't able to be with his children. He dated a couple of women and partied to try to ease the pain.

"When I moved in, we lived a pretty fun lifestyle. We were a couple of playful men just living the life. With my airplane, we buzzed boats on the lake and once we even buzzed Earls Restaurant on Regina's main street – okay, it was kind of on the approach path to the runway – and then we went in and drank with all our buddies and had a party. In the summer, we went boating and had a boatload full of girls, thanks to Sean's popularity. Sean also had a cool '57 Chevy, and we both had motorcycles. We did a lot of cruising and had a lot of fun with our toys that summer. That winter, we also snowmobiled together throughout Saskatchewan and the B.C. mountains."

Westerman also has fond memories of the months he and Graham lived in the same house. "I have probably never had as much fun in a short period of time. It was night after night of parties and morning after morning of headaches ... Graham was always the entertainer and loved to show everyone a good time. We went out to the lake one time with his boat and Graham decided to bring the parasail. We must have had 15 people out that day and it was his goal to make sure everyone got a turn."

While Westerman drove the boat, Graham became the coach of the parasailing for the day. All went well and everyone had a turn in the parasail except for Westerman, who naturally agreed to let Graham drive the boat while he went up in the parasail. "It was the most amazing experience. As I was floating in the air looking down at the captain of the boat, Graham decided to turn around and head back to the beach and drop me off," recalls Westerman. "Everything was going well but as he turned downwind for the beach, I started to slowly come down. I was all smiles and sad to see the ride end. Graham, being telepathic, must have sensed this and decided that I needed to continue my ride. Unfortunately, I was too low and almost in the water by then. So Graham gunned the boat!

"The look of horror on my face must have been priceless. The sail did not have enough air in it to lift me back up and by gunning the boat, all it did was speed up my descent. I hit the water and the combination of ropes and harnesses and the now-submerged sail dragged me to the bottom of the lake and, as I was bouncing off the bottom, I was getting wrapped up in all the ropes!

"One of Graham's favourite sayings is 'Never say whoa in the middle of a slough.' He did not give up. He was bound and determined to get me up out of the water, so he gunned the boat engine even more. This made the situation worse and I could not get above water. I was preparing to meet my Maker," laughs Westerman. "Finally, after what seemed like ages, Graham decided that no matter how much gas he gave it, I was not going to come up and he let off. I floated to the top and slowly got myself disconnected. I swam for my life to get away from Captain Death. I am convinced to this day that he was trying to 'off' me for some unknown reason. Fortunately for my pending lawsuit, this entire episode was caught on tape. When reviewing the disaster later on, I could hear Graham in the background say to the other passengers in the boat, 'Well … that didn't work too well.' " Westerman has refused all subsequent offers from Graham to go parasailing.

Graham's separation was making news not only in Saskatchewan business circles but within the Freightliner corporation as well. "The main office was concerned how this divorce might affect the franchise, so they flew their dealer operations manager out and he met with me to investigate. My wife and I had a very nice life. We were always travelling and the kids travelled with us. She didn't work outside the home. It was nice clothes, nice car, nice house and everyone knew how absolutely devoted and loving I was with my wife and kids. It was the fairy-tale life. So to find out about the years of betrayal that had been going on shocked a lot of people."

Graham made it through the meeting with the corporate representative and leaned heavily on his best friend Roger Pettigrew to run the companies. "My focus was completely off the business as I mourned the loss of my marriage and family. I'm so thankful that Roger was there to pick up the slack that I literally was incapable of handling. I was also inundated with court and legal battles as I fought to maintain access to my children and the rights to my companies."

In October 2000, Graham helped purchase a new home for his wife and children to move into in Regina. "I really wanted to move back into the home I had built because I felt it was really important to try and provide a familiar home setting to the children, one that they had been raised in since birth. The house was too large for their mother to take care of on her own and I had built it before I married, so it held a lot of sentimental value to me."

While Graham attended a school bus dealer meeting in North Carolina, his wife moved out of the White City home and into the Regina one. Upon Graham's return he moved his few belongings back to his house and discovered that his wife had even taken the toilet paper off their rolls.

"I was alone and miserable. I was sitting on my mattress on my bedroom floor, working late Friday night on my laptop, in an empty house with no toilet paper on the rolls, and I got all mixed up and lost in some files on my computer. I'm not very computer-literate. I had this laptop and I just didn't know what I was doing on it, and I was starting to get pretty frustrated when up popped an e-mail that Dionne had sent me years earlier. I literally can't explain how it appeared."

Through Dionne's work in Freightliner's corporate service department, Graham and Dionne had maintained a collegial relationship since they first met in 1984. They talked by phone or e-mail when one of Graham's service men won a Technician Of The Year award or when other Freightliner business demanded that they connect. They had become workplace friends who knew a bit about each other's families, who shared a similar sense of humour and had joked about each other's attractiveness in a non-offensive way. They had also chatted about their Freightliner co-workers' marriages, illnesses and other life changes that affected their workplaces.

Graham knew that Dionne had gone through treatments for breast cancer and that he had always liked her, but they hadn't actually seen each other in years. On this dark lonely night in early October 2000, he re-read the July 1998 e-mail that had magically popped up on his laptop.

Titled 'Surprise!,' Dionne had written the e-mail to tell Graham about her appearance in the magazine article about the *Look Good ... Feel Better* program.

'Hi, Graham. How goes everything????? You guessed it. I am back but on a part-time basis for now. I can tell you one thing. A lot sure can happen when you are absent for a year. Holy comoly. Where is everybody, who is this person?

I hope the wife and kids are great and you guys are enjoying your summer.

I have spoken to my co-worker fighting cancer and she is doing wonderful. She feels good and looks great. I do miss her around here, though.

I have another surprise for you, Graham. I am in a magazine article that is in the Chatelaine and Canadian Living magazines this month. If your wife does not get these magazines, let me know and I will send you a copy. I would like to share it with you because I feel it would make you proud of me. The only other place you can get the magazine is at the make-up area in Shoppers Drug Mart. They should have them on display. If not, ask for one there.

My husband and I also renewed our wedding vows on Saturday July 4th. I planned a family and friends BBQ and surprised him with a minister at 9 p.m. It was a beautiful evening and God even sent us a spectacular rainbow, too. It was like we were given a second chance to start off fresh and new, which we definitely needed.

Well, Graham, I better get back to work. Take care of yourself and remember to smell the flowers, enjoy the warmth of the sun and that laughter can heal pain.

Dionne

P.S. I still think you are the sexiest man alive. It's too bad your wife got you first!'

When the e-mail was written in 1998, neither Dionne nor Graham thought much about the postscript.

"To me, it was just a nice compliment," says Dionne. "I knew he was happily married. He was funny. He was genuine. Let's give him a little woo woo! And he made everyone feel comfortable around him. I just said nice things to blow his head up. He was a well respected person and was one of the Freightliner dealers who was nice to everyone no matter what. There was never a bad thing said about him. Many women in the office said, 'There are very few Grahams.'

"I knew who I could joke with and have fun with and not step over the line," adds Dionne. "I always thought he was a very good-looking man. A lot of us thought that. And he has a smile that can light up a room. I just boosted his ego. I meant it all in a good way."

Although Graham felt an initial connection with Dionne in 1984, it was never something he acted on. "It wasn't proper to entertain those feelings," he says. "We were totally platonic." Graham was already married and then Dionne got married. And frankly, Dionne scared Graham a bit.

"I always found her intimidating. She's so confident and so beautiful and I'm a Prairies stubble boy. I made trips into Toronto and I would see her in the office with everyone else. Dionne was in charge of all the technicians' training programs in Canada. She was always flamboyantly dressed – totally styling in a positive way. Not slutty, but not conservative at all. She did not match or fit in with anyone else."

Dionne doesn't remember what exactly was happening in her own life when she added that postscript to the 1998 e-mail, but she can guess. "Maybe my husband and I had just had an argument and Graham had always been a nice person in my life. I don't remember. I know that I thought his wife was a very lucky woman. She had a very good husband. Working in an office environment, you see a lot of things going on. Graham loves marriage. He was dedicated to his family. He had said to me, 'I don't like being single. I like being married.' "

"I didn't even take it as a compliment," says Graham of the postscript. "I probably thought, 'Oh, she's a silly girl.' I didn't even think of it. It was like goofing around. It didn't mean anything to me because I was happily married. When your heart is full, that stuff bounces off it. But then when I was single and I found that letter on my computer … It was late at night. I was frustrated. I was ready to throw the frickin' computer through the window. And then the letter appeared. I read it and all of a sudden, that 'P.S.' took on a whole new meaning."

Graham phoned Dionne at the corporate office on the following Monday, knowing she would be a friendly ear listening to his problems. "I said, 'I'm sure you heard about my Jerry Springer separation.' She hadn't heard, so I was telling her some stuff and when I finished, she said, 'I know exactly how you feel. I've been through the same thing.' And I was shocked because I still thought she was married. She hadn't changed her name on corporate e-mails she was sending to all the dealerships."

Graham and Dionne talked for awhile, sharing the stories of their broken marriages, and before they finished their conversation, Graham asked her out on a date. "I said, 'Have you ever been to the symphony?' She said, 'No,' and that surprised me because, as I like to always say with some humour, 'I always thought she was such a classy broad.' We made arrangements to get together in Toronto and I think we had to wait two weeks," he says. "I had a NASCAR trip to host with customers and her grandmother was coming from New York to visit her."

Meanwhile, Graham sent Dionne a photo of himself and asked her to send him a recent photo of herself. Dionne refused. "I said, 'No. I'm not stupid. You want to see what I look like now, come see for yourself. Take it or leave it.' He hadn't seen me for a very long time. He wanted to see how different I looked, whether I'd gained weight ... he sent me a picture of himself, so obviously he felt he looked good," teases Dionne. "Men are more visual than woman when choosing mates," she adds with a smile.

Dionne had dated a couple of men after her marriage. Shortly before she heard from Graham, she had broken up with a man who lived in another province and had a child. "His ex-wife-to-be was a wacko. He was willing to move to Toronto and I said, 'You're the only sane person in that child's life, you can't leave.' So we broke up."

After Graham's phone call, Dionne began looking forward to their date. I thought, 'Why shouldn't I go out with him?' I liked him as a friend. I knew he was a good husband, a good father. We always had this great friendship and awesome connection. I was very excited."

On October 19, 2000, two weeks after their phone conversation, Graham flew to Toronto on a commercial flight. He did not go to Freightliner's offices. He was there only for his date with Dionne.

"We went to a nice restaurant in downtown Toronto. I was done my meal a half hour earlier than she was," he says with a smile. This was not a concern to Dionne.

On their way to the symphony concert after dinner, "three men slammed into me while staring at her," says Graham. "She was so beautiful. I said to her, 'Does this happen often to you?' " Dionne was polite enough not to answer.

"We enjoyed the first half of the Toronto Symphony Orchestra playing. After intermission, they had a guest choir called the Armageddon Choir. It was 150 people strong," says Graham. "They lifted the rafters with their voices. The music was so beautiful and when I glanced over at Dionne and saw tears streaming down her face, it was like the scene from *Pretty Woman*. On the second night, she took me to a medieval feast with live horses and knights performing and we had to eat with no utensils. We enjoyed the meal and each other's company. We immediately had this love connection."

Dionne was ecstatic after their two evenings together. "Going from a husband who told me I was damaged goods, here was Graham who knew what I had been through. To him, I didn't look like damaged goods."

Graham was as happy as Dionne that first night. Where he normally shook hands at the end of a date, never wanting to appear too forward, he did not do this with Dionne. "Not only did I go in for the full kiss on this night, I returned back up the 11 storeys to her door after leaving her the first time because it felt like a second kiss was in high order! After those two kisses, I don't think I slept a wink. I was on cloud 11!"

Dionne couldn't stop thinking about Graham either. He was kind and genuine, and he obviously cared about her.

And he had given her an angel.

On the morning that he was to fly to Toronto for their date, Graham thought he should turn on his answering machine. "I went to the phone and my hand brushed something that I heard fall on the floor," he says. "I bent over and picked it up. It was an angel pin. I had never seen it before in my life. And here it was in this empty house lying beside my phone. I remember standing there wondering, 'How did that come to be there?' and then I'm not exactly sure why, but I took it with me to Toronto. I pinned it on a rose when I went to pick up Dionne." During that first date, Graham was pleased to learn that Dionne had a love of angels because of her two cancer battles.

Their first dates went so well that a second weekend of dates was quickly planned for two weeks later, in early November.

Graham had always been romantic, buying flowers every week for his former wife and lighting candles to create the right mood. Now he set about wooing Dionne. He bought a subscription to *Victoria's Secret Magazine* and "took great interest" in ordering dress clothes for her that were shipped directly to her office. He had purchased a boat shortly before visiting Dionne and when he mentioned it to her, she asked what the boat was named. Graham had not even thought about naming the boat but within a few weeks of their first date, the back of his new boat proudly bore the inscription 'Pretty D,' with an angel figure beside it.

Shortly before going to Toronto for his second weekend of dates with Dionne, Graham walked into a store in Regina called The Angel Shop to look for a gift for Dionne."It was operated by a good witch," he says. "She was into astrology and angels and stuff like that. While looking for a gift, Graham told the store owner about what had happened with his first wife and how he unexplainably had these feelings for this beautiful young woman in Toronto 16 years earlier and that there was definitely a connection with her now.

"She said to me, 'Sometimes we have to be with the wrong person to know when we're with the right one.' My jaw dropped. The store owner asked, 'What's wrong?'

"About 45 minutes earlier, Dionne had forwarded me a poem that a friend had sent her with the exact same quote in it. The store owner looked at me with the most knowing and confident look and said, 'Young man, the universe is trying to tell you something.' At that moment, I decided she was right and that I was going to just go with it and not put any guards up around my heart."

So, two weeks after their first date, Graham headed back to Toronto with a plan.

Daimler Benz, the parent company of Freightliner, had just purchased the Chrysler company and adopted a new corporate protocol which insisted that all meals, entertainment and fraternizing by employees be properly documented. Everything had to be above board and open for examination. "They wanted to make sure dealers weren't bribing corporate people or improperly influencing them," explains Graham. "I was used to when corporate people like my factory sales manager came to visit, he'd come to my house to eat or we'd go to a hockey game together or we'd go to *The Nutcracker* at Christmas time. Now we had to report everything.

"When Dionne and I went out for dinner on our first date, it was so romantic," he says sarcastically. "We each had to report the value of our meals so no one could point a finger at us and say, 'Graham is trying to bribe Dionne.' At the end of the meal, I said to Dionne, 'Okay, here's what you have to report.' Even though it was a personal date, we were so scared because we didn't want to get each other in trouble with this new code of ethics."

Dionne was very concerned about breaching the code and what might happen if they were seen together on a date. "I was worried about all of it because I was a little person in the company. Graham owned a business." So she asked Graham to speak to her boss, Craig Smith, to get his approval so they could date openly. "We had a whole scenario set up," laughs Dionne. "It was almost like an ambush."

Graham phoned Smith to say he was coming to Toronto in a couple of weeks and asked if they could get together to chat somewhere near Smith's home. Smith was slightly confused, not knowing Graham's real reason for being in town, but agreed to meet Graham at a show home sales office in the area. "In fact, Craig was excited to take me to an aircraft museum located not far from his home while I was there."

On the appointed day, Graham and Dionne pulled up at the show home shortly before Smith arrived. Dionne went inside the home to hide from her boss, leaving Graham outside in his rental car. "I had a lady trying to sell me the house and I was not interested whatsoever," says Dionne with a laugh. "When I saw Craig's car pull in, I finally had to tell her what was happening. I said, 'Honestly, I'm not here to buy a house. You see that man out there? He's about to ask my boss if it's okay that we date.'

"She said, 'Really?'

"I said, 'Yeah, but my boss doesn't know that I'm actually in here.'

"She said, 'This is great! It was so slow in here. This is awesome!' "

Since Dionne couldn't look out the window and risk being seen by her boss, the sales agent became Dionne's eyes and filled her in on what she saw happening. "She was watching the faces of the two men in the vehicle and she was telling me, 'Oh. They're smiling now.' 'Oh, there's some laughter.' She was giving me a play-by-play while I was hidden in this sales office and she was so enjoying this."

Graham, meanwhile, was chatting with Dionne's boss. "I said, 'There's somebody in the corporate office I'd like to date and according to the new corporate integrity laws, I've got to be up front with it. This person *does* look after our technicians and I don't want anybody assuming there would be extra concessions coming to my dealership or anything.'

"And he said, 'Dionne?' and I said, 'Yeah.'

"And he then read me the Riot Act and said, 'You'd better make sure you don't mess around and you'd better treat her right.' We talked for a few more minutes and then Craig said to me, 'Okay let's go to the aircraft museum.' I then had to say that I couldn't go to the aircraft museum because, unbeknownst to him, Dionne was in the model sales home waiting for my signal. He looked confused for a second and then he burst out laughing!"

Inside the show home, the sales agent told Dionne, 'Oh, they're really smiling and laughing now. Oh, they're getting out of the vehicle.' So I said, 'Okay, well, I have to get out there some time. And out I went.' When I came out, my boss smiled and giggled. He gave me a big hug and said, 'I'm very happy for you guys.' "

What Dionne didn't know was that Graham had not only told Dionne's boss that he wanted to date Dionne. He also said that in two more weeks, he was going to ask Dionne to marry him.

On To Saskatchewan

"What if Graham gets cancer?" – Graham's father Goff Warner

On November 24, 2000 Dionne boarded an Air Canada flight bound for Regina. She thought she was simply going to visit Graham and attend a Tragically Hip concert. The weekend turned out to be much more eventful than she anticipated.

Although Dionne has a diverse taste in music, the Canadian rock band Tragically Hip was new to her, so she asked her friend Kim Robulack-Mendes about the band. "Kimmie brought me every Tragically Hip CD she had and said, 'You have to listen to this.' "

Robulack-Mendes was the only Freightliner employee aside from Craig Smith who knew that Dionne and Graham were dating. They also were the only two who knew Graham's real plans for the weekend.

Dionne finished work that Friday, changed into a comfortable sweatshirt and a pair of blue jeans, and boarded a plane for a fun weekend in Regina. She was immediately bumped up to first class. "I thought I had won the lottery. I had no clue what was going to happen," she says. "I had never experienced first class before. Whoa, it was good!"

Graham, meanwhile, was alternately pacing and sitting on a chair inside the control tower of the Regina Airport.

Two weeks earlier, when Graham had arrived in Toronto before going on his second date with Dionne, he had taken two brown envelopes to the Air Canada office in the Toronto airport. "I explained to a lady there what I wanted to do. She went and grabbed another friend and they became very enthusiastic deputies of my plan. I asked them to hand one envelope to the captain of Dionne's flight in two weeks and the other envelope was to be given to the head flight attendant. These two office girls were so excited about the plan, they upgraded Dionne to first class without telling me," he says.

Dionne's flight was supposed to land in Regina at 10 o'clock that Friday night, and Graham had made arrangements to be in the Regina control tower before it landed. "It was 9:30 and we couldn't find the flight on the radar screen," he says, "so the Regina controller radio-telephoned the Winnipeg controller. He confirmed it got away late, it was over Kenora, Ontario and it would be in the Regina sector in about 20 minutes. I had to chew the fat for 20 minutes. I remember it being kind of uncomfortable."

Finally, the blip blip of Dionne's flight appeared on the radar screen and Graham's heartbeat quickened in anticipation of what was to come next. "The controller picked up the mike and said, 'Air Canada Flight 1119. This is Regina Tower. Do you copy?'

"The Air Canada captain came on and said, 'Flight 1119. Affirmative.'

"So then the controller said, 'I have Graham here, who says, '*Go ahead.*' '

"What had been handed to the captain in the brown envelope was a photo of Dionne and me and a request to relay my proposal over the P.A. system at about a half an hour before landing. So the captain went on the P.A. system of Dionne's flight and said, 'Ladies and gentlemen, this is your captain speaking. We've just received an unusual but pleasant request from a fellow pilot in Regina who has asked that I relay his request for eternal partnership in marriage to a beautiful young lady on board named Dionne. So if she would kindly let the flight attendants know her answer, they'll let me know and I'll let Graham know, who I am sure is anxiously awaiting.' "

On the airplane, Dionne wasn't paying much attention to the announcement. Then she heard 'Dionne.'

"I turned to the gentleman beside me and said, 'Did I just hear my name?' " she recalls. "I was shocked. This was my first time to Regina and already he wanted to marry me. I was happy-shocked. I knew we were getting serious. I just wasn't sure what level we were at ... Graham loves being married. I wasn't sure, especially going through his divorce."

The second brown envelope for the head flight attendant contained a photo of Dionne, along with a request to allow her to get off the airplane first because Graham planned to be standing at the bottom of the escalator with the engagement ring. "But there was one flight attendant on board who could barely contain her excitement and her confidentiality, so the other flight attendants had to keep her away from Dionne for most of the flight, they told me later," laughs Graham. "During the announcement, they let her go and apparently she's the one who was crouched at Dionne's side when Dionne screamed, 'YES!' That flight attendant was off like a shot to go tell the captain."

On the airplane, after eagerly accepting Graham's proposal, Dionne was completely overwhelmed with emotions. She was shaking and grinning and laughing, all at the same time. The other passengers were clapping and cheering at the storybook proposal they had just witnessed.

In the control tower, however, all was quiet.

Graham was left wondering what had actually happened.

"Then the captain came on the radio," says Graham, "and he said, 'Regina Tower, this is Air Canada Flight 1119. Is Graham there?'

"The controller said, 'Yes, he is.'

"The captain said, 'Is he sitting down?'

"The controller said, 'Affirmative.'

"And then nothing for 45 seconds. That is so long, especially on air," laments Graham. "I literally thought, 'Oh my God, I asked too soon. I've been too forward. What have I done? This is totally humiliating.'

"Then the captain came on in this big John-Wayne-like drawl ... *'Welllll ... tell him she's gonna go through with it.'*

"Almost immediately, another call came through on the control tower's radio. 'Regina Tower, this is Northwest Flight 1172. Our request isn't quite so exciting. Could you give us the wind and weather, please?'

"We all laughed. And I recall the Winnipeg tower radio-phoned and congratulated us, too."

The flight landed and Graham was happily waiting at the bottom of the escalator to give Dionne the ring. What he didn't know was that the flight attendants had decided to ignore the second part of his instructions because they wanted to be part of the big moment. "The only way to do that was to keep Dionne on the plane until the last person had left," says Graham, still bristling slightly at the memory.

"They didn't tell me, so I was standing at the bottom of the escalator, wearing my new suit, anxiously looking for Dionne. Instead, I got slaps on the back and high fives, my hand was shaken by about 150 passengers and not one of them went to get their baggage. They wanted to be a part of the big moment, too. But it took *so long* for her to come down. I remember feeling the nervousness of the passengers behind me thinking, 'Oh my God, she stood him up.' And I admit even I was beginning to wonder if maybe she slipped out the back gate because something has changed. But eventually she came down with the captain, co-pilot and all the flight attendants."

Graham slipped the ring on Dionne's finger and they exchanged a kiss, which was supposed to be captured in a photo taken by a security guard. "But the photo didn't turn out – and in true 'Scare Canada' fashion, they lost her bag on that direct flight. Yep, she had to sleep naked in the guest room that night," says Graham with a laugh.

"I think losing my luggage was just another plan devised by Graham that he just isn't owning up to," laughs Dionne.

All of this fairy tale proposal occurred before the airport security concerns stemming from the tragic events of September 11, 2001 of course. "Can you imagine trying to do that now?" asks Graham.

The next day, when Dionne phoned Robulack-Mendes in Toronto, they shared a laugh over the anxiety that her engagement had caused her friend. Craig Smith knew about the engagement after Graham told him about it at the show home but Graham didn't tell Robulack-Mendes that Smith knew when he enlisted her aid in figuring out the correct ring size for Dionne. Graham had suggested that he could take Dionne shopping and they could just kind of look at rings as part of their shopping, but Robulack-Mendes squashed that idea. Dionne would quickly figure out what was going on, she said. Instead, Robulack-Mendes offered to look at the hands of every woman who worked in the Freightliner corporate office until she found a ring finger that seemed the same size as Dionne's. And she was right, laughs Graham.

Keeping that secret from Dionne was a lot harder than searching for the right ring size, though. "I can keep a secret but I have to tuck it in the back of my brain and pretend it doesn't exist. I can't lie," says Robulack-Mendes. "Dionne likes to surprise people but she doesn't like to be surprised, so she will pick, pick, pick to find out what she wants to know. Nothing will get by her, even when you think it does. That's why it was so stressful to keep the engagement secret."

After Dionne left work that afternoon to fly to Regina, Smith came out of his office and said to Robulack-Mendes, 'Boy, I'd like to be a fly on the wall of that airplane for that.' Robulack-Mendes looked at him and said, 'What? You knew? I have been going crazy holding on to this secret for two weeks and I wasn't able to tell anybody anything and you knew? I could have talked to you!'

Dionne's suitcase arrived in Regina on Saturday and then Graham introduced her to about 25 of his family and friends during a horse-drawn sleigh ride he arranged to go through Wascana Centre, the large park south of Regina's downtown that contains the legislative buildings, University of Regina, arts centre and rehabilitation hospital. It was a typically cold evening in November but everyone was welcoming and excited to meet Dionne.

To this day, Graham regrets that his children did not meet Dionne that night which had been a big part of his plan. They did not find out about the engagement until after Christmas that year. "There was a last-minute decision by their mother to not allow them to come to the sleigh ride. This severely affected their relationship with me and Dionne," he says sadly.

Graham's mother and some of his other family were there, though, and the next day, they went to see both of Graham's parents at their house in Regina. "My father wasn't well enough to come out to the sleigh ride. My mom had met Dionne the night before but I didn't tell her the news. So I sat my mom and dad down at their kitchen table and told them I had proposed to Dionne. The first thing my mom said was, 'What if she gets cancer again?' and my dad interjected without hesitation, 'What if Graham gets cancer?'

"It was so cool," says Graham. "There was this rough, tough pioneer road worker, very emotionally smart and very character-smart, and he nailed it. 'What if Graham gets cancer?' That was an important line to me. And of course, they gave me their full support. Just like now."

Graham will always remember that insightful comment from his father, who passed away in February 2002 and did not live to see Graham and Dionne get married. "Rather than him assuming that D was going to get cancer again – the way life goes, what if I did? He recognized I was just totally in love and that Dionne was totally in love, so it didn't matter ... that's just the way life could be. I could get cancer next, so what would we do then? Unfortunately, he was wrong in the end, but that was quite the statement."

With that news announced and celebrated by his parents, Dionne and Graham drove up to Saskatoon with his friend Sean and his girlfriend to see the Tragically Hip in concert the next day.

And how was the concert?

"I loved it," laughs Dionne. "They were great."

Years later, Graham still cannot get over his good fortune in Dionne accepting his proposal. "When they removed the tumour for her brain cancer, they removed some good judgment cells, and that's the only way I stood a chance with her," he jokes. "She's way out of my league."

Before Dionne went back to Toronto that Monday evening, she and Graham had discussed a plan for what would happen next. Since Graham had his business in Regina, they decided that it would be best for Dionne to quit her job and move to Saskatchewan.

One of the reasons she might have been more willing to do so, aside from loving Graham, was that he told her a little white lie about Saskatchewan's temperatures in winter. "I told her it never got below minus 10 Celsius in Saskatchewan," he says with a smile and a twinkle in his eye.

Dionne may have bought the line – or not – but she did buy into a life with Graham, and she agreed to leave Ontario behind and move west. "We wanted to start off 2001 together in Saskatchewan," she says. "So I was going back to work to let them know I was leaving."

Dionne had two different bosses at Freightliner at the time. Although Craig Smith knew all about the engagement, the other boss was the person Dionne had to speak with about her decision to move to Regina in a few weeks. "I was unaware that he had been fighting for me to keep my job during a lot of layoffs in our company. He said, 'Now I'm going to have to fight to fire you, to let you go.' "

He asked her to return to work in the new year so he could officially release her, which she did. On January 9, 2001 Dionne was officially but happily let go from Freightliner and given a severance package.

Dionne will forever be grateful to that boss for recognizing her years of service to Freightliner and for arranging that she receive a severance package. "It was a well-kept secret. He was happy Graham and I were together and he was supporting us in starting a new life. I thought that was just so incredible that he would do that for us. I walked out of there not crying but with a big smile on my face."

Graham jokes about taking Dionne away from her job. "I always tell people that Freightliner didn't give me enough concessions on trucks so I went and got my concession I deserved, which was Dionne."

On December 17, 2000 Graham jumped into his Suburban truck and drove for 32 hours straight all the way to Toronto. Although Graham said at the time he was "running on adrenalin," others knew the truth. He was in love and anxious to be with his lady.

He and Dionne went on a one-week Caribbean cruise and after Christmas, they packed Dionne's belongings into Graham's truck and a tandem U-Haul trailer he'd rented for the occasion. Three of Dionne's cousins, whom she considers her brothers, helped with the packing. That part of the move has become a source of good-natured ribbing ever since.

"Her cousins hauled all her stuff down from the 11th storey for me to load into the U-Haul," says Graham. "They used an elevator, but they moved it all from the 11th storey down. I thought they were such great guys until six hours later when I realized I had frostbite on my nose and they were fine.

That's when I figured out what their real motivation had been in offering to do all that work inside. It was only minus 15 but with the humidity, it was way colder." Graham was used to the 'dry cold' of the Prairies and he teased Dionne's cousins relentlessly about trying to freeze him so he wouldn't take Dionne away to Saskatchewan.

"My brother and I went down and helped her load up, and that was the first time we met Graham," says David Ballantine in self-defence. "Graham's a constant joker. I was actually a furniture mover for years. It's very important when moving people's stuff to have one person in control of packing the load because if anything gets broken, that person is responsible. My rule is if you want to be on the truck, be on the truck. Graham comes from Saskatchewan, so he should have been used to the cold anyway," teases Ballantine.

Peter Ballantine supports his brother's side of the argument. "Graham's got a deluded way of looking at things," he smiles. "My brother and I worked for moving companies. Divide and conquer. We're both big guys and we're always volunteering to do the heavy lifting. We were running up and down and we figured we were getting the short end of the stick!"

For her part, Dionne has tried desperately to avoid taking sides on the issue. "Can I plead the Fifth? I love them all. I think my cousins were just the smart ones. It sucks to be Graham," she laughs. "If something doesn't work out here in Regina, they're the ones I'm calling to pack me up and move me back to Toronto."

On December 29, 2000 less than three months after they started dating, Graham and Dionne left Toronto and headed west. Without any furniture, "we packed the trailer and Suburban to where we had to actually tilt the driver and passenger seats forward because the stuff was right behind our heads," explains Graham. "We even went and bought Rubbermaid storage bins at Canadian Tire and I strapped them to the roof of the truck." They stopped overnight twice and each had their own precious cargo that they babied along the way.

Graham had sampled Honey Brown beer from the Sleeman Brewery in Guelph, Ontario while visiting Dionne's family there, "and I absolutely fell in love with it. My little luxury, other than bringing Dionne, was two 12-packs of this Honey Brown beer," he says. "I had to nurse those beers all the way home. We moved in December and in Dryden, Ontario it was

45 below Celsius. So every night, I had to unpack the truck and take the beer into the hotel. In the morning, I'd take it back out and repack. It took us three days to get here.

The day after New Years, we went out for dinner and I was telling the waitress at the Keg all about this beer and she said, 'Well, we have that here.' "

"Yes, it was quite funny how he babied this beer," adds Dionne. "Our family laughed at us. 'Are you sure?' 'Yes, we don't have that beer in Saskatchewan.' "

The differences in their backgrounds and environments became more apparent as the couple drove west. Dionne was cruising along at dusk through the rocky Cambrian Shield in northern Ontario, trying to break her own personal long-distance driving record. "I was proud. I had been driving towards my new home for nine hours. Woo hoo! I can do this!"

Then Graham suggested she might want to slow down a bit because there were moose in the area and they often came out at that time onto the highway. "It was like someone had scratched a needle across the record," smiles Graham. "Errrchhh! She pulled right over. 'Here you go, babe.' I didn't want to slow her down, but I didn't want her to hit a moose."

They also chuckle at Dionne's first experience with block heaters on vehicles. In Dryden, Ontario she wondered why every vehicle was plugged in. "She said, 'Everybody must have electric cars here.' I was incredulous she didn't realize this," says Graham.

Dionne also had her own safety concerns during the trip, which proved to be not so silly after all. Being a Toronto girl, she was worried about theft and she took her own precautions every time they stopped at a restroom. "I said to Graham, 'If something happens, I've been shoving the engagement ring into my sock. So if I don't come out, the ring is in my sock.' He kept telling me I was crazy. 'That would never happen.' "

"Plus, I said, 'That doesn't happen in Saskatchewan. You don't have to worry about that in Saskatchewan,' " added Graham confidently.

"I'm a city girl from Ontario. You lock up everything. I had this beautiful ring on my finger. In the areas where we were stopping ... he just thought it was crazy to think this way but I wanted him to know where the ring was anyway. I'm always protective of my stuff."

"Paranoid's a strong word," teases Graham. "Let's just say she's extremely suspicious and cautious."

"I live in a reality world," argues Dionne.

On their last leg of their trip, they were about 130 kilometres east of

Regina when a blast of wind in a developing blizzard caused two of the three bins to blow off the roof of the truck and scatter the contents in the ditch and field. "At the time, the highway wasn't divided in that spot. I had traffic on my tail and the shoulders were plugged with deep snow so I couldn't pull over to the shoulder," says Graham. So he drove another 200 metres to an intersection and took the remaining bin from the top of the truck. There was no room inside the vehicle, so he set the bin down into the ditch near the stop sign and they quickly drove back down the highway to try to retrieve the other items and bins.

"We were up to our knees in snow," recalls Dionne. "We were picking up everything – Christmas decorations, clothes. My sweaters were in the field. Oh my goodness. At one point, I said to Graham, 'Just forget it. Let's go.' He said, 'We're going to get everything together and we'll put it back in and it will be okay.' We spent maybe 10 to 20 minutes gathering up everything and putting it back into the bins and securing them back onto the roof to get back to that one lonely bin."

When they returned to the intersection to pick up the bin they'd left by the stop sign, they discovered that the bin wasn't there.

"So I looked at him and I said, 'Hmmm … I thought things like this didn't happen in Saskatchewan!' "

Graham was angry that the bin had disappeared but hoped it was a case of someone being helpful rather than being a thief. They turned in at the first gas station they saw and Graham looked at every vehicle there to see if he could see a bin anywhere. "I did it with a clear frame of mind," he says. "I thought maybe somebody just picked it up thinking it had blown off and they were here having a coffee or beer at the café." He and Dionne never recovered the bin, even after Graham went on CKRM-Radio to tell listeners where it could be returned if they had it.

Dionne was thankful that the lid of that storage bin had opened before Graham set the bin in the ditch near the stop sign. She saw her baby album in the bin and asked Graham to hand it to her so she could put it in the cab of the truck. "I had a lot of photo albums in there. My baby book was the only album I saved. My wedding album from my first wedding was in there. These things are not replaceable. It's all I have."

Graham is still slightly embarrassed by his assurances to Dionne that there was no cause for her to worry on their way west. "Every restroom we stopped at, she took her engagement ring off and put it in her sock or gave it to me so that if something happened, it wouldn't get stolen. That was all the way through Ontario and Manitoba. And I said, 'You don't need to worry about stuff like that in Saskatchewan' ... and we didn't even make it to our house and she got robbed. In a blizzard. On New Year's Eve."

Moving from Toronto to the flattest part of the Canadian Prairies had its challenging moments for Dionne, but it was not as difficult as some of her friends and family thought it might be for her.

Dionne's Aunt Janet found it difficult to have Dionne so far away, and their relationship fizzled shortly after the move. Freightliner employees had questioned Dionne about why she would want to go west to Saskatchewan where it is cold and flat.

"I told Graham what they were saying and he tried to tell me the bonuses. 'It never got below minus 10. It was a dry cold. The whole province isn't flat, just the southern part.' These were the things he was telling me to tell people," laughs Dionne.

Kim Robulack-Mendes was one of Dionne's many friends and co-workers who was at first baffled by Dionne's announcement that she was moving west. "I had met Graham quite a few times through Freightliner functions. He was funny, handsome and charismatic – but a match for Dionne? No! He lived in freaking Regina! Dionne is a club girl. She loves to go dancing. She loves to go shopping. She loves her friends and family. She won't last in Regina!" thought Robulack-Mendes.

"I was confused about how she could pick up and leave her life for a man she really didn't know for all that long. I kept thinking, 'What will happen if she gets sick again?' I knew she took a genetic test that had an extremely high percentage that the cancer would reoccur. I just wanted someone whom Dionne could count on. I didn't realize at the time how selfish that was of me. But when I saw them together, I was happy that Dionne had found somebody whom she loved and who loved her back. A lot of times, she has loved. She gives it very freely but she's very cautious because she's been burned so many times – not just from men but from her family. I was happy that Dionne was happy, that Graham treated her like a queen, and that she felt like the beautiful and smart woman she is and not the young girl who had cancer."

"Graham knew he probably had all of Ontario against him. He was taking our girl. Once we spent a little bit more time with them, we fell in love with Graham, too. He tried so hard to get to know us. If Dionne would call, Graham would get on the phone and be interested in my life and my husband's life and get involved in the conversation – and a lot of men wouldn't do that. That makes a big difference. You couldn't be upset or angry. You just wish they lived closer to you. I still wanted her then and I still want her now to be part of my day-to-day life."

Dionne's father says he was shocked at first to hear that Dionne was moving to Regina because he knew she would miss her family and friends in Ontario. "I questioned her with regards to divulging her medical condition fully to her new suitor. When she said she did and he still wanted to marry her, I gave her my blessing."

Dionne's cousins were also supportive.

Peter Ballantine recalls asking Dionne, 'Are you sure this is the right move? This isn't a rebound from your marriage, is it?'

"They didn't date very long and he went after her with guns a blazing," says Ballantine, who was quickly won over by Graham as well. "He's a great guy, though. He's quirky and he's got a bit of a different sense of humour. He's a great guy because he's been great for her."

Peter's brother David was also taken aback by Dionne and Graham's rapid romance and by the call to come and help her move to Saskatchewan with her fiancé. In the end, he trusted his cousin's judgment and he understands and shares her attitude about living life. "She was willing to take a chance and go for it. We either go for it or we don't. It was one of those whirlwind romances at a time when both of them needed something like that in their lives. They were both looking for someone to lean on a little bit."

For David Ballantine, one of the more shocking parts of the move was how rapidly Dionne embraced a new lifestyle where she became much more 'outdoorsy' than she had ever been in Ontario. "If she was going to move away from Mississauga, we probably thought she'd move to New York, not Saskatchewan. If you were going camping, she'd be the one to say, 'Go have fun.' She was not a tomboy or an outdoorsy girl at all, and here she is on a snowmobile, out for a weekend travelling to places. People were shocked."

"I never thought I'd be on a Ski-Doo, but Graham loves to sled," says Dionne. "You gotta go with the flow. This is the entertainment out here." Dionne quickly learned how to dress properly to stay warm in minus-45 weather and how to pee while wearing a snowmobile suit. She and Graham went on weekend snowmobiling trips with Graham's two children, who lived in Regina until about two years after Graham's divorce from their mother.

Snowmobiling also became much more fun after Graham's snowmobile dealer convinced him to upgrade Dionne's sled to a newer, more comfortable sled. Dionne immediately loved it and after her first test ride, yelled out, "Wow, this is better than sex!" And for the men standing just outside the showroom, she added, "This is what it feels like to have something powerful between your legs!"

Dionne soon purchased a new snowmobiling outfit to go with her new sled. "The sled was hot, but the girl on the sled has to look hotter," she laughs. One of the funnier moments on the snowmobile trails happened when they stopped for a break and Dionne commented to Graham about the friendly sledders they had met coming at them on the trail. "The last gentleman gave me the peace sign, so I waved back," she said, showing him a full five-fingered wave. "So Graham told me, 'He was telling you there were two more people behind him! Now he was looking for the other five people behind you!' I didn't know that! I should not really have done anything," she laughs. Then Graham explained she should have actually held up her fist, which means no other riders behind her.

Oh, well. Maybe next time.

Dionne also went on a snowboarding trip with Graham and his children to Kimberley, British Columbia when she first moved to Saskatchewan, laughs Graham. "We talked about how she would take one afternoon of lessons and then try it. The snowboard instructor was a 6'5" dark-haired Italian god, with six-pack abs and V-shaped torso. A freak, I'd say. Well, Dionne ended up taking lessons *all* five days in a row and still couldn't snowboard with a ... No, I'm kidding. She did well. She liked to phone her girlfriends, though, just to tell them about her find."

Dionne took photos of herself with the instructor, so she could share him with her girlfriends. 'Catch me, I'm falling...' was a common refrain, she jokes.

Dionne found many things she loved about living in Saskatchewan in the warmer months as well. She would pull over on the side of the road often to indulge her love of photography and take photos of the farmers' fields. "I'd never seen a beautiful yellow canola field or a field of flax. The sky is beautiful here and I remember looking up at night from our yard in White City and seeing the Northern Lights for the first time. Oh my goodness!"

She learned about country living from Graham's cousins at their ranch near Mossbank, about 90 minutes southwest of Regina. "They taught me how to shoot a gun and I did skeet shooting. I got to see a calf being born. Oooohh! It was a whole different world for me!"

Dionne's cousin Yuri Collesso also found it amusing "to watch the 'big-time big-city girl' transform into the 'country girl/city girl hybrid' we have today. She used to dance on top of speakers at Club Richards in Mississauga. Now she'll dance atop tractors just the same," he laughs.

"I was very happy for her," adds Collesso. "I was definitely sad to see her go and sad that she was no longer less than an hour away, but I was very happy that she found happiness and a life partner who just plain adored her."

"Even if Dionne didn't have cancer, she would have loved him," says Robulack-Mendes. "She takes chances. She takes risks all the time. I just think that Graham was who she was meant to be with."

A few weeks after moving to Saskatchewan, Dionne wasn't so sure that she'd made the right decision. It was the day of their first big fight.

After Dionne moved in with Graham in White City, the party life that Graham had lived for the past few months quickly came to an end. His former roommate, Sean Westerman, was not pleased about this change.

"He was kind of jealous, I think," says Graham.

"He made my life a miserable hell," adds Dionne. "Graham was caught in the middle. It was a very hard time for me and for Graham."

On this particular day, Dionne decided she'd had enough of the tug-of-war for Graham's attention. She stormed out of the house, upset and confused. "I threw the ring at Graham, got in my truck and started to drive out onto Highway 48."

After a few minutes, she pulled over onto the side of the road, realizing she didn't know where to go, and had a little pity party. "I had no friends. I had nowhere to go. I had a cry and then I went back."

She and Graham still laugh about that incident. However, guidelines were quickly put in place in case something like that ever happened again.

It turned out that, even if she'd wanted to go back to Toronto, Dionne had absolutely no idea which way to turn onto the Trans-Canada Highway to get there. "She clarified that if she was ever going to leave, she just needed to know which way to Toronto," smiles Graham. "She also wanted to make sure that the truck was in her name and I assured her it was. She said, 'Okay, I will take the truck and go to Toronto.' Then I think her next worldly possession was she had bought one of those mosquito magnets. Then when we had another squabble, she said, 'I'm taking my mosquito magnet and my truck and going back to Toronto.' Then she got a snowmobile. Then it was, 'I'm taking my snowmobile, mosquito magnet and my truck and going back to Toronto.' I pointed out that she doesn't have a trailer to pull this snowmobile. As time's gone by, I've reminded her that she'll look like the Beverly Hillbillies with the whole back full. It's made quite a cute little running joke."

Dionne has told Graham repeatedly that he always has a choice in their relationship. "I've said to him, 'If someone else ever comes along – this journey's tough, I understand – just tell me.' But when I first moved here, I added, 'The only thing is you'll need to tell me which way to point me because I'm not sure which way is back to Toronto.' "

As for her relationship with Westerman, they are now among the best of friends. "We were all leery of the girl from the big city and it's no secret that Dionne and I butted heads at first," says Westerman, "but I was just testing her to see if she would stick it out," he jokes. "If she could handle me – and she did! – I figured she could handle our tough winters and three-pound grasshoppers. She passed the test with flying colors and has stuck it out ever since, and we have all grown to love her and respect her."

Westerman adds that "all will agree that one of the first things you will discover is her ability to fight – not as in boxing, but her fight to live. She has been to hell and back and still has a great attitude towards life and still does not give up. Her spirit is unbelievable and she always seems to just bounce back with a smile. As far as boxing goes, Tyson would have a tough time with Dionne as she just *won't* give up. I have never avoided an argument with Dionne but get me in the ring with her and I would be high-tailing my butt out of the country. You can't beat someone who won't give up!" he laughs.

Shortly after Dionne moved to Saskatchewan in 2001, Graham approached his friend Craig Clendening, owner of Camera One to create a portrait of Dionne and Graham that had an angelic feel to it. "We wore white to try and create that kind of a feel," says Graham. "What Dionne didn't know was that I took a 12-inch-high black angel doll that she had just received down to the photo studio a day after our normal photo shoot. Craig had just started working with digital photography and he used his new fancy digital gizmotry to create the black angel looking down on us from three different angles. I then supplied the love poem, *Finding True Love by Ba'al Shem Tov: From every human being there rises a light that reaches straight to heaven and when two souls that are destined to be together find each other, the streams of light flow together and a single brighter light goes forth from that united being.*

"Craig combined all of that to make a very romantic angelic portrait that captured everything I had wanted. At that time, this combination of digital manipulations was truly amazing and we were awestruck with what he had done with the black angel subject. I surprised Dionne with it by hanging it on the wall of our living room before we came home together one evening. She seemed adequately pleased with it."

Never Leave Your Wingman

"In practicality, you're actually each other's wingman.
You never leave your partner vulnerable." - Graham

S hortly after moving to Saskatchewan, Dionne began working as a full-time receptionist at Graham's company and immediately began to meet new people and make her own friends.

Karen Drysdale, who has worked for Warner Industries since 1997, remembers being apprehensive at first about this woman who had captured her boss's heart. "The way he described Dionne before we had met her – what an extraordinarily beautiful woman she was, just gushing on and on – I had this vision of a Toronto socialite dressed to the nines in designer clothes. On the day she was coming into the office for the first time, I was looking at the clock, anxious to meet this woman. My office was on the second floor and I could all of a sudden hear this laughter. I just thought, 'Oh.' I went and looked and there's my Miss D the way you see her now – in jeans and a T-shirt and runners. She's my kind of girl.

"We just struck it off," adds Drysdale. "She's down to earth, totally opposite of that picture I had in mind. That laughter precedes her wherever she goes. I was in a restaurant one day. It was fairly big, busy and noisy. I said, 'Yep, D's here.' I could just hear her laughing."

Drysdale became one of Dionne's closest friends at Warner Industries. The two have had many coffee and lunch dates together as well as gone to movies and other social events. "Over the years, not only has Dionne become my dear friend, but my inspiration for life," says Drysdale. "If she can do anything for anybody to help them, she'll be there. There is just a positive energy that always comes from her no matter what."

Drysdale recalls her boss's face whenever he talked about Dionne then. "He would get this look like a little 16-year-old boy. His eyes would light up and I thought, 'Oh, wow, this woman has to be somebody.' I witnessed my boss fall totally head over heels in love, right to where they are today, head over heels in love. They'll never change. Graham will never lose that look in his eye when he talks about her and I can say the same about Dionne."

Many years later, when Graham is asked why he fell in love with Dionne, he doesn't hesitate. "I always see her and she's a light."

For Dionne and Graham, working in the same office led to some interesting moments, such as the time when Graham walked around the corner to the customer lounge to discover that a customer had just asked Dionne out to a movie. "Dionne was waiting for me to finish up for the day and here was this long-distance trucker waiting for his truck. I guess he liked what he saw," laughs Graham. "I heard Dionne say, 'Well this is my fiancé, Graham Warner, the owner of the business.' She didn't say to me, 'He just tried to pick me up,' but I remember the guy looking at me very strangely, kind of sheepishly. I just thought, 'Okay. Whatever.' "

Graham was getting used to Dionne attracting attention. After all, she'd attracted him, and now they were planning their wedding for that August at a venue in Regina.

Almost as soon as Dionne arrived in Saskatchewan, she and Graham began travelling together. Whether it was going away for fun or attending dealer meetings and other business events across North America, the two enjoyed the freedom they now had to see many places and spend time together. "I loved being with Graham and being able to travel with him. And he wanted me to travel with him and be on these trips."

When Dionne was away, one of the other office staff filled in on reception, which became more and more difficult as time went along.

One Monday afternoon at the end of March, just three months after Dionne moved to Saskatchewan, Graham noticed that his fiancée did not look well. On the way home from work that evening, she began complaining of severe cramps in her left side. After a few more minutes of driving, she and Graham decided they should stop at a medi-clinic.

"The walk-in clinic that we went to, because of my case history, advised us to get me to emergency right away," says Dionne. "At the hospital, they ran test after test and I was admitted." The doctor who was working in emergency that night couldn't find anything wrong with Dionne but ordered an extra test to be safe. This meant Dionne had to stay in the hospital for a couple of days until the results came in.

On Wednesday evening, March 28, 2001 the emergency-room doctor came into Dionne's room and she knew immediately that something was wrong. The doctor quickly noticed that Graham was not in the room and asked Dionne, 'Where is your fiancé?'

Dionne had insisted that Graham keep with his regular Wednesday evening schedule and have supper with his children. "He was hesitant to go but I told him, 'Just go. I'll be fine on my own. This is time with your kids and it is very important for you to do this.' "

When Dionne told the doctor that Graham was out with his children, the doctor said he'd come back later when Graham was there, but Dionne would not hear of it. "I said, 'No, you obviously came in to tell me something.'

"He said, 'I don't think you should be alone when I tell you this.'

"I said, 'Just tell me, so I can have some time to go through this myself to figure out what I'm going to do next.' I knew it could not be good news."

Finally, the doctor relented and told Dionne that he still could not find out what was causing her pain, "but with this one other test that I did, I did not expect to find what I did."

"Well, what is it?" Dionne asked him.

"You have liver cancer."

Strangely enough, the liver cancer was not connected to the pain she was feeling on the other side of her body. The doctor had simply decided to do another test for possible kidney stones and liver cancer had shown up.

"When would I have discovered I have liver cancer if you had not done this additional test?" Dionne wanted to know. She was told that she would have eventually had some side-effects and pain. She decided it was probably good that this test had uncovered the cancer.

"With most of my cancers, I've been lucky. It's been early detection where something could be done."

After the doctor left the room, Dionne phoned her Aunt Janet in Guelph, Ontario. "I wasn't going to interrupt Graham during his dinner. His children were very important." Dionne's aunt immediately wanted her to move back to Ontario to be cared for by the oncologists who had treated her breast cancer and brain cancer. Dionne would not agree to that idea just yet.

"I said, 'I don't know what I'm going to do. I have not spoken to Graham. I need to talk to him first.' "

Then Dionne hung up the phone and spent the next few minutes crying. "I was upset. I was scared. I knew nothing about the liver as an organ and what it can do. I was devastated. I was doing so well – 1997 was my last diagnosis with brain cancer and it was now 2001 and I was sick again."

When Graham returned after supper, Dionne told him the news. It was one of the most memorable moments of her life.

"I told him that he didn't have to marry me. I would go back to Ontario. My family was there and I'd be okay. He didn't have to worry about this and take all of this on himself. And Graham, the man that he is, said, 'You never leave your wingman.'

"It took my breath away. He told me, 'I could get sick with cancer. Would you leave me?' I said, 'No – but women are wired differently.' "

Graham repeated, "I'm not going anywhere. We'll get through this together."

Dionne called her family again and told them she would not be moving back to Ontario. "I'm going to stick it out here. Graham and I will get through this together. We're going to find a good doctor here to look after me.'

"I knew I'd be okay," she says. "Regina would be my new home and I'd be okay."

The wingman comment came from Graham's long-time interest in Second World War history. "When bombers or fighters were flying in formation and were being attacked, the enemy always tried to separate the formation – because once they were separated, they were vulnerable. So from that, it was gleaned that you're stronger if you never leave your wingman. It's a pledge of loyalty.

"In practicality, you're actually each other's wingman. You never leave your partner vulnerable. I have that with Dionne. She's my wingman."

Dionne stayed in hospital for the next several days, having tests done and meeting with doctors to sort out a possible treatment plan. Graham spent as much time as he could with Dionne and then went home at night. At about 10 o'clock one evening, he left the hospital and drove to his house in White City, about half an hour outside Regina's city limits. "I drove home, had a shower, crawled into bed and lay in bed for about two minutes and absolutely hated it. I couldn't take it. I got up, got dressed and drove back to the hospital. I didn't really sneak in but I kind of walked by security and climbed into bed with Dionne in her small hospital bed. By then it was probably about 11:30 or midnight. I slept with her. I just couldn't sleep in my bed alone."

Dionne was touched by this pure act of love.

"That was quite a moment for him to do that. I just thought, 'Wow!

This man loves me! He loves me a lot. He misses me. I'm not afraid. We'll get through this.' "

Karen Drysdale recalls her boss coming into the office to tell some of the staff that Dionne had liver cancer. "He was just shell-shocked at first. He looked devastated. I hadn't seen D because she wasn't feeling well, but Graham came and told Ruth Patron and I at work. He tries so hard to keep his calm demeanour at the dealership, but he was struggling with that."

The first oncologist that Dionne and Graham saw was not the right fit for her or Graham, says Dionne. "He said, 'You should get your affairs in order. Probably six months is all you have. You're lucky you survived this much.' "

Graham adds, "He was an old crusty doctor who was ready to retire and he just didn't care." Graham and Dionne knew they could do better than that. However, the second oncologist they saw didn't exactly endear herself to them either. "Graham was at my side, of course. He never left my side for all of this," says Dionne. "He wanted to be part of the meetings and I wanted him to be part of the meetings. This doctor said to me, 'Graham should leave the room.' I asked why and the doctor said, 'Because he may not want to marry you when he finds out how sick you are.'

"I said, 'He's going to be my husband! I don't want any secrets from him – we don't want any secrets between us. He needs to know what's happening with me.' "

The doctor continued, "With what I'm going to tell you, he may not want to marry you."

While the oncologist continued to insist that Graham leave the room, Dionne continued to argue that Graham was not going anywhere. "He's going to stay here with me and we'll deal with whatever you have to say."

So the oncologist went through the diagnosis of liver cancer and told both Dionne and Graham about steps that might occur. Dionne and Graham did not like this doctor's approach either, so they decided to keep looking for another oncologist as well as treatment options. "There has to be somebody else with better compassion and a better bedside manner," they thought.

Graham phoned the Mayo Clinic in the United States. "Although they were willing to see us, they recommended we see a doctor located right in Regina first."

That doctor was Dr. Muhammad Salim, an oncologist in Regina who also collaborated with the Mayo Clinic and would become a critical link in Dionne's health care for many years. Both Dionne and Graham found Dr. Salim to have the right combination of caring, compassion, humour and knowledge. Although Dr. Salim had worked in Florida for many years and was an esteemed oncologist in both the Allan Blair Cancer Centre in Regina and associated with the Mayo Clinic in Minnesota, his thick East Indian accent often left Dionne and Graham wondering what they had just heard. "We'd walk out of the room after meeting with him and say to each other, 'Okay, what do you think he said?' " laughs Dionne.

Communication struggles aside, Dionne does not want to think about what would have happened had she not met Dr. Salim. "He's a gem in my life for sure. I was just so thankful to get him as a doctor."

Dr. Salim ordered a CT scan, bloodwork and other tests for Dionne. The CT scan is also known as a CAT scan (computerized axial tomography) and uses X-rays and a computer to see soft tissue and other parts of the inside of the body that cannot be seen by a conventional X-ray. Through Dr. Salim, Dionne learned that her liver cancer had metastasized from her breast cancer and that the tumour might be able to be removed since the liver is the only organ that can rejuvenate and grow back. Two weeks after her diagnosis, Dionne was sent to Calgary to see if specialists there could or would operate on her.

A young doctor walked into the Calgary hospital room and both Dionne and Graham initially thought he was not a physician, because he was wearing a plaid shirt and jeans, not the standard white lab coat. Dionne decided to have a little fun with the young doctor. When he tapped on her back during his examination, she asked, 'Have you ever got a knock back?' The young doctor burst out laughing and it lightened the mood during this serious situation.

After she returned to Saskatchewan, the Calgary doctors told Dionne they would not operate on her. She and Graham were pleased to hear, though, that the Mayo Clinic was willing to meet with them but before those arrangements could be made, Dr. Salim spoke to Dr. Roger Keith, a surgeon in Saskatoon, about two and a half hours north of Regina, who was willing to consider Dionne's case.

A week after the disappointment of the Calgary trip and three weeks after diagnosis, Dionne heard from Dr. Keith. "He looked at my scans and felt comfortable enough that he could do the liver surgery and he could remove the tumour, so that was great news for us. It was wonderful news. It was something more supportive."

Their summer wedding was now officially postponed. Dionne was admitted to Saskatoon's Royal University Hospital so that on May 28, 2001 she could have surgery for her liver cancer.

Dr. Keith had told Dionne that if he opened her up and found anything different from what he'd seen on the scans such as more than one tumour in her liver, for example, he would just close her up again. "I totally understood that," says Dionne. "I was just grateful that someone would take a chance and just go in and look, especially after getting a 'no' from Calgary and so many different doctors' attitudes I had to deal with before finding a surgeon here and a good oncologist at the Allan Blair. Dr. Keith was willing to try."

Graham recalls the moments before Dionne went in for her liver cancer surgery as being among the saddest and loneliest of his life.

He had walked with Dionne as far as the hospital staff would let him go before they got to the operating room. He and Dionne kissed and hugged and then Dionne walked the rest of the way with the doctor to be prepped for surgery.

"I was watching her walk down the final hallway to the operating room," says Graham, sadly reliving that moment. "The doctor was walking beside her, but she looked so tiny and frail. It was a terrible feeling. I felt like I was sending her off to fend for herself. It was lonely. It was the most scared I've ever felt."

Although Dionne herself was frightened by the unknown of the surgery and of course, the outcome, she had total confidence in her surgeon. Dr. Keith was not only completely competent, but he was blessed with a sense of humour that was much appreciated. "He and Graham just clicked," smiles Dionne. "He has a wonderful heart and soul. I felt very good having him look after me. It put a calming over me that I could put my mind at ease and be okay to do this."

During the next six hours, the surgical team removed 51% of Dionne's liver, which included her tumour. They also removed her gall bladder to ensure the cancer did not spread to that area. When Dionne was later told they had also removed her gall bladder, she honestly didn't care. "I just said, 'Okay. As long as you've got the cancer out. I'm alive. I'm breathing. I'm okay. I woke up. That's fine, and I can still function on what liver I have.' I was just so relieved to know they were able to get to the tumour because Calgary said they wouldn't touch me with a 10-foot pole."

Dionne learned some valuable lessons from her breast cancer and liver cancer. "Get a second opinion. Get a third opinion. Don't just go by one. With my breast cancer, the first doctor told me it was nothing to worry about. That second opinion helped save my life."

Her recovery from the liver surgery was more difficult than her previous cancer surgeries. "I had to work a lot harder to build up my strength because they moved everything around in there to get to the tumour. "She had to exercise her lungs by blowing through a breathing tube to get the ball inside it to move. Considerable energy was expended just to get up and move around, but Dionne was determined to not stay in the hospital a moment longer than the two weeks they told her she had to be there. "I said, 'I will be out in two weeks because I hate hospitals,' " she laughs.

Graham spent at least part of every day in Saskatoon during those two weeks. "I would get up at 5 o'clock in the morning, work at the dealership until noon, stop at McDonalds to get food on the way to the airport, eat in the truck as I drove to the airport, file my flight plan, check the weather, pull the airplane out of the hangar, fly to Saskatoon. I'd be there by 2 o'clock, leave at 7 to 8 p.m., fly home, repeat the process the next day."

Sometimes he stayed overnight at a motel near the hospital. On one memorable evening, he gave Dionne a special goodbye before heading back to Regina.

"I buzzed the hospital," explains Graham.

"I was going to fly home but I told Dionne I would phone her from the runway before I took off and for her to look out the window shortly after that. The tower cleared me for takeoff. I phoned Dionne. I purposely left the Mode C transponder off. That's a device that tells the tower what altitude I'm at and where I am. The Royal University Hospital sits on the South Saskatchewan River. I proceeded to fly down along the river and I think D was on the fourth or fifth floor. Anyway, I flew by just above her window."

Dionne knew that Graham was coming by and she flagged down a nurse who was walking by her room just in time to share the excitement with her. "I said, 'Come in here! Come in here! You see this plane that's coming? It's coming for me! It's coming for me!'

"She said, 'Yeah right. Come on, you're kidding me.'

"I said, 'Seriously, seriously. And I bet it's going to wave its wings.' "

The nurse didn't believe Dionne, but Dionne convinced her to just stay and watch for a minute. "So here comes Graham and he gets closer and he did! He rocked the airplane side to side, waving the plane's wings! I said, 'Yeah, see – he's waving! Oh my goodness, that's my fiancé!' "

The nurse was suitably impressed and shouted, "Oh my gosh!"

This only added to Dionne's joy.

Meanwhile, the Saskatoon Airport Tower had become suspicious and had radioed Graham to find out the problem. "They were not happy," he smiles. "They wanted to know why my transponder was not on. I just said I would recycle it and see if it came on. I then proceeded to shoot skyward to gain altitude before I turned it on, and everything was good in the world."

"Graham has a motto he uses – 'it's easier to ask for forgiveness than permission,'" laughs Dionne.

"Just sometimes," adds Graham. "You have to decide when."

"It was a very, very neat moment to have," recalls Dionne. "And for that nurse to say, 'Oh my gosh!'" That special wave from Graham's airplane will live on in Dionne's memory forever.

There were plenty of other special moments during Dionne's stay in the Saskatoon hospital – all brought to her by Graham. He purchased the *Sex and the City* VHS series and a small television that could play the tapes, then brought them to her room so they could lie in her hospital bed together and watch the shows. Often, nurses and other hospital staff would stop in to watch parts of the series with them.

"The nurses would come in and hang out with us. It was cute," says Dionne. "As I got better, Graham brought in food. He'd often bring in extra for the staff. Graham always took care of everybody. He had mini donuts one time and milkshakes one other time. That is G – 'Let's do something for the night staff now.'"

Graham flew one of Dionne's girlfriends, Kim Maki, up with him from Regina one day. Maki had met Dionne during the sleigh ride on Dionne's first trip to Saskatchewan. Maki was dating an acquaintance of Graham's and ended up sitting beside Dionne at Boston Pizza after the sleigh ride. "We hit it off instantly," says Maki. "It was like we had known each other forever."

Maki had wanted to go see Dionne in hospital and was planning on driving up to Saskatoon one evening, but Graham told her, 'No, we'll just fly up.'

"I got to fly the plane and everything!" says Maki, still smiling at the memory. "It was a really big deal to me!"

On June 9, when Dionne's two weeks in hospital were up, she was released from Royal University Hospital. She felt fine and was anxious to go home and had no intention from the beginning of spending a moment past her 14 days in the hospital. Dr. Keith stopped in to see her before she was discharged and Dionne later heard that this visit was rare. "The staff said we were lucky because he rarely comes back to visit patients later.

He's a very busy surgeon in Saskatoon and I knew that. It was really nice that he came to see us. He really enjoyed Graham. I was just thankful he would even try to do this surgery."

From that surgery, Dionne has a huge scar that extends from her breastbone down past her belly button. At first, she vowed she would never wear any of the two-piece swimsuits she owns because of that scar and the other marks on her abdomen that show where the catheter was connected. Although Graham had repeatedly told her there was no reason to be embarrassed and no reason to hide her scars, it took Dionne a few months to accept that reasoning and be comfortable enough to wear her swimsuits as she had done before the surgery.

"They're survivor marks and I had to figure out that I shouldn't be ashamed of them. Oh my goodness, I'm slashed from here to here. I couldn't cover that up. I saw other people wearing two-piece swimsuits who shouldn't be in two-piece swimsuits and I thought, 'Why am I covering myself up? It's nothing to be ashamed of or embarrassed about. It's just something I had to go through in life.' When kids came up to me and pointed out my scars to their mothers, I'd say, 'Oh, yeah. Shark bite. You should see what I did to the shark!' " she laughs.

A few days after returning home, Dionne was back working part-time on the reception desk for Graham's company. Her co-workers were all shocked at her quick return, but it was impossible to convince Dionne to stay away from work. "I'm not a person who can sit around and do nothing. I'd rather be surrounded by people than have my mind wondering, 'What's next?' "

On July 12, 2001 she began chemotherapy treatments in Regina at the Allan Blair Cancer Centre. She was scheduled for five treatments, once every two weeks.

Nadine Desrosiers, a staff person at the cancer centre, remembers seeing Dionne in the chemo waiting area for one of those early appointments. "She was sitting with G, curled up in the chair like a child. She looked so young, I even remember the striped T-shirt she was wearing. She seemed quite shy. I remember thinking, 'She is so beautiful and young. I hope she isn't a patient,' but gut feeling told me she was." Desrosiers, like so many others, felt drawn to Dionne and approached her after a couple of treatments to get to know her better. "She seemed so very excited to introduce G. She just beamed like she was introducing me to a prince. I guess that a wingman is like a prince."

Fifteen days after her first chemo treatment, Dionne phoned her girlfriend Kim Maki to ask if she would come to Dionne and Graham's house in White City and shave Dionne's head. "Our little head-shaving party with Kimmie Maki was at 9:00 p.m. on July 27, 2001," says Dionne. "Kimmie was a hairdresser in Regina at the time. She had her own business in the basement of her home. After my second chemo treatment, I could feel that tingling sensation I was used to having before chemo hair loss, so I asked Kimmie if she would come out and shave my head for me. I knew I would be in good hands and this was one way she could help me take control of the situation. Kimmie graciously, without hesitation, came out and we set up shop in our downstairs bathroom.

"Graham was with us and volunteered to shave his head. Kimmie and I both thought it was very sweet of him to offer but I knew my hair would grow back after treatment and his might not, so we let him off the hook," laughs Dionne. "I saw the look of relief in his face.

"It was quite a bonding moment for Kimmie and me. I will never forget how wonderfully Kimmie took care of me that night. There may have been a few tears along the way, but the love in that room overpowered any sadness, that is for sure."

Dionne was given Tamoxifen, a drug that interferes with the activity of the female hormone estrogen. She completed three of the five chemotherapy treatments and then stopped because the chemo was too strong for her. She was not given any further treatment. Regular check-ups and tests were scheduled and Dionne carried on with her life.

On December 13, 2001 Dionne had day surgery at Regina General Hospital to remove her ovaries, a suggestion she'd first heard in Toronto a year earlier after her genetic testing results were known. "They said I should have had a double mastectomy and had my ovaries removed because my cancer was hormonal and I had the abnormal BRCA1 gene. The doctor here decided that because this liver cancer had come into my life, I should at least have my ovaries removed."

After the surgery, Dionne was fading in and out of consciousness in the recovery room while Graham sat at her bedside. "The fascinating and wild thing about this was when the doctor asked how I was feeling," laughs Dionne. "I said, 'Oh, pretty good.' Then she said, "The surgery went well. We did have one little issue.'

"So I said, 'Okay...'

" 'We seem to have misplaced a tool and we think it might still be in you,' the doctor said.

"And I thought she was joking. I thought Graham had put her up to it – because this is my fiancé, the joker. And Graham was looking at me, saying, 'Hon, I had nothing to do with this!' And I was saying, 'Ha ha ha!' Because I was still kind of high as a kite. 'Yeah, right, Graham, you're funny!'

"He just kept saying, 'Hon, no. Seriously, seriously.' It probably took him 10 minutes to convince me that this was not a joke."

Once Dionne realized that the doctor was not kidding at all, she asked if this meant she would have to go back into surgery. The doctor, now at the foot of Dionne's bed, said, 'No, I'm just going to feel around and see if I can feel it first of all.'

So Dionne was casually thinking, 'Hmm ... okay,' in that half-awake, half-asleep state that occurs upon waking up after anaesthesia. "The doctor then proceeded to put her finger in and she said, 'Take a deep breath,' and she just yanked! I never screamed so loud in my life! Graham ran around the corner of the curtain."

Dionne later thought about being a fly on the wall in the operating room when staff realized they had misplaced a tool. " 'Okay, this is back, this is back.' Then they're looking at each other – 'Oh oh, this thing is missing. I thought you got it.'

" 'I thought you got it.'

" 'Oh oh. It's still in the patient.'

"I think it was a filter kind of thing," says Dionne. "I was still kind of half out of it. But I do remember screaming because it still had to come out! The doctor just reached in and grabbed it! Ooohh! ... It just gets more and more interesting with the things that happen along the way."

The 36-year-old Dionne was now welcomed into the world of menopause. Although some of the possible side-effects of Tamoxifen are menopause-like symptoms such as hot flashes, vaginal dryness, joint pain and leg cramps,[6] Dionne had not experienced any of those symptoms. After her ovaries were removed, she jumped into menopause with a fury.

With her hormone-related cancer, she could not take any pills to combat the hot flashes or other symptoms. Doctors offered her an anti-depressant medication that might help, but she refused to take it. "I said, 'I'm not depressed. If you've got anything for the hot flashes, bring it on, I'll take it – but I'm not depressed. I don't want to get into the mode of popping those types of pills. I'll deal with the hot flashes. I will see what my body can handle first before I start popping pills."

Mood swings have also been a frustration. "I remember the one time

[6] **U.S. National Cancer Institute**
http://www.cancer.gov/cancertopics/factsheet/Therapy/tamoxifen

saying to Graham, 'I could just cry right now. I don't know why. I could just cry.'

"It's kind of cute when we're driving down the highway and it's 40 below Celsius and she's plastered to the side window trying to cool off," smiles Graham.

"Graham just laughs when I ask him to put the air conditioning on for a bit, 'Pleeeaasse.' Meanwhile, he's freezing. There were times I would wake up with night sweats. It feels like you could just peel the sweat off me. There are times he'll reach over to cuddle me … 'Oh, you're hot flashing, aren't you?' But he's never kicked me out of bed."

Cancer and menopause bring certain changes in intimacy and a woman's feelings about her own body, says Dionne. "I used to be that cuddly, snuggly person lying in bed, but it's tough now. You're either hot flashing or the sex drive on the woman's side is not as strong as it used to be. It comes part and parcel with me and the disease. When you get your ovaries removed, things change. You've had a lot of stuff ripped out of you. Sometimes you feel a little bit less of a woman." For Dionne, there are no products available to help with any of these symptoms, because they are all hormone-based. "You really have to have a good man who can understand."

Dionne had decided long before she met Graham that she would not have children, so the removal of her ovaries was not a concern from that perspective. Nor was it for Graham, who had two children and had already had a vasectomy before he met Dionne.

"Thank God I never did have a child with my first husband because I wouldn't be able to be here with Graham. Everything happens for a reason. I would be sitting in Mississauga, probably miserable."

Dionne and Graham did talk about adopting, but decided against that option.

"We were travelling so much, plus I had my hands full with my kids in the early stage before they moved away," says Graham. "I said what we could do was adopt an 18-year-old big-bosomed female at the time."

"If it was Shania Twain, he'd be happy," laughs Dionne.

"Now I'm okay," concedes Graham, years later. "I wouldn't know what to do with it."

After her day surgery in December 2001, Dionne returned home and rested for as short a time as she could. She wanted to keep busy so she went back to work part-time and then full-time once she was strong enough. She and Graham continued planning their wedding, this time for October 2002.

"Everything was looking good. I was feeling pretty good. Everything was great."

At about this same time, Dionne began thinking about leaving her job at the dealership. She and Graham had come to realize that their main topic of conversation away from work was still work. "I didn't know anybody else, only the people at work. I like to meet lots of people, but when we came home, that's all we did was talk about work. It was tough," says Dionne.

Dionne was away from work often, between travelling with Graham and being sick, and there was strain in the office with Dionne being on staff. "You can't leave a full-time job and say, 'I'm gone for five days because my fiancé has a business trip.'" It was causing strain on other staff to fill in rather than hire another permanent staff person. Graham had also caused a stir initially by stating that Dionne be paid her Ontario salary for her work in his Saskatchewan office. Dionne had warned Graham that he couldn't afford her, "but he never listened to me," she said. This did not sit well with some staff members who saw the boss's fiancée receiving preferential treatment. So Dionne and Graham talked about all these issues as well as Dionne's interest in volunteering and agreed that she should resign from her job.

This meant that Graham had to admit what all men hate to admit – his woman was right.

"It was either I start sleeping with all the girls or hire a replacement for Dionne," jokes Graham.

"None of the girls wanted to sleep with him, so they hired a replacement for me," adds Dionne with a smile.

She had been thinking about volunteering at the cancer clinic, but this presented its own problems for her to overcome. Even though she knew Graham was able to support both of them financially so she didn't have to work, it was difficult for her to accept that concept at first. "Yes, he's well off and he can take care of me, but I'm still an independent person. I have to be my own person. I was used to always taking care of myself. I don't like to depend on anybody and that was a very tough thing to let go of, to feel that it was going to be okay," she explains.

"My mother depended so much on my dad for everything and this was always in the back of my mind. I said I didn't want to be like that. I have to take care of myself and do the things that I want to do in life. I remember saying to him, 'Now that I don't work, when I go shopping for your birthday, I feel like you're still buying your own birthday gift.'" It took quite a while before Graham was able to convince Dionne that she was contributing to the success of his business in her support for him and that she was entitled and deserving of sharing his wealth.

Giving Back

"These are people who supported me – angels who are still in my life and people whom we've lost along the way, too." - Dionne

In May 2002, Dionne began volunteering at the Allan Blair Cancer Centre on the main floor of Regina's Pasqua Hospital. Having spent time there undergoing chemotherapy for her liver cancer, she knew some of the staff and volunteers. This made her entry into volunteering somewhat smoother but her focus was still, of course, on the patients.

"Since I'd been through so much, I thought I could help somebody else and give them that hope and courage and strength. I just loved it and I met so many wonderful people from the nurses to the patients. A lot of my friends are survivors whom I met along the way."

Dionne volunteered on Tuesdays and Thursdays from 8:30 a.m. to 4:30 p.m. She chatted with patients, helped them try on wigs and pushed a food cart that offered juices, water, hot chocolate, ginger ale, crackers and cookies to help patients feel more comfortable while they received treatment. The volunteers also served sandwiches to patients when Dionne started, but that practice has since ended.

Dionne enjoyed being able to sit with patients and talk about any topic they chose. As the staff and other volunteers grew to know Dionne and her story of overcoming three cancers, they began asking her to visit certain patients as soon as those patients walked into the clinic. Dionne would laugh and say, 'Okay, they just checked in. Let's let them get the first treatment over with and I'll go visit and talk to them." The response was often, 'No, they need to hear your story now so you can give them that strength and that hope.'

"It was kind of cute how they said, 'Go! Go! Go! They need to hear your story!' " she says.

Dr. Salim occasionally asked Dionne to visit patients in the third-floor cancer unit who were having a difficult time with their diagnosis or treatment. "He'd ask me if I would go up to the ward and introduce myself to the patient, see if they could warm up to me and see if I could sort of take them out of that funk, that 'Woe is me!' kind of thing. I would go up and try to do that, and I never got booted out! I have many friends from that, too."

When she was not attending to patients' physical needs, she relied on her natural intuition to spot patients who were suffering emotionally. She introduced herself and sat with those patients, almost always putting them at ease and making them more comfortable as they went through their own battle with cancer.

"Dionne has a renowned enthusiasm and vibrant personality. She readily became a member of the team," says Wilbur Heinrich, co-co-ordinator of Volunteer Services at the Allan Blair Cancer Centre. "Dionne is well known for her infectious laughter, her fun-loving nature and her generosity in giving her time and energy in fighting cancer. She exudes positive energy wherever she goes and is an inspiration to all of us."

Shortly after Dionne began volunteering at the Allan Blair clinic, she donated about a dozen of her hats as well as her hat stand to the cancer clinic. The hats and stand sit in the wig room, just inside the entrance to the cancer centre. Fashion has always been a big deal to Dionne, and covering up one's bald head to help make a person feel better was therapeutic and easy for Dionne to encourage.

Her fashion sense went beyond caring for the patients, though. She often made her own fashion statement in refusing to dress the same way as all the other cancer centre volunteers, which led to some strife at times. "At first it was an issue because the volunteers used to wear these green jackets that were the colour of Kermit the Frog," says Nadine Desrosiers. "Dionne said, 'It's gross. I can't co-ordinate anything with it!' She and Lou Beltramini, who trained her as a volunteer and then became one of her closest friends, volunteered together for years and they were both excited when the volunteers got burgundy jackets. Then they became rebels and just started wearing their regular clothes. They were called in. Dionne complained the jackets were too hot … She's really something," laughs Desrosiers.

"People have said to me at times, 'Why would you go back to volunteer at the cancer centre when you've dealt with so much cancer?' It's a place that I belong. I can help others. There are patients who don't even want to think about this disease. That's a part of their life that they're done with and they never want to look back. I don't look at it that way. I want to help others try to get through their journeys. I think that's so important.

"I wish I had known somebody to contact when I was diagnosed with the brain cancer. There was nobody. When I was diagnosed with the liver cancer, there was nobody I could speak to who could tell me what they'd gone through, to sort of help me. It was the best decision Graham and I ever made, for me to do the volunteering. It also opened up our conversations."

In late August 2002, Dionne had a follow-up CT scan to see if there had been any change in her cancer. On August 27, when Dr. Salim entered the room where she and Graham were waiting to hear the results of the scan, Dionne knew that something was wrong.

"As a cancer patient, you get to know the look after awhile when it's not good news. I said to him, 'What now?' He looked at Graham and I and said, 'My dear, I dreaded coming through this door and telling you any more bad news after all you have been through.'"

Then he told Dionne that her liver cancer was back. This time, it was on the other side of her liver.

"I think my first words to him were, 'Can we rip it out again?' I didn't know how much my liver had rejuvenated, what I could survive with ... Was this possible?"

Dr. Salim quickly answered Dionne's questions. Yes, her liver had rejuvenated enough to do another surgery, but the procedure would have to be done fairly soon. He had already contacted Dr. Keith in Saskatoon, who was willing to examine Dionne again to see if he could excise this new tumour.

Dionne asked if she and Graham would still be able to get married before the surgery. The answer was yes, but they could not have a honeymoon. They would have to have their wedding, then go straight to the hospital in Saskatoon.

Dionne was distraught by this news but, as usual, she did not let it get her down for long. "I have a 24-hour rule with my cancer. After I get the diagnosis, I give myself 24 hours to absorb what's been said to me and take it in as best I can, but I have to let it go after that and figure out what's the next step. I could sit here forever and cry. It's not going to make a difference. I'm a person that even if I'm lying in bed and I can't sleep, I'd rather have the TV on than let my mind work overtime on the 'what ifs' and 'what could happens.' I take myself to another place."

Due to this new diagnosis, Dionne and Graham decided to cancel their Regina wedding and get married in Guelph, Ontario during the Thanksgiving long weekend in October. They had to forego their deposit at the Hotel Saskatchewan to do so, but it was worth it.

"We went to Guelph because marriage licences are $10 cheaper there," jokes Graham.

Dionne laughs. "I really wanted to see my family again before this next surgery. Everything happened so fast. The hotel was able to take us and there was no official invitation. It was an e-mail that said, 'We're coming, we're going to get married there and we hope you can join us for a special evening at our wedding.' "

Dionne and Graham chuckle about having to recycle the 130 invitations they had purchased for their Regina wedding. Graham had suggested that they could just cross off the date and location and write the new information over the old details. "Why couldn't we? Everybody would understand," he said.

Dionne vetoed that idea. "Not at my wedding!" she laughs. "There was no crossing out of dates, but I did keep the envelopes."

Nadine Desrosiers and another woman who worked at the Allan Blair Cancer Centre held a small bridal shower for Dionne in the back conference room one day. "There were only a handful of us there as not many people knew this quiet and, at times, shy young lady yet," says Desrosiers. Dionne was starting to experiment more with her photography then and Desrosiers remembers her bringing in her camera and asking the women in their scrubs to pose for pictures. "She'd say, 'This one's for the boys' and she'd make us pose and be silly. Then she'd bring back 8-by-10-inch photos with little borders and sayings on them. It was quite cute."

On Friday, October 11, 2002 Graham and Dionne were married in a hotel in Guelph in a simple ceremony performed by a justice of the peace. It was a romantic setting with soft lighting and white roses everywhere. Tiny white lights hung over the trellis leading to the spot where Dionne and Graham would exchange their vows surrounded by Dionne's aunt, father and half-sister, other family members and friends as well as Graham's two children, his mother and his Aunt Evelyn Lowe from Moose Jaw.

Graham's attendants were Dionne's cousin Yuri Collesso and Graham's son Maxwell. Dionne's attendants were her girlfriends Claire Fletcher and Kim (Kimmie) Maki, and Graham's daughter MacKenzie. As Graham stood at the front of the room, waiting for his bride, Dionne surprised him by having Collesso's stepdaughter Candace Zeller sing *The First Time Ever I Saw Your Face*, a song made famous by Roberta Flack. "That song has always made me think of Graham," smiles Dionne.

Dionne's father had come from Jamaica to witness his daughter marrying the man he calls "a godsend for Dionne. Every night, after I offer prayers for them both, I always thank God for bringing Graham into her life," says Rupert Walford.

Partway through the ceremony, the justice of the peace and the other attendants stepped back and Maki surprised the happy couple by singing *Whither Thou Goest*, a decades-old wedding song that Maki's father sang to her mother on their wedding day. "I thought it was a really good song, more of an older church song, and one of the easiest ones I could sing," smiles Maki. "It was quite the surprise because I had been making plans from Regina with the minister, without Dionne and Graham knowing about it. They were standing there, kind of looking at each other and wondering 'What is going on? What is she doing?' "

"We didn't know she could sing!" laughs Dionne.

It did not come as a surprise to most of the guests that the theme of the wedding was angels. The happy couple had purchased ceramic angel candleholders for centrepieces and instead of wedding gifts, the 80 guests were asked to find an angel pin and wear it to the wedding.

"It was great," says Dionne. "Everybody was beautiful with their pins on. I loved it."

All night long, guests shared stories of how they chose their angel pins and what the pins meant to them, especially with Dionne heading into her next surgery. "There was a lot of love and support in the room that night. You could just feel it," she says.

For their wedding song, Dionne chose the Celine Dion song *The Colour Of My Love*. Although she is a huge fan of Celine Dion, the words of the song were what attracted her to it: "*I'll paint a sun to warm your heart, Swearing that we'll never part, That's the colour of my love. I'll draw the years all passing by, So much to learn, so much to try, And with this ring our lives will start, Swearing that we'll never part, I offer what you cannot buy, Devoted love until we die.*" [7]

The wedding ceremony was followed by dancing and desserts. The only speech was given by Graham and Dionne, who thanked everyone for coming and then invited them to Aunt Janet's home the next day for a get-together. The bride and groom provided wine that Graham had made and put a bottle of red and a bottle of white on each of the tables for their guests to enjoy. A photo of the couple was on each bottle.

At one point during the evening, Dionne and Graham were on the dance floor when *The Prayer*, sung by Celine Dion and Andrea Bocelli, came over the speaker system: '*I pray you'll be our eyes, and watch us where we go. And help us to be wise in times when we don't know. Let this*

[7] www.songlyrics.com

be our prayer, when we lose our way. Lead us to the place, guide us with your grace, To a place where we'll be safe.' [7]

"Everybody came off the dance floor and left the floor for Graham and I," says Dionne. "It was heavenly. It felt like we were floating, surrounded by angels."

There was no official wedding cake but that didn't stop two of the guests from jumping to that conclusion. Graham and Dionne had placed two small angel ornaments on top of a small chocolate cake that was sitting on the desserts table. During the evening, a guest thought she'd like a slice of the cake and cut into it, only to hear her friend yell, 'Oh my God, you just cut into the wedding cake!' In a panic, the women quickly thought of a plan to hide the mistake. They turned the cake around so the slice could not be seen and quickly walked away from the dessert table. Unfortunately for them, someone told the bride and groom what had happened.

The next day, the young women arrived at Aunt Janet's house to visit the family. Graham calmly answered the door and then launched in with, 'Can you frickin' believe some jerk cut our wedding cake last night? Can you believe someone would do that?'

"And I just let it hang on them," laughs Graham.

"Oh, yeah, you were good," giggles Dionne.

"They almost were in tears," adds Graham.

"They broke down right away," laughs Dionne. "They screamed, 'Oh my God, it was us! We didn't know!' Everybody else in the house already knew that we were setting them up for this. We laughed and said, 'We got you! We already knew you did it! We were waiting to see your reaction. My gosh, the two of you sold out so quick! You didn't even try to deny it! You could have gone, 'Oh my goodness, you're kidding?' It didn't matter to us. It was never a wedding cake."

The young women were relieved to hear that they hadn't actually assaulted the wedding cake, but admitted that their mistake had ruined the rest of the wedding night for them.

Although everyone laughed at that moment at the expense of the young women, the last laugh was actually on Graham and Dionne a few days later as they headed home. While in Guelph, a number of gag gifts were given to Dionne at a party before the wedding, and more were left on their wedding bed at some point during the reception. While packing up to head back to Saskatchewan, Graham decided to take some of these amusing items home to show some of their friends in Regina who had not been at the wedding, except it didn't work out that way.

[7] www.songlyrics.com

"I had started to box up our centrepieces and, being the efficient freighter packer dude that I am, I thought I'd take some of these gag sex-toy gifts and pack them wherever I could in the angel candleholder boxes. I was pretty proud of the job I did because I had a box for each member of my family to carry through security as carry-on. There were probably five or six smaller boxes within each large box."

Forgetting what was in the boxes, Graham sent his son through security first when they got to Toronto's Pearson airport. "My son was 11. He had a skateboarder's kind of chain on his pants. He hadn't had any problem flying to Toronto with it but now the security officer there decided it was a security risk. He had my son remove the chain from his belt and hand it to me to hold on my person during the flight. Apparently an 11-year-old boy will strangle the pilot with a chain but a 38-year-old man won't," smiles Graham.

"Then my daughter came through. Everything was okay until the candleholder box she was carrying caught the security guards' attention as it went through the X-ray machine."

The guard who had just dealt with the skateboarder's chain looked at the X-ray screen and walked over to Graham. "Sir, we have a problem."

"He was being very discreet," says Graham. "The guard said to me, 'There appears to be some objects in this box that will not be allowed on the plane. I'm going to open it from the bottom and we'll see what you have.' And I was thinking, 'What is he talking about?' Then the first thing he pulled out was a set of black fur-lined handcuffs."

Dionne had gone through ahead of Graham. At the first hint of trouble, she kept walking. Graham's mother, meanwhile, was waiting behind him and his daughter to come through the security scanner. Graham was sure she was wondering what was going on ahead of her, but she thankfully couldn't see what the security guard pulled out of the candleholder box next – a whip adorned with metal studs.

The security officer did his best to remain discreet. "He kind of leaned over to me and said, 'Sir, we have two options. You can either leave it here or check it in your luggage.'

"I said, 'Thank you so much. Just leave it here.' It was just one of those moments. I totally forgot I had that stuff. And my daughter was saying, 'What's that, Dad?' She was 13 years old.

"I don't even know what else was in there," says Graham, who was more than a little flustered by this point.

Dionne laughs that they have since told friends and family travelling through Toronto's Pearson airport terminal to check the display case for items that are not allowed in carry-on luggage. "Those are probably our fur-lined handcuffs in there," she laughs.

Dionne also remembers smiling about what was going through the heads of the people in the line-up behind Graham and his family. "They were probably thinking, 'These people are freaky. I can't believe we're stuck in this line and this guy is pulling out handcuffs and a whip.' "

"I was just dying," says Graham.

And what did he say to his daughter and his mother afterwards? "I don't know," says Graham. "I probably just said, 'Don't worry about it.' "

Dionne and Graham have also had a few laughs over the years about the time Dionne actually asked Graham to be her husband – 10 years before their wedding – as a temporary fix to an annoying problem. They were in a Toronto restaurant club with a group of other Freightliner employees after a business meeting. Graham was deep in conversation with Kim (Kimmie) Robulack-Mendes about the parts side of the business while Dionne was trying to fend off a man who was hitting on her.

"He wasn't part of the Freightliner group. I finally said to Graham, 'Can you do me a favour? If this guy comes up to me again, can you just pretend you're my husband?' And Graham said, 'Okay, sure.' So this gentleman came up to me again and I said to him, 'I'm here with my husband.' He looked at Graham and said, 'It doesn't look like he's paying you much attention.' Years later, who would think we'd be married? We played husband and wife just to deter him," laughs Dionne.

Graham nods and adds, "I remember specifically that Kimmie and I were in this huge debate. It was all pure business. And here was Dionne getting hit on and I was not there to defend her honour. Well, I still defended her but it was just, 'Yeah, okay, back to Kimmie.' "

Shortly after returning from their real wedding to their home in White City, Dionne and Graham received a phone call from the hospital in Saskatoon. Dionne's liver cancer surgery had been scheduled.

One of Dionne's girlfriends flew to Regina from her home out of province to spend the two weeks in Saskatoon while Dionne was in hospital. This allowed Graham to travel back and forth between Regina and Saskatoon for those two weeks, splitting his time between caring for his business and caring for his wife. Dionne and her girlfriend decided to drive up to Saskatoon so Dionne's girlfriend would have a car during that time. When the two women were about halfway between Regina and

Saskatoon, Dionne's girlfriend yelled out, "Oh my God, there's an airplane!"

"Just past the A & W at Davidson, we looked over and saw Graham flying low over the field – right there beside us! 'Look! Look! Oh, wow! Oh my gosh, there's Graham!' He had planned to fly up and he'd timed where he thought we would be. He'd been looking for us. It was beautiful," says Dionne.

Graham and the women continued on their way and met at the Royal University Hospital. On October 28, 2002 Dionne had her second surgery for liver cancer. This time, the doctors removed 31% of her liver, including the tumour. Dionne was thrilled and was looking forward to recovery.

"I knew I would have to go through the two-week minimum and rebuild everything again. It was easier this time because I knew what to expect and what I needed to do. I felt more comfortable also because I knew the staff and they knew me."

Immediately after the surgery, Dionne was placed in intensive care for a few days to recover. Graham recalls that she was hooked up to machines, hoses and lines when someone carrying a tray of freshly made French fries with gravy on them happened to walk down the hallway just as the door to the ICU swung open. "Dionne caught not only a whiff of the delicious treat but sight of them, too," smiles Graham. "This created quite an interesting dilemma for Dionne. She now was craving this favourite food of hers but didn't have the means to obtain it. She was pretty doped up with morphine and other drugs when she asked me to leave her $20 before I left. I told her, 'You don't need $20 in ICU. Everything is provided for you.' It was most amusing to watch the wheels in her drugged-up mind still turning, trying to figure out how she could get me to leave the cash so that she could get those French fries without telling me that was what she was trying to do," Graham chuckles.

"There was not a hope in hell that she could have eaten them had she convinced someone to go get them for her, but once Dionne's mind is made up, it's pretty tough to change." Although Graham doesn't think Dionne ever lost that craving, she did not get French fries until after she left the hospital, he explains.

A few days after Dionne was transferred from ICU to a normal hospital patients' room, Graham returned to Regina for the night. The next morning, he walked into Karen Drysdale's office and asked, 'How busy are you today? How would you like to make a trip to Saskatoon with me?' Drysdale was surprised and thrilled. She and Ruth Patron had made

Graham promise that he would phone them to tell them how the surgery went. She did not expect him to drive the two of them up there to see Dionne for themselves.

Drysdale remembers walking into Dionne's hospital room and receiving an excited welcome. " 'Ooohh!' Dionne insisted on getting out of bed and said, 'We're going down to the cafeteria for a coffee. Now I can start healing.' And she did," says a still-amazed Drysdale. "She's the strongest woman I've ever met and I ever will meet. No doubt about it."

The women spent all afternoon visiting. They left Saskatoon with Graham at about 5 p.m., arriving back in Regina around 7:30 p.m. with Graham happy in the knowledge that the trip had given all of their spirits a boost.

During the two weeks that Dionne was recovering from surgery in Saskatoon, Graham would often bunk down in a motel room just across the river from the hospital, says Dionne, who giggles about a nighttime pastime that they created when they were separated by the river. Dionne and Graham would look out their respective windows and blink flashlights back and forth at each other while talking on the phone. " 'Can you see my light?' 'Yes. Can you see mine?' You find things to do when you're stuck somewhere," laughs Dionne.

Finally, a hospital staff person suggested that they should perhaps stop their flashlight antics because someone might think one of them needed help. This added another memory for the two to discuss during their long hours in the hospital.

When Graham was unable to stay overnight, he flew his Cessna to Saskatoon for evening visits. Dionne's out-of-province girlfriend would take a break from the hospital while Graham visited with Dionne, or Graham and Dionne's friend went for supper and then returned for another visit before Graham headed back to Regina.

One day, Dionne was pleasantly surprised to see her girlfriend Kimmie Maki arrive in her hospital room. Maki had driven up from Whitewood, about four hours southeast of Saskatoon, to spend the day with Dionne. She brought Dionne a small stuffed lion. Dionne has lovingly turned to 'Leo the Lion of Courage' many times since then.

Being the mischievous person she is, Dionne decided that things were a little too boring in hospital the afternoon that Maki was there. She decided to "shake things up a little." Graham was out of the room and Maki was sitting by the window, looking out at the river view, when a nurse came in to check Dionne's blood pressure. When the nurse started to pump up the blood pressure cuff, Dionne went full-tilt into a pretend spasm, as though she was having a convulsion.

"Kimmie yelled at the nurse, 'What are you doing to her? What are you doing to her?' " recalls a still-amused Dionne. "I laughed and said, 'It's okay! I just wanted to spice things up a bit. It's too quiet around here.' I just did it for fun to see their reactions," laughs Dionne, who adds that it took quite awhile for both the nurse and Maki to calm down and trust her again.

"I will never ever forgive her for that," says a still-irritated Maki years later. "It's the worst feeling in the world, to be sitting there beside your best friend and she's in spasms. Dionne said the look on my face was priceless. She figured she'd better say something because I looked like I was going to pummel the nurse if she didn't tell me. The nurse wasn't too thrilled either and I thought, 'Well, obviously you don't know D and her sense of humour. She was quite the character before she met Graham, but now that she's been with him for awhile, her sense of humour is even more so."

Still, Maki says she could not have survived some of the ordeals in her life without the support of this amazing couple. "I wouldn't have made it through without the support of both of them and their attitude of, *'Keep your chin up. It will be fine. Everything will work out.'* "

Another surprise visit to Dionne occurred from close friends Pat and Joan Ozirny from Edmonton, Alberta. Pat was Graham's mentor for more than 20 years in the Freightliner business and Joan is a survivor herself, of multiple sclerosis. "There is a special connection between us because shortly after Dionne was diagnosed with her first liver cancer, Pat phoned me with profound news," says Graham. "I remember I was standing in my furnace room when I took his call. 'Misery loves company,' Pat said. 'Aaron, my 20-year-old daughter, has just been diagnosed with cancer,' Pat informed me. This devastated me and I felt the pain for Pat, as he felt mine.

"Unfortunately, Aaron lost her battle and passed away only a few months later. Since then, Pat has loudly, proudly and passionately called Dionne his hero. So on that quiet sunny Sunday afternoon, with Dionne sleeping and me sitting in a chair at the end of her bed feeling a little blue, the sight of Pat and Joan walking in was sure a sight for sore eyes! They had driven for six hours just to see her and this gesture meant the world to both D and I."

At the end of two weeks in hospital, Dionne had built up her strength again and happily got into Graham's truck for the ride back to White City. She was not given either chemotherapy or radiation, but Dr. Salim did change her main medication from Tamoxifen to Arimadex. "They felt that Tamoxifen was not working because I got sick with the liver cancer, so they switched me to a new drug."

After her second liver surgery, things went along much more smoothly for Dionne. She was back volunteering at the cancer clinic, Graham was concentrating on work and growing his business, and they were enjoying spending time together.

Dionne began volunteering again shortly after her surgery, as soon as she felt well enough to do so but much sooner than others thought she should. "Wilbur asked me, 'Are you sure you're okay to be here?' I told her I was fine. If I didn't feel good, I would go home," says Dionne. She looked forward to visiting with the patients and working with the staff and other volunteers, especially Lou Beltramini.

Beltramini recalls being at first concerned that he would not be able to relate to this woman from Toronto who sounded 'too sophisticated' for him. He quickly found out that was not the case and he and Dionne became instant friends as they worked on the same days at the same time. "I call her my shadow," says Beltramini. When Dionne was away, the people at the clinic would say, 'Where's your shadow today?' This is a joke between us. You can't live without your shadow."

Dionne sometimes received glares from people who did not appreciate her normal exuberant attitude. "My girlfriend Bev Holfeld and I are both happy people. We'd laugh and joke with the patients. The higher ups at one point heard us, I guess, and didn't think it was the greatest thing to have that much laughter in chemo. Then the nurses said to us, 'We need this laughter in chemo.' When I first did my treatment and Graham was there and a lovely nurse was taking care of me, I thought we'd probably get kicked out of there because we were giggling and laughing so much."

In 2002, after Dionne's first liver surgery, some of the women who worked at the cancer centre and had come to know her through her treatments and volunteering activities approached Dionne with an idea of creating an 'angel network' for her. This would not be like *Oprah's Angel Network* of charity work that Oprah Winfrey began in 1997 after she met a child who collected pennies for charities.[8] This Angel Network would build on Dionne's fondness for angels and the women's desire to love and support Dionne in any way that she needed. The women, of course, would benefit from this friendship as well, for it is impossible to be counted as

[8] http://oprah.about.com/od/philanthropy/p/angelnethistory.htm

Dionne's friend and not be the recipient of her special gift of love and support.

"People just started saying to me, "You have to get an Angel Network and we're going to be it," says Dionne. "These are people who supported me – angels who are still in my life and people whom we've lost along the way, too."

"This Angel Network of women began in Regina with a few of the cancer clinic staff getting together with Dionne once or twice a month to the best of our ability," says Donna Kish, a nurse at the clinic. "It was our kind of 'me' time and 'girl time.' The more we got to know each other, the more time we spent together. It grew from there."

Over the next few years, Dionne and her new friends relished in each other's company and shared a special bond through joy, laughter and pain. They met for coffee or a movie, chatted on the telephone or watched weekly TV shows like *The Bachelor* and *Dancing With The Stars*. Graham was included in some of these excursions – he has never been ashamed to show his feminine side and he gets along equally well with men and women – and during the next few years, Dionne's Angel Network expanded to include more friends and 'friends we consider family' from across North America and beyond.

"In Toronto, it wasn't a very big thing. I just collected a lot of angels and I had a group of family and friends that I called 'D's Angels,' but it was never an Angel Network until I came to Saskatchewan," says Dionne quietly. "That's when it became strong. It's grown ever since. I love it."

Dionne's first husband was not very accepting of her fondness for angels. He found they brought back bad memories of her cancers. During Dionne's years with Graham, she has been given as well as purchased dozens of angel ornaments, signs, statues and trinkets. These are displayed throughout their home as well as in a special cabinet that Graham purchased for the collection. One section of the 'angels cabinet' is in memory of friends lost along the way.

Dionne's first angel Emma, given to her by her friend Kimmie Robulack-Mendes in Toronto in 1997, cannot be found in the special cabinet. "Emma is safe in a box. She's very special. She's my first."

The Good Life

"I enjoy giving back, after all I have been through. There are people who don't even want to discuss it after they're done treatment. I'm different." - Dionne

L ife was good for Dionne after her marriage to Graham and her second liver cancer surgery. She had regular check-ups including routine CT scans every six months. Although Dr. Salim saw three little spots on her liver, he and Dionne both hoped they were just scar tissue marks and no cause for worry.

"Everything else looked great. They were checking my brain and I had scans and mammograms," says Dionne. "I was feeling great. Everything was fine."

By this time, Dionne was seeing Dr. Salim's wife, Dr. Najma Kazmi, as her family physician. "She's very compassionate and thorough. If their family moved away from Regina, I'd be in trouble. I'd lose two of the best doctors I've ever had," says Dionne, who has teased the couple repeatedly about sharing in her care. "I told Dr. Salim one time, 'Now you can talk about me in bed.' He said to me, 'Do you not think we have better things to talk about?' "

Dionne simply smiled.

Many doctors have called Dionne a medical miracle – a woman who had well surpassed the expected survival rate of six months for brain cancer and had also overcome two liver cancers. This was simply remarkable. Dr. Salim has been the personal investigator for more than 10 years for the North Central Cancer Treatment Group which is a big consortium in the U.S. attached to the Mayo Clinic. At a medical conference in New York in 2003, he discussed Dionne's case with other North American oncologists because her cases were so unique. He told his colleagues about a female patient who had breast cancer, brain cancer and then liver cancer. He asked the doctors if they would have operated on the liver cancer.

"Eight out of the 10 doctors at the table said they would not operate on me because it was too risky," says Dionne. "Then Dr. Salim proceeded to tell the doctors that not only had I had one surgery for liver cancer but I'd had two, and they would never know it to look at me that I'm a cancer patient," smiles Dionne.

"The very first time I saw her, in terms of resecting the liver, there was not much information at the time that you could do it and it would make a difference to her, so I wanted to check that out," says Dr. Salim. He spoke with the head of Mayo Clinic's breast cancer treatment program about Dionne and said, " 'This is what I'd like to do – remove the tumour from the liver – what do you think?' We had a discussion that the data is scanty but it is probably the logical thing to do, so we did." Dionne then agreed to go for surgery on the liver and was sent to Saskatoon, he added. Dr. Salim does not blame the other physicians for saying they would not have sent the patient for a resection, because there is no data to show that as a reasonable option. This is the reason that cases such as Dionne's are discussed – to share the results of treatments that others might not consider.

"When he was telling us what the other doctors said, Dr. Salim looked at Graham and I and said, 'See. It pays to think outside the box.' And that's why I trust Dr. Salim as much as I do," says Dionne. "I said to him, 'Thank God I have you in my corner!' "

Of course, Dionne is also thrilled to have Graham on her side as well.

Loving, romantic, generous, genuine and humourous are characteristics that everyone who knows Graham will quickly attribute to him.

"I'm not selfish," Graham says of his personality. "I find great pleasure in my employees being the highest paid in the industry, and in trying to be nice to people. I am fiercely loyal. I'm not a quitter. That is probably almost a detriment. One of the sayings by which I live my life is, 'You never say whoa in the middle of a slough.' Because I deal with so many Americans in my business and they don't know what a slough is, I had to change it to 'in the middle of a mud puddle,' but I still like slough. I'm in Saskatchewan, right?

"The other phrase that I like came from one of our former staff members. 'Character is what you are in the dark.' I don't like superficialness. It's easy to be the good guy when everything is going well. It's when it gets difficult or nasty or dark – that's when you find out what the person's really like. The wingmen in my life have proven their character in the dark – they've proven their character when no one's looking."

Graham's passion for flying is also obvious to all. When they became a couple, Graham and Dionne planned to take vacations and mini-vacations and to travel together for Graham's work meetings all across North America. They went on cruises and saw many beautiful places including New York, Chicago, Baltimore, Hawaii, New Orleans, Cancun, Dominican Republic, Italy and many parts of Canada.

"We've been to Moose Jaw, Maple Creek, Swift Current, Battleford, Balgonie..." adds Graham with a grin, naming communities in Saskatchewan and finishing off with his own chorus of *'I've been everywhere, man!'*

Some of their trips together were more memorable than others.

Sean Westerman recalls a particular weekend getaway trip to Radium Hot Springs in British Columbia that he, Graham, Dionne and Crystal Kalyniuk took in Graham's plane. They had a wonderful weekend and the weather was fine until it was time to head back to Saskatchewan, says Westerman. "When we got to the plane, it was completely covered in frost. Apparently in the 'plane world,' it is frowned upon to try and take off, let alone fly with heavy frost on the wings – something about no lift and crashing comes to mind," he smiles.

"We were at a tiny runway that had no service. In fact, there was no staff. As I looked around, it became apparent to me that we were in fact the only plane and the only idiots stupid enough to be at this runway. As we tried to figure out a game plan, a passerby came and told us that this was the last day the runway was open because it was almost winter and they didn't have any de-icing equipment. Graham, being of the 'never-say-whoa-in-the-middle-of-a-damn-slough' mindset, was not worried. He somehow broke into the little airport office and found that the power had not been shut off yet and there was a very small water heater that was still working. He found a couple of small pails and little paper coffee cups and he instructed us to keep filling up the cups with hot water, to run them out to the plane and pour them over the wings until the frost was gone. WHAT???? I contemplated taking the girls and hitchhiking back to Regina but being the idiot daredevil loyal friend that I am, I decided to go along with this ridiculous plan and we started dousing the plane with hot water. It took forever to do this, running back and forth with damn coffee cups of water and dousing the wings, but eventually we got the frost off, Graham assessed the situation and determined we were set to go," laughs Westerman.

"We taxied down the runway and found, at the end of the strip, about 10,000 birds. Not just little birds. Big frickin' birds. This was not good.

Graham assessed the situation, again, and decided to go slowly down to the end of the runway and scare them off and then turn around and take off. The problem was that the stupid birds simply flew to the other end of the runway and landed. Now we had to scare them off again! Finally, it was clear and Graham gunned the plane, but as we started taxiing down the runway, a bunch of the birds decided to start coming back again. There was madness at the end of the runway. We thought we were screwed. We were going too fast to stop without crashing off the end of the runway, so we only had one option – Graham gunned it! Does this sound familiar?" he asks.

"All of us were frozen in fear. Were the wings in fact clear of ice? Were the stupid birds going to get out of the way or not? As we were almost about to lift off, I heard Graham over the headset and he muttered something like, 'I sure hope one of these birds doesn't hit the prop or we're dead.' WHAT???? Nice warning, Graham. As luck would have it, we barely missed a few of the birds, we made it up and over the mountains and had a fabulous flight back to Regina. Life with Graham and Dionne is always an adventure," laughs Westerman.

Graham's business continued to do well in the new millennium. He added a trailer company to his enterprises in 2002 and a decision was made that year to rename all of the company's divisions to be more in line with their specific products and services. "We realized that trying to sell a bus to a customer in the city of Saskatoon or North Battleford was a little bit difficult when you were presenting yourself as Freightliner Truck Sales Regina Ltd.," says Graham. "It was Dionne who came up with the 'Warner Industries' name."

Each division was named for its product. Warner Truck Industries Ltd., Warner Bus Industries Ltd., Warner Fire and Rescue Industries Ltd. and Warner Trailer Industries Ltd. were born. All of the enterprises were collectively known as Warner Industries. In 2003, Graham purchased an 8,550-square-metre concrete building near the main shop for storing school buses indoors. This saved about $175,000 in fuel costs within the first year due to the reduced idle time for the buses.

Graham continued to watch for opportunities to grow his business as well as ways to fulfill his plan of semi-retiring at age 40 to become a charter pilot.

One day in 2004, Graham was watching the television news and heard how the Turks and Caicos Islands, a collection of 40 islands in the

Caribbean, might join Canada. He started searching the Internet to learn more about the islands and somewhere deep in the website, he saw a seaplane listed for sale. Perhaps this was an opportunity to pursue an aerial sightseeing business in the Caribbean.

He and Dionne had already booked a vacation to Dominican Republic, which is not far from the Turks and Caicos, so they decided to take a couple days to check out the seaplane for sale on Providenciales Island, one of the Turks and Caicos Islands. Also known as Provo, it has a population of about 15,000 people.

Although they had planned on renting a car and driving to Santiago to catch a commuter flight that would take them to Providenciales, it was determined that driving conditions in the Dominican Republic were just too risky. "Dionne was scared that when we travelled through the jungle-type terrain, we would get ambushed and she would be raped and I would have to watch," Graham chuckles. "I pointed out that, in fairness, there was the possibility that we could be ambushed by six-foot-tall beautiful Amazon women who would rape me and make *her* watch.

"Dionne said, 'That wouldn't be rape … and regardless of what you say, I am not making the drive.' "

So Graham came up with another idea, and they rented a Cessna and flew to Santiago from Punta Cana. "English is the international language in aviation," Graham pointed out, "so that wasn't an issue in that Spanish-speaking country. The aircraft was a little worse for wear, but I kicked the tires and the brakes seemed fair – which reminded me of Johnny Cash's *Hot Rod Lincoln* song – so off we went," he laughs.

"After we got to Provo, we walked out on Grace Bay Beach," says Graham, still in awe of that moment. "It was so beautiful. I said to Dionne, 'We need to live here.' In a day and a half, we fell in love with the island. We changed our lifestyle to live there in the wintertime and try to get this seaplane business going. Because of Dionne, it sparked that 'You have to go for your dreams and live every day' thing. In 2005, we rented a house and stayed for three months. We bought a condo in 2006."

They visited Provo to ring in the new year for the next few years, spending longer and longer on the island each time they went. Graham thought the warmer climate would be beneficial for Dionne's health and, of course, they'd leave Saskatchewan's cold winters behind.

"It was a little restitution for that 'It never gets below 10 below' indication I may have made," he smiles. "Although I actually got away with that little white lie for the first three years because Dionne was *'in love'* and never even noticed," he grins.

"The deciding factor in 2004 was that my general manager Roger Pettigrew and I communicated one entire day by e-mail and he was only 20 feet away from me in his office. Our banking is all electronic. We also have quite a few cameras in both our dealerships in Regina and Moose Jaw, so I can visually see what was going on from anywhere if I have a computer. My general manager is so strong that, to some degree, the company is not big enough for both of us. It was kind of a good way for him to grow and take over more and allow me to pursue business in the Caribbean."

Graham did not buy the seaplane he saw on Provo because it was full of corrosion, but he did buy one from another location and then got it fixed up to the stringent United Kingdom standards that were required. "It was ready to go, sitting in West Palm Beach, Florida, and 72 hours after it was ready, Hurricane Wilma came and destroyed it before I could get it to the island," he says.

The plane was written off but eventually rebuilt just over a year later. Then on Graham's first day flying his newly rebuilt airplane from Regina to the Caribbean, the landing gear collapsed and the plane skidded on its belly for 400 feet during what had been a planned normal landing in North Platt, Nebraska. "It was 17 below Celsius and it took three hours to get the aircraft hoisted up and off the runway. That was a long, cold, disheartening evening, let me tell you." Graham learned later that the landing gear had not been properly adjusted and that there were no nuts on the bolts holding the pilot ailerons or rudder-control pulleys, as well as other problems with the repairs. "I think there was definitely an angel watching over me on that flight."

It was December 22, 2006 and Graham now had to figure out how to get home. He decided he could rent a car the next day to drive as far as Minot, North Dakota about five hours southeast of Regina. He phoned Dionne to ask her to drive down to meet him in Minot. Dionne refused – at first.

"One of the few fights that Dionne and I have ever had was that day," says Graham. "I phoned her and I was standing on the runway beside my crashed, broken airplane that I had saved from turning into a big ball of smashed-up aluminum. 'I had a little accident, but I'm okay. I need you to come to Minot to pick me up tomorrow night.' She didn't want to come. She had a dinner party with her friends planned for that night," says Graham, still incredulous at her refusal.

"He wanted me to drive down there by myself, in the winter, which I had never done!" states Dionne. "I couldn't ask anyone to come with me – it was Christmastime!"

"So we had a little discussion," explains Graham. "In the end, how I convinced her to go was I told her, 'Look, the hotel is in the mall. You can go shopping.' "

Now, one thing that all of Dionne's friends know about her is that she not only loves to shop but she is very good at it and will accept any shopping opportunity that is presented. Nadine Desrosiers and many others admit that Dionne actually taught them how to shop. "D knows stores. She knows when they have sales and how to find sales. She told me, 'Honey, you always go to the back of the store – that's where you get all the deals. So that's what we do. She just knows. You never pay full price for that stuff. You have to get it on sale."

"She can find deals in every store. She magically makes things drop in price and fit my body," laughs Crystal Kalyniuk. "Things just fly off the hanger at her and they're cool things and amazing deals. One time we were in an outlet mall and she asked if I wanted a cart. I said, 'No, I don't need a cart. It's just one store.' She asked, 'Are you sure?' In probably 10 minutes of walking behind her, my arms were full and my fingers were numb with hangers. I quickly realized I had to go get a cart ... She should be a personal shopper."

"Dionne lives every second of every day and if she gets a bargain, she lives it twice," adds Desrosiers. "She gets so excited. 'Woo hoo!' If she finds a bargain, she will buy the same item in several different colours. She had an open house one time and invited some girlfriends to come and pick from the many shirts she had of the same style. 'No fighting!' she told us. She never leaves her shopping partners in the dust either. She's interested in what you're buying and wants to know if you are getting something for your family. Then she knows where you should go and what you should get there."

"It's all about the sale," giggles Dionne. "It's the words 'clearance, liquidation, out of business, 75% off the lowest ticketed price.' It's about making the time to search through those racks. Some women can't do that. I even had to teach Graham's daughter. And it's about the timing of when to purchase your summer things for summer next year and your winter things for the following year."

Dionne attributes her love of shopping to being the only girl in her family and having her mother take her to the Square One Shopping Centre in Mississauga every Saturday. "I was a spoiled little girl. I got the outfit every Saturday. So really, it was imbedded in me back in the day that shopping is so much fun."

With the opportunity to go shopping as the carrot dangling in front of her on that cold December day, Dionne dutifully drove down to Minot to pick up Graham. She even made it in record time. "I had to get to the mall to start shopping before Graham could slow me down!" she laughs.

She and Graham returned to Regina together and he arranged to have his seaplane repaired properly. He later sold the Cessna that he had won and purchased a second seaplane for the business he hoped to create in the Turks and Caicos. "I wasn't using the Cessna as much as I had been because business had changed and we were living in the Turks and Caicos more. I only logged about 20 hours in it one year. Dionne wasn't happy about the sale. She wishes I had kept it."

Dionne continued volunteering at the cancer centre and the more she volunteered, the more comfortable she became in sharing her story and helping others. In 2003, she and Graham attended their first Relay For Life in Regina. The Canadian Cancer Society's Relay is an event held in communities all across Canada to give the public an "opportunity to celebrate cancer survivors, remember and honour loved ones lost to cancer and fight back against all cancers."[9] Regina's Relay is held in Wascana Centre, near the Legislature and manmade Wascana Lake, with participants from the various teams taking turns to walk the route continuously during a 12-hour overnight period.

Carla Redler has been the chair of Regina's Relay For Life survivor committee since it began in 2002. "The day I met Dionne feels like it was yesterday," says Redler. "We were working down at the Cancer Society offices two or three days before Relay 2003. Dionne had come down to volunteer. I was just awestruck. It was like Halle Barry had walked into the room. She was beautiful and incredibly vibrant with a warm personality. Instantly, there was a connection."

Dionne helped Redler prepare name tags for survivors who were attending that year's Relay. "The next day, Dionne gave me this CD. She said, 'Carla, I just want to welcome you into my Angel Network. You're one of my angels.' The CD had instrumental music that she had pulled from wherever. It's heavenly."

Carla and her husband Tony did not meet Graham until the day of the Relay, May 30, after all the survivors had finished their Victory Lap to officially start the 2003 Relay For Life. Graham and Dionne have been members of Regina Relay For Life's survivor committee since 2003 and have contributed more than they will ever know to the success of the event, says Redler.

[9] http://convio.cancer.ca

"Graham is awesome," says Carla. "He shares the same mentality as I do – 'You go big or you go home.' There is nothing he wouldn't do for D or other survivors. At the first meeting, he was quiet. He took everything in. Then he said, 'We can do more. I can provide the barbecue. I can provide food for the survivors.' Graham and Dionne are not a big part of us just because of what Graham can financially give us – it's their love story and their life that inspires us. I don't think I've ever met two people who were so openly in love, so fun-loving and so giving of themselves."

The Warners and Redlers share a similar story with their cancer battles. Tony Redler was diagnosed with non-Hodgkin's lymphoma in 1982. It reoccurred in 1990 and again in 1992. He has had stem cell therapy and two bone marrow transplants. Dionne and Tony have become very close and Carla teases her husband that Dionne is the only person who can make him smile. "I'm not in a photo on our fridge with him but Dionne is, and I'm totally fine with that," smiles Carla. "She's so much a part of our life. We absolutely love and adore both Graham and Dionne. Our life is enriched because we know them and consider them such good friends. They really knew the journey we had and we could understand where they were," says Carla.

"Dionne and I have travelled a long distance," adds Tony. "We're not using each other as a crying shoulder. We're using each other as a motivator. We've been there. We've gone through different bouts of treatment and we just keep bouncing back. Her morale is just over the top. The Allan Blair is a better place with Dionne there because of all the hope she brings in."

Survivor Jayne Clendening had invited Dionne to attend Relay 2003 and remembers Dionne arriving in a white sweatshirt on which she had used neon colours to hand paint words and pictures that signified her journey through cancer. "The rest of us admiringly autographed her symbol of victory before we set out to join the throngs of people in the park," says Clendening.

"I had survived malignant melanoma and breast cancer, so our common experience allowed us to easily connect," she adds. "Dionne and I walked the Victory Lap together that night, hand-in-hand. Our journey was illuminated by white paper-bag lanterns dedicated with hope and prayer to individuals living with cancer, and in memory of friends and family lost to the disease. The crowd roared and cheered us on, with many of their faces lit by the reflection of the lanterns. It felt surreal, like a multitude of angels applauding and high-fiving us all the way. Our tears flowed as we held each other and walked down the path, smiling, wrapped in this heavenly energy."

A few months after Relay, in October 2003, Dionne participated in her first CIBC Run for the Cure event. This was another emotional experience because of the Run's goal of raising breast cancer awareness and funds for the Canadian Breast Cancer Foundation. She and a couple hundred other participants walked or ran all or part of the five-kilometre course through Regina's Wascana Centre, clad in T-shirts decorated with pink symbols of hope. The following year, Dionne visited her family in Guelph, Ontario and was a guest speaker at that city's CIBC Run for the Cure.

"I was asked to speak out and tell my story to give patients hope that there's life after cancer," she says about the Guelph event. "I enjoy giving back, after all I have been through. There are people who don't even want to discuss it after they're done treatment. I'm different."

In January 2004, a bone scan showed that Dionne had osteoporosis in her left wrist area and right hip. "So along with the menopause, I now had osteoporosis," she says sullenly. A drug was prescribed specifically for osteoporosis and Dionne was sent on her way.

Dionne met many patients and built many friendships through her volunteering. Kelly Greenwood was diagnosed with an early stage melanoma in March 2004. She also happens to work at the Allan Blair Cancer Centre. She knew of Dionne only as a volunteer and will forever be thankful that she found the courage to walk up to Dionne one day and ask for a few moments of her time.

"Knowing as much as I know and being in our new patient office, I was surrounded by the yuckiness of cancer all the time and I was having a really hard time with my diagnosis," says Greenwood. "I didn't really know Dionne. I just knew she had this amazing attitude and a laugh that could light up a room. After struggling for several weeks, I was sitting at my desk and I heard that laugh. I said to myself, 'I have nothing to lose. I am going to talk with that Dionne lady and see what makes her tick.' I wondered how can she have been through this battle and still be as happy as she is, and how can she not only come to the Allan Blair for her own appointments but put in extra time by volunteering, too? So I went up to her and asked her if we could talk in private and she said, 'Yes, of course.'

"I told her what I was going through and that I was having a hard time dealing with things and I asked her how she did it," says Greenwood. "Dionne's answer was simple – she just chose not to let this wicked disease get the best of her. She relied on her family and friends for support but at the end of the day, this was her battle and she was going to give it everything she had."

Dionne and Greenwood had a long conversation that day and before Greenwood had to get back to work, she went to the bathroom to wash her tear-streaked face and settle down for a moment. "In the five minutes that this took, I came back to a package on my desk," says Greenwood. "It was from Dionne. It was one of those Willow Tree Angels – the Angel of Courage – standing with her arms up to the sky. She had a little note with her telling me I was a lot stronger that I thought I was, that things would get better and that I had a forever friend in Dionne from there on in. Needless to say, I bawled like a baby, but that angel has been on my bedside table ever since. She is the last thing I see when I go to sleep and one of the first things I see in the morning – besides my husband, of course."

Dionne has long been known for her generous nature, giving gifts both planned and impromptu to family, friends and individuals she has only just met, like Greenwood. "Yeah, I'm a giver," admits Dionne. "That's where Graham and I are exactly the same. We love to give. We love to share. If I saw something that was breast cancer-related and I knew a patient would like it, I would get it for that patient. Or if patients admired something I had on my wrist, I would take it off and give it to them. I can always get another one or find something else similar for myself."

"When it comes to friendship, D is like a lioness protecting her cubs. She always has your back and will do whatever is needed to help a friend out," says Crystal Kalyniuk. "To balance that out, she will be the first to tell you the way it is and give you a kick in the pants if you need it. Dionne (& Graham) are two of the most giving people I know; they both have such open hearts and are constantly thinking of others and willing to lend their hands, share their knowledge, their time and their love."

"I don't know where Dionne gets her strength," says her cousin Peter Ballantine. "If we could bottle it, it would be a best seller. I guess it's a combination of life experience and genetics. We've heard so many times, 'This is it. Sorry, Dionne, the prognosis isn't good. They just didn't take into account her desire and willingness to do whatever is required to live."

In the summer of 2005, Dionne's father came from Jamaica to visit Dionne and Graham. It was his first visit to Regina and they happily showed him around the city and did the usual summer activities of boating and enjoying the outdoors. The highlight of that trip for Dionne was putting on her 10-year-Survivor T-shirt that she had made for Relay For Life a couple months earlier and taking her father to the site of that Relay in Regina's Wascana Centre.

"We did our own victory lap down in the park," she says. It was a special celebration for Dionne, sharing that time with the two men who mean the most to her.

In October 2005, Dionne decided to do more for cancer than just volunteer at the clinic. She created her 'Little Shop of Hope' to sell cancer awareness merchandise including pins, ornaments, magnets, bracelets, T-shirts and more. On the days she wasn't volunteering or out of town, she went to the Warner Industries dealership and sold the items from an office near the front desk. When customers from all across southern Saskatchewan came in to pick up a truck or for parts and service, they often stopped to see Dionne and purchase a few pieces of her cancer awareness merchandise. "I was there for about a year every day that I didn't volunteer."

Dionne also sold the merchandise on her *Cancer Survivor In The City* website, at a simple table in front of the Warner Industries heavy-duty truck display at the Western Canada Farm Progress Show, and at a table on the Regina Pats junior hockey team's Breast Cancer Awareness Night. The items ranged in price from $5 for the popular silicone wrist bands to $60 for a Swarovski crystal cancer awareness bracelet.

Dionne was thankful to Brandon Tooke for designing her web site "to help me get my story of *hope* out." On her web site Dionne stated, "Many thanks to all of you wonderful angels for your help in getting my web site out to your family and friends, who continue to share it with their family and friends. I have welcomed many new people to my Angel Network, thanks to my web site, and I want to thank all of you for sharing your stories of survival and loss with me. Each and every one of your stories touched my heart. As a volunteer at the Allan Blair Cancer Clinic, I continue to meet and be inspired by many survivors. Thank you for sharing your stories with me."

In only 18 months, Dionne raised an amazing $50,773.03 by selling her various cancer awareness items. "Most of her sales ended with tears or a hug," says Graham proudly. She donated all of the proceeds to Saskatchewan Cancer Research Fund.

Dionne spent a lot of time educating patients and customers about the colours for the various types of cancer. Everyone knows that pink is for breast cancer, she'd say, but there are at least 20 other colours including grey for brain cancer, emerald green for liver cancer, gold for childhood cancer, light blue for prostate cancer, and lavender to support all cancers.

During her years of volunteering, Dionne has gained the admiration of many patients and staff who have come to know and love her. "I have had numerous patients ask if Dionne is 'in' today," laughs Nadine Desrosiers, a staff person at the cancer centre. "They always want to talk etc. I think they get a fix from her positive energy. One patient asked where Dionne got her wigs from, so I e-mailed D and she was more than happy to share that information. She has also gone out of her way to order things for people through her Little Shop of Hope. If she didn't have it, she would comb the earth to find it."

"Dionne's laugh and energy are infectious to anyone around her," says Michael Melville, a clinical assistant at the Allan Blair. "Dionne has a way to make people smile, make people laugh and most importantly, to give people hope. After meeting Dionne for the first time, I knew I wanted to get to know her. She is more than just a cancer survivor – she's a crusader for helping others."

Balking at normal procedure, Dionne and Desrosiers took a special interest in one female cancer patient who came for her appointments alone. They stayed with the young woman, held her hand and gave her little gifts to make her days a little brighter. "Dionne always seemed to be there if there was somebody who needed a hand or someone to talk to. She would source that out," says Desrosiers. After this young patient became more ill and was isolated in the hospital, Dionne and Desrosiers were among the few people who visited her.

"D ended up being a very big part of her life," adds Desrosiers. "She absolutely beamed to get Dionne's company. We talked about it a lot. It was really comforting for that patient to know that D had been that sick and yet D was still doing so well. Dionne had beat it and was strong and healthy. That gave this young woman hope. She felt she could beat it, too. Unfortunately she didn't – but without hope, where would a lot of us be?"

"They try to teach you to not become attached," says Dionne about volunteering at the cancer centre. "Nadine and I became attached to that young lady. This girl had only a few people there for her. We tried to make up for what her family didn't give her. I celebrate these people. Everybody has touched my life."

Dionne has sat with other patients who were alone during their chemotherapy as well. She gets upset thinking about the men she has seen who do not stay with their wives through their treatments. "They will sit outside or wander, or go shopping. Yes, they might have other things to do but, right now, their wives are having chemo treatment. Right now, their wives need them more than ever. It just devastates me that they sit there on their own because their husbands dropped them at the door with, 'When are you done? Three hours? I'll be back to get you. See you.' As volunteers, those are the patients for whom we pull up a chair and sit with them because there's nobody around them. We just sit and talk so they don't feel like they are alone.

"I've heard those women say, 'Oh, he can't deal with it, so he'll just be back to pick me up.' Then there are the husbands like the one I am very blessed to have. You see them in there all the time. It's incredible.

"I met a lady when I was fitting wigs one time. She told me she sleeps in another wig at home because her husband doesn't feel comfortable if she doesn't have a wig on in bed. I was thinking to myself, 'This is your home, this is your sanctuary – and you still feel like you have to cover up?' I just couldn't fathom that. If I've been out somewhere and I'm sitting at home and I still have my wig on, Graham will say to me, 'You can take your wig off, hon. You can relax. You're at home.' "

Dionne often wishes that more women had a husband who is as supportive as Graham is to her.

Marla Fehr-Sinclair will always be grateful that she met Dionne Warner. In 2007, Dionne was sent by Dr. Salim to visit Fehr-Sinclair in her hospital room "to give me a good kick in the butt while I was going through treatment," says Fehr-Sinclair. "I was diagnosed with a rare and aggressive form of childhood lymphoma and spent five months in hospital for treatment. I was not having a great day and was starting to go stir-crazy when in walked an angel with the most contagious laugh. It was Dionne, of course. She introduced herself and told me about her story. I began to instantly have hope again and quit feeling sorry for myself. I looked forward to her visits, usually twice a week until I got out. Dionne also introduced me to the Relay For Life and at the time, said, 'You are going to be in it next year with me.' She held me to my promise."

Allison Cann worked at the Allan Blair Cancer Centre in 2003 when she met Dionne, the volunteer. "Shortly after meeting her, I became diagnosed with cancer myself and she was a very strong support system for me to lean on while coming to terms with my diagnosis," says Cann, who now works for the Alberta Cancer Line. "Dionne, in a word, is inspiration. She is bubbly, outgoing, fun, loyal, a great friend, loving, caring, courageous ... I don't know how else to describe someone whom I have come to think of as a hero. She inspired me to overcome my feelings of self pity when I was sick and to see the world in a whole new light. She inspires me to be a better person and appreciate life to the fullest."

One of Dionne's favourite stories from her volunteering days at the Allan Blair Cancer Centre occurred when she was working in the wig room one day. A female patient stuck her head in the doorway and told Dionne, "You look too pretty to be looking after sick people."

Dionne asked the patient to come further into the wig room, where Dionne pointed to a snapshot of an attractive bald woman. She asked the patient, "What do you think of this picture?"

The patient was aghast and said, "What woman would let somebody take a picture of her with no hair?"

Dionne replied, "Actually, that's me. I am a four-time cancer survivor. I've had breast cancer, brain cancer and two liver cancer surgeries."

The patient grew very quiet and then she grabbed Dionne's hand, looked at her and said, "My dear, if I look as good as you after all my treatments, it will all have been worth it."

Dionne had put the photo of her bald self, taken by Graham, on the wall of the wig room in 2005 "because I wanted the women to know that I know what it's like to be bald. I know what it's like to try and find that wig that fits so you feel better."

Dionne and the patient hugged and laughed. "It was quite a moment for the two of us."

Although Dionne never had her own children, she has been blessed to be a special mother figure – twice. On September 8, 2002 she became godmother to Joshua Collesso, son of her cousin Yuri Collesso and his partner Diane Stein in Ontario. On May 8, 2005 she became godmother to Shaya Dionne Nordick, daughter of her good friend Kimmie Maki in Saskatchewan.

"These children are two of my most precious gifts. I never lost out in the mother role, thanks to Diane and Yuri and Kimmie," says Dionne gratefully.

Diane Stein explains that Dionne is "incredibly strong, positive and inspiring – the reason we chose her to be our son's godmother. We could not think of a better person for Josh to emulate."

Kimmie Maki agrees. "Graham and Dionne were on the island when Shaya was born. I had the name Shaya picked out. I decided her middle name would be Dionne because Dionne is just the strongest person – an inspiration to everybody. If Shaya, by having that name, can take on half of what Dionne is, I would be more than happy in life. Dionne couldn't have kids of her own. She did have Joshua, who is a boy, and what perfect way to give her a boy and a girl of her own? Shaya definitely loves her Auntie D, that's for sure."

In October 2005, Dionne reached two major milestones. She had been cancer-free for seven years and she happily acknowledged her 40th birthday. Every new day for a cancer survivor is a special day, but a 40th birthday for Dionne was an incredible celebration, considering all she had overcome since her first diagnosis 10 years earlier.

To fulfill his wife's birthday wish of having "a big party for me and my friends," Graham rented a ballroom at the Travelodge. As usual, Dionne was on the dance floor all night, enjoying every minute of her party and living her life to the fullest.

One of the important cancer charities that Dionne and Graham support is the annual auction hosted by the Regina Progress Club to benefit the Camp Circle of Friends, to raise funds for a camp for children who either have or have been affected by cancer. Jessica Martorana, a survivor of childhood cancer, is one of the eight people who routinely sit with Dionne at the table purchased by Graham for this charity event. "Dionne invites some of her angels to go. Her husband's company pays for the table and we have a ladies' night. Our table is the table of silly, fun-loving ladies. There is entertainment, supper, a live auction and a silent auction. They've joked about raffling off a spot at our table so others could join the fun because our table is always the life of the party."

Martorana and others enjoy many laughs watching Dionne go head-to-head with the men in the room to bid up an item. "We just love this camp and we love the kids!" says Dionne. "We've been there, we've helped out, we've seen the children. For me, whatever it is, I'm going to buy it. It's going for the kids, so … Yahoo!"

Dionne's more memorable purchases include a white glove service, being a weather girl for a day on the local TV news, and an evening with some of the Saskatchewan Roughrider football players, although that was not initially the item that was placed for auction.

"Every year, they have the 'white glove service' for the next year. It's a table in the middle and you get special attention," explains Martorana. "It's the prestige of it all. Dionne will just battle with some of the men there to get that service. It's always a lot of fun and it's all for a good cause, too."

One year, Dionne won the bid to be a weather girl for the day, but Graham was not told of this win until well after it happened – and then he was sorry, and still is to this day.

"It's a sore point with me," says Graham with a smile. "One day at supper time, weeks after the auction, she told me, 'Make sure you watch the news tonight,' because our girlfriend Michael was going to be on the news. I said, 'Okay.' Dionne was going out with the girls and I would be home by myself."

Unknown to Graham, Dionne actually went over to the local Global TV station to be the weather girl on the late-night news. She had learned the ropes the night before, when she'd made some other excuse to leave the house, and she was now ready for her big Christmas gift to Graham, all dressed in a little red Santa outfit befitting her shapely figure.

Graham usually goes to bed well before 11 o'clock but he struggled desperately to stay awake on this night to watch for their friend's TV appearance.

"I watched the bloody news. No Michael," explains Graham. "I've seen the news enough to know that they do the news, then the sports, then they do the weather at the end. They go into the sports – okay, there's no Michael – so I turned the TV off and went to sleep. Dionne came in quite late and woke me up, all excited and pumped. I told her, 'I didn't see Michael,' and I started to go back to sleep. So she informed me what she'd done but said I wasn't going to get a copy of it because I'm a bad husband and I went to sleep after I didn't see Michael."

"It was for Christmas!" says a frustrated Dionne. "I was all in red and I had a Santa hat!

"I learned it's not easy to be the weather person. You're trying to move away from the screen and be on time. I asked them if it was okay if I had a little fun with it and they said, 'Of course.' So because the weather was getting warmer, I said, 'Regina! Is it getting HOT in here?' while I seductively fanned myself. After that, I could hear the sports guy laughing. After they went off air, I asked if I did okay and the cameraman said, 'See that big guy over there? He never laughs. You had him laughing.' They gave me a tape of it but I refused to let Graham see it. I told him he had to get his own."

Graham continues the story. "So the next day, after I told every person who would listen to me, to determine that I was not in the wrong – I then went to the Global TV station myself and pleaded to them, to convince that I was not a bad husband, to save my marriage and to give me a copy of this tape so I could see what my wife had done for me.

I'm still totally innocent," he insists.

Graham usually attends the fundraiser with Dionne and their friends, but was at a meeting in the United States when a more recent auction occurred. Roughrider pennants and a helmet were put up for auction, but not much happened bidding-wise until Dionne yelled, 'Throw in a couple of the 'Riders! Then you'll get some bidding going!' Some women at Dionne's table cheered and others shouted their encouragement and soon, a date with a couple of the Rider players was added to the item up for bid.

"The bidding started and our table was going wild and screaming," says Dionne.

The bid reached what Dionne thought should be her maximum and she decided to stop bidding. "I said, 'Okay, you guys, I can't go any further. Graham will kill me. At least the money's up. Somebody's going to pay this and they're going to get it for the camp. We'll bid on something else.' Then out of nowhere, this lady at another table yelled, 'You girls can't give up yet! I'm coming with $100! Bid it up!'

"She didn't know us. We saw her take $100 from her husband and put it on the table. After that, nobody else bid. They cheered and said, 'You have to have this,' and they gave it to us. We got the pennants, a helmet autographed, and Stevie Baggs and Weston Dressler came to our home to hang out with us one night. We had a bunch of people come over. It was just open conversation and it was great! But the crowd went *crazy* in that room that night. Oh my goodness, we have had some fun nights!"

Dionne and her friends also bid on the white glove service at that auction. "So we spread the money around. I never said anything to Graham and he found out when he went to his executive business club luncheon a few days later. Someone came up to him and said, 'Boy, Graham, your credit card should be burning.' He said, 'Huh?' He came home and said to me, 'What did you do?' I said, 'It was all for the camp.' … Maybe I batted my eyelashes once or twice, too," she giggles.

Graham actually has no concerns about the amount of money Dionne spent for that auction. Although the visit by the Rider players went for about $3,000 and the white glove service went for slightly more, both he and Dionne are pleased that they could contribute with their friends to such a great cause. "It was a lot of money but it was for the kids," says Dionne. "One hundred per cent of it helps out with that camp. They have a silicone wristband that they sell for the camp. It says, 'Until there's a cure, there's camp.' These kids have to have somewhere they can go and have some fun and enjoy life and forget about the disease."

Dionne and Graham have visited the camp and met some of the

children there. "It's just beautiful to hang out and play games with the kids. It's not about the cancer. They have a time where they share the poems they've written or the pictures they've taken. One of the boys had his book published – he's passed away since – about fighting a dragon and cancer was the dragon. I took his little book to the island because I know they don't have anything for children with cancer there. Now there is something at their cancer building that they can give to a child to look at and read or share with another child."

By 2006, Dionne and Graham were spending from January to late spring each year on Provo. Dionne had been raising more awareness of cancer whenever they were there and she got to know Lucille Lightbourne, the head of the Providenciales Turks and Caicos Cancer Society. In spring 2006, Dionne was the keynote cancer survivor speaker at the island's cancer gala fundraiser. She surprised the 150 people at the gala with her bluntness.

"Cancer was very hush on the island," says Dionne. "They were shocked when I asked cancer survivors to please stand. You could see their surprise as they looked around – 'I didn't know that person had cancer or that one.' There may have been five of us who stood up and acknowledged our cancer. Everybody came together and I asked to get a picture with those survivors. Nobody had ever done that before. I wanted to do that so I could say, 'Congratulations!' "

This simple request from Dionne began to change the mindset on how cancer is viewed in that Caribbean country. "She changed the culture of an entire country," says Graham proudly.

In June 2006, Dionne was the ambassador for Relay For Life in Regina. As the face of the Relay, she met with media and attended the Survivor rally as well as gave an emotional speech to celebrate and encourage the survivors and all those affected by cancer.

Leading up to the Relay, Dionne was still in Turks and Caicos when the media event inviting survivors to participate was scheduled to happen in Regina. Even though she wasn't physically present, she sent a video DVD from the Turks and Caicos to be played at the Regina event. "In it, she was sitting on the beach inviting everybody to come out to Relay in June," says Carla Redler. "She did it talking about the importance of Relay and where the money is going. She was encouraging teams to continue doing what they're doing and she was thanking the survivors. She and Graham did a slideshow ... It was G-and-D style. Even if life has them in a different place, they make sure they're still in contact."

"If they commit to something, they will do it," adds Tony Redler.

"They don't do to show off. It's just their style," adds Carla. "I could have read her words, and I would have done that, but to see her on the big screen and the words coming from her, it was so much better. It was more than we ever expected it would be."

"They make the impossible possible," adds Tony. "They were back in Regina for the Relay. She spoke as our very first Relay For Life ambassador. She's like a little general. She has to make sure everybody has everything, and Graham's right beside her."

Graham's interest in mechanics and his long-held ability to be creative and improvise has led to him being nicknamed 'MacGyver' for the 1980's television show character who always made something from very little. "He's kind of a MacGyver kind of guy," says Carla. "If he gets an idea, he's out there and before you know it, there's something happening."

Graham has come up with ideas to improve parade floats for Relay and ways to cook burgers for Relay volunteers – not always without some kinks, though. "I have a Tim-the-Toolman-Taylor barbecue on chrome mag wheels," says Graham happily. "One year, we burned the barbecue down. We couldn't unhook the trailer from the van and we emptied two fire extinguishers." The show must go on, though, and he was back the next year with a totally rebuilt barbecue to feed the hungry volunteers who were setting up for the Relay.

Dionne and Graham invited Lightbourne to come to Regina to experience the 2006 Relay For Life in person. She stayed with the Warners while she was in Saskatchewan. "Dionne wanted her to experience what this was about first-hand so she would be able to maybe take it home and start Relay on the island," says Carla Redler. "I guess we'll just wait and see if they do anything."

Dionne has shared her message of hope at a Relay For Life in Moose Jaw as well as at the Terry Fox Run in Regina. "They'd heard my story and wanted me to come share it and be their speaker." Her answer to these requests is always "Of course."

Organized by a group of female Harley Davidson riders, the Ladies of Harley in the Regina HOG Chapter, the Annual Ride for Breast Cancer Screening has taken place in September every year since 2004. In 2006, Dionne and Graham participated for their first time in that motorcycle ride from Regina to Moose Jaw and they have taken part in it every year since.

The year 2006 was also significant for Dionne and Graham as they moved out of White City and into a comfortable three-bedroom home in Regina's east end, so that Dionne's girlfriends could visit more.

In January 2007, Dionne and Graham stayed on Provo for three months, enjoying a vacation from Saskatchewan's cold winter and allowing Graham to do further investigating into his seaplane sightseeing business in the Turks and Caicos. They had met Leslie Foss at an outside restaurant on the island the previous Easter and had become friends with her and her husband Todd. Dionne had overheard Leslie tell a waiter that she was from Saskatchewan and Dionne quickly invited Leslie over to their table. In fact, when Dionne heard where Leslie was from, she yelled to her, "Saskatchewan? Get your butt over here!!" They have since become close friends and spent many hours together both on the island and off.

"We've gone to the beach together, enjoyed many dinners together and I dragged Dionne out as my workout buddy to the gym," laughs Leslie. "We would go for our workout and then often go for coffee after and just hang out. As a couple, the four of us have had many beach outings, boat rides, and dinners together. We have taken trips off island to Fort Lauderdale and elsewhere. D and I have done quite a few girls' trips, going to New York twice and to Las Vegas."

In 2007, Graham used his business expertise to counsel Todd Foss on how to improve the Grace Bay Car Rentals company he had purchased on the island. "When Todd bought the car rental company, it had 10 old dilapidated cars that if you looked at the floorboards when you were driving, you could see the ground going by through them," says Graham, who was invited to invest in the company and used his MacGyver-like skills to upgrade everything at the start from the office door to customer access ways and finally, in building a three-bay shop to repair the cars. During the following two years, Graham and Dionne spent more time on the island, and Graham kept busy hanging around with Todd and helping out with day-to-day duties and customer services.

"I've given Todd two or three seasons and never expected nor wanted to be paid a dollar," says Graham. "It's kind of nice just to see a guy like Todd start from scratch and watch him succeed like he has. In return, Todd – a humble dedicated bodybuilder – has helped whip me into the best physical shape that I've been in in years and I know I would have never done that on my own. We have become the best of buds – bruthas from another mutha, I'm proud to say!

"Everything happens for a reason and my seaplane business was so wrapped up in bureaucracy," continues Graham. "I couldn't sit on the beach for six months. Helping Todd gave me something to do. That was really what it was about." By 2009, Grace Bay Car Rentals had a thriving business with 212 cars – none of which have any holes in the floorboards, Graham likes to point out.

Graham had obtained his commercial pilot's licence rating in November 2004 and his seaplane rating the following spring, specifically for the seaplane business. However, after five years of investment, that business never did go forward "due to excessive bureaucracy and restrictive rules that the British air regulators changed after I started my process," he explains. "I spent a lot of time, money and energy trying to get a sightseeing seaplane business going. It's the only business I failed at. In the Caribbean, I intend to just fly for beer now."

On the island and in Saskatchewan, Dionne continued to add to her Angel Network – not because she was collecting friends but because they were seeking her out for comfort, wisdom, laughter, and hope. She met many individuals either through her volunteering, speaking engagements or through other friends, who quickly became her own cherished friends. Many of these lucky individuals found it easy to immediately like Dionne, and even easier to love her when she cheerfully addressed them as 'Earth Angel' after only a few minutes – and meant it.

In June 2007, Dionne celebrated 10 years as a brain cancer survivor, something two doctors told her they had never seen. "See! You can beat the odds and give other patients hope!" she wrote on her *Cancer Survivor In The City* web site.

"Today at the hospital, my doctor called me his walking miracle after all I have survived ... I will never say this journey was easy. I always gave myself 24 hours to say, 'Why Me?' and then after those 24 hours, I would come to my senses and say, 'Why Not Me? And what am I going to do to beat this?!!' "

While Dionne may have been a miracle patient for Dr. Salim, he held a very special place in her heart as well. She refers to him as 'My Doctor of Hope.'

In 2000, Dionne had celebrated being a cancer survivor by having two tattoos inked on her upper back. Her tattoo of a pink ribbon symbolized that she had officially made the five-year mark as a breast cancer survivor, with the love and support of her family and friends. Her tattoo of a heart with wings symbolized that she was loved by many angels. She would show them off "with pride over having climbed the

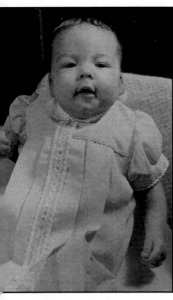

Left and centre below:
Dionne Walford, born in
Toronto, Ontario, Canada.

Right: Graham Warner,
born in Kipling,
Saskatchewan, Canada.

Left: Baby
Dionne.

Centre and right:
Graham in his
younger years.

low: Graham on a packer near Balcarres, Saskatchewan a few days before his 11th birthday, August 1973.

Above: Dionne, third from left in the front row in Grade 8.

Below left: Dionne being carried by her friends on the school playground in Mississauga, Ontario.

Above and above right: Dionne, age 12, and with half-sister Shayna.

Right: Ready to party, 1988.

Left: Graham in his Regina Lions Junior Band uniform.

Right: Graham in Grade 12.

For more photos, see slideshow on Accompanying DVD.

ve: The Regina Hino dealership.

right: Graham in front of the Freightliner
ck Sales Regina Ltd. dealership in Regina,
katchewan, Canada.

Right: Inside the
Freightliner
dealership with
his father Goff
Warner, 1984.

Left: Dionne on vacation in Italy, 1994.

Below left: At the medieval feast for their second evening out together,
Toronto, Ontario, Canada, November 2000.

Above: Graham in the six-seater Cessna Skymaster
plane he won in 1998.

For more photos, see slideshow on Accompanying DVD.

Top left: Photo by Craig Clendening of Camera One, Regina, 2001.

Top right: Dr. Roger Keith performed Dionne's liver cancer surgeries in Saskatoon, Saskatchewan.

Left: Dr. Muhammad Salim, Regina, Saskatchewan – Dionne's 'Doctor of Hope.'

Right: October 11, 2002.

Left: Dionne happily makes a snow angel in her new province.

Right: Rupert Walford with his daughters Shayna and Dionne in Jamaica.

Left: At Graham's cousins' farm in Mossbank, Saskatchewan, 2003.

Right: Fun in the snow at Moose Mountain Provincial Park, Saskatchewan.

For more photos, see slideshow on Accompanying DVD.

Above: Dionne's shirt for 2003 Relay for Life.

Top right and right: Dionne announces names of the survivors at 2004 Relay For Life, Regina, wearing her hand-decorated T-shirt.

Left and below left: Dionne loves her new city and the blossoming canola fields in Saskatchewan.

Below: On Provo, Turks and Caicos Islands, 2004.

Below: Dionne and Graham and friends at 2004 IBC Run for the Cure, Guelph, Ontario.

Below: Graham and Roger Pettigrew.

For more photos, see slideshow on Accompanying DVD.

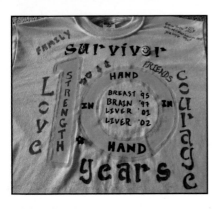

Left and right: Dionne's 2005 Relay For Life T-shirt and a victory lap with her dad later that summer in Wascana Centre.

Below left and centre: Enjoying Provo island.

Above right: Visiting with Peter Ballantine and family in Guelph, Ontario, August 2005

Left and below left: Dionne enjoys sledding Moose Mountain Provincial Park but enjoys warming up afterwards even more, 2005.

Below right: Graham unwittingly collects some snow in his helmet while sledding nor[t] of Yorkton, Saskatchewan, 2005.

For more photos, see slideshow on Accompanying DVD.

Left: Ready for the Annual Ride for Breast Cancer Screening, beginning in front of the Saskatchewan Legislature.

Right: A luminary from Graham, Relay For Life 2007.

Left: On vacation in Italy, June 2007.

Right: Dr. Salim walks the Victory Lap with Dionne, Regina Relay For Life 2007.

Below right: Graham dresses up, courtesy of the restaurant, for his birthday supper, 2007.

elow left: Dionne was honoured with other survivors at the 07 Regina Pats junior hockey team's Breast Cancer game.

elow centre: The Cancer Survivor Garden is in front of egina's Pasqua Hospital, the location of the Allan Blair ancer Centre.

elow right: Graham enjoys wakeboarding, Provo, 2008.

For more photos, see slideshow on Accompanying DVD.

Silly Dionne and Graham *(clockwise from top left)*: A pretend wedding kiss in a chapel on a 2008 Alaskan cruise; 'I want that Louis Vuitton bag!'; Graham gets up close and personal with a TV host in Chicago, 2009; Who's up for Thanksgiving turkey?; Playing around in Chicago; 'Green beer, anyone?'

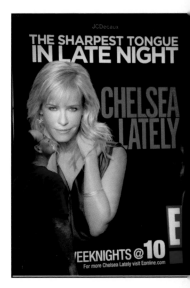

For more photos, see slideshow on Accompanying DVD.

Above: Celebrating life as a cancer survivor, on Grace Bay Beach, Provo, Turks and Caicos Islands, 2009.

Below: Graham's semi pulls Relay For Life's 'Hope' float during Regina's 2009 summer fair.

Left: Dionne and Dawn Williams.

Right: Dionne with fellow survivors Linda Rattray *(left)* and Katheran Krall, honoured by the Regina Pats junior hockey team.

Below left: At the unveiling of the Terry Fox Canadian dollar, Regina, Saskatchewan.

Below right: The 2009 volunteers of the Allan Blair Cancer Centre, Regina, Saskatchewan.

For more photos, see slideshow on Accompanying DVD.

Left: Ready for the executive association's annual Christmas ball, November 2009.

Right: Dionne with her new Stage IV diagnosis and picc line, December 11, 2009.

Below left: The picc line gets a cleaning.

Below right: "My brave beautiful angel is about to head into her third radiation treatment. I'm pretty sure all the lights in Regina momentarily dim when the switch is thrown on this baby!" – Graham

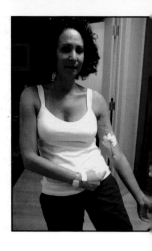

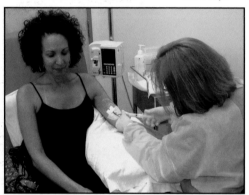

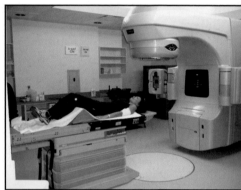

Left: Utilizing a good 'pole-dancing' opportunity, to the surprise of angel friend Bernie Desrosiers, December 14, 2009.

Right: Warner Warrior is ready to do battle during her first chemotherapy treatment, December 17, 2009.

Right: Angel friends Crystal Kalyniuk (left) and Nadine Desrosiers support Dionne during her treatment.

Far right: Graham 'bribes' clinic staff with milkshakes.

For more photos, see slideshow on Accompanying DVD.

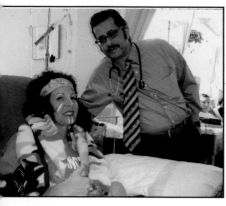

ove: Warner Warrior is visited by Dr. Salim and Wilbur Heinrichs, co-co-ordinator of Volunteer Services
th the Allan Blair Cancer Centre.

"In the immortal words of Bugs Bunny: Of course you realize that this means war!"

With Graham at her side, Dionne is ready to attack her cancer.

Left: Putting the 'Ho' in Ho Ho Ho!

Below left: Still conked out from her chemo treatment, at home on her couch.

Below right: She woke six hours later to see the snow angel Graham made for her in their front yard.

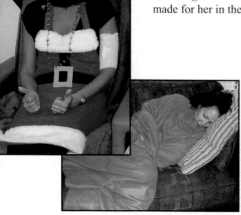

For more photos, see slideshow on Accompanying DVD.

Above left: 'Angel vandals' from the Relay For Life committee left this hope-filled sign in the Warners' front yard, December 27, 2009.

Above right and below right: Dionne with her goddaughter Shaya Nordick and Shaya's mother Kimmie Maki, and Dionne with her godson Joshua Collesso.

Above: Graham with his brother Brent and mother Audrey Warner.

Right: Ringing in the new year in the chemo treatment room with angel friend Kimmie Maki.

Below right, left to right: Partying with Michael Melville, Kimmie Maki, Bev Holfeld and Nadine Desrosiers, December 31, 2009.

Below: The Cancer Survivor Garden sign is particularly beautiful surrounded by snow.

For more photos, see slideshow on Accompanying DVD.

Above left: On January 1, 2010, Dionne called to Graham, "Hon, would you come here? And bring the camera."

Her loss of hair prompted a trip to a local hair salon. The end result was a beautifully shaven, proud Dionne.

Below right: The photo that is on display in the wig room at the Allan Blair Cancer Centre, Regina.

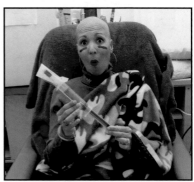

Left: The chic, ultra fashionable Toronto girl turned redneck, or at least a little militant with her mid-January 2010 theme of 'I'm Killing Cancer – Back Off!'

Right: Dionne's smile faded quickly when she saw the size of the needle they actually use to inject her chemo drugs.

For more photos, see slideshow on Accompanying DVD.

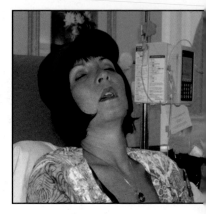

Above: Graham found this completely purple-attired mannequin in the hallway at home just before leaving for the clinic, ready for the theme 'I just *love* the colour purple!' Dionne displays some messages of support from Leslie Foss of Provo island and then, as the chemo started to take effect, Graham was quick to point o "Man, these conked-out shots just never get old, do they?"

Left: This theme became even funnier when Dionne had to answer a female onlooker's serious query of 'What's a ta-ta?' Good thing she didn't ask Graham.

Right: Winnipeg angel friend BJ Langdon came bearing ... er wearing his wife Karri's ta-tas shirt!

Left: Valentine's Day 2010 found Dionne and Graham in Tijuana, Mexico for some new therapies.

Right: This is the cost of not taking your wife's T-shirt seriously enough. "Can you unlock me now please?"

Bottom left: Graham reads to Dionne while she undergoes a sauna heat-type of therapy.

Right: With their new-favourite chef and friend Mariana Brito.

For more photos, see slideshow on Accompanying DVD.

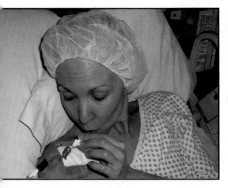

Top left: With huge new picc lines inserted, Dionne says, "I'm going to blow me up some boobs." Silly girl.

Top right: With Dr. Ariel Perez (left) and Dr. Juan Manuel Garcia (right) in hospital in Tijuana, Mexico.

Left and below: In her tribute to the Olympic Games, Dionne borrows the Games motto of 'Believe' and shows some of the things she believes in every day, February 2010.

low: Crystal Kalyniuk arrived in Mexico to e Graham's place while he went off to ASCAR.

Below: Perfusionist Vera Lopez and Dr. Garcia watch over their patient patient during her hyperthermic treatment.

For more photos, see slideshow on Accompanying DVD.

Left: When Dr. Garcia took out the picc lines, the pain on Dionne's face tells the tale.

Above: With cousin David Ballantine in Toronto.

Left: Visiting with some of Dionne's family and friends in Ontario.

Above: Cancer centre staff blow the foam off the St. Patrick's Day beer, March 2010.

Below: Graham happily found some Easter bunnies on Provo's beach: *(left to right)* Tara Czarnecki, Cindy Alston, Dionne and Leslie Foss.

...ring their 2010 Easter trip to Provo, Dionne was able to realize some wishes: to feel the sand between her ...s, feel the warmth of the sun on her face and enjoy the view of the crystal clear turquoise waters from ...ce Bay beach. They also enjoyed a meal on the beach with friends they consider family.

...ove right: Some girlfriends had fun with sunscreen, trying to give Dionne an angel wings suntan tattoo.

...ow: Having fun with some angel friends on the island, and simply relaxing and enjoying the view.

For more photos, see slideshow on Accompanying DVD.

Above: "Woo Hoo! I love Provo!"

Top right and right: Bringing a little of the island to the cancer centre.

Above: Hola, Chef Mariana Brito! Welcome to Regina! Now it's time for a Mexican fiesta theme!

Right: Cancer centre staff Harry Mundy and nurse Donna Kish as well as nurse Heather Choquette *(below right)* partake in a little Mexican party fun.

Below: The beautiful señoritas and handsome señor.

For more photos, see slideshow on Accompanying DVD.

Left: Looks like someone has had a *little too much* tequila!

Right: We thought chemo was supposed to *remove* the hair!

ove: Chef Mariana treats Regina CKRM country radio show hosts Jamie Lewis (left) and Willy Cole
ht) to her organic cupcakes with gluten-free icing and tells some of her secrets on air, April 28, 2010.

Left: Chef Guido and his lovely helper compare their kitchen tools.

Right and below right: After she licks the spoon, Dionne shares with angel friend Carla Redler.

Left: Chef Mariana has way too much fun in the kitchen!

For more photos, see slideshow on Accompanying DVD.

Top left: Nominators Heather Choquette *(left)* and Nadine Desrosiers with Dionne at YWCA Women of Distinction gala, May 2010.

Above: Dionne's cousin Yuri Collesso made a surprise visit for the gala from Guelph, Ontario.

Left: Dionne and Graham with angel friends Tricia and Roger Pettigrew.

Left: The gardener gets busy watering the beautiful but surprised flowers, May 2010.

Below: Watch out for those butterflies!

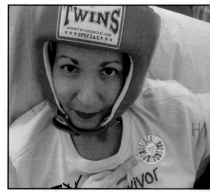

Above: Nadine Desrosiers was pleased to find that her work outfit matched the theme of the day.

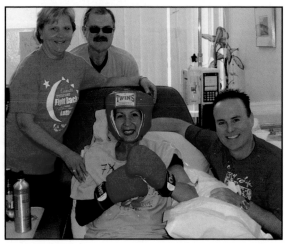

Left and above: It's time to Fight Back with Relay angel friends Carla and Tony Redler, and to recognize the many colours of cancer.

For more photos, see slideshow on Accompanying DVD.

Carla Redler takes her best shot *(left)*, but Dionne wins in the end (right), and Graham doesn't fare so well!

Left and above: Captain Graham enjoys a day at a local lake with his Pretty D boat and a boatload of pretty ladies: (left to right) Crystal Kalyniuk, Mariana Brito, Mandy Sauer and Dionne.

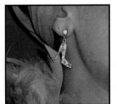

It's *Sex and the City* theme time! Dry martinis, cigars, Louis Vuitton bags, Jimmy Choo shoes for every-one!!
"No cracks about the tiara. This guy knows people who know your people, see?"

The Jamaica theme, v
Dionne's father in
attendance, was a litt
too popular!

2010 Relay For Life: *(above left to right)*
Graham, Mariana Brito, Dionne and her dad with
a sign for the Survivor Bracelets program
sponsored by Warner Industries; Warner Warrior
D dressed for the rain; Mariana Brito and Dionne
feeding burgers to the volunteers.

Above right: Kelly Greenwood and Dionne – happy survivors!

Below: Survivor Tony Redler in front of survivors waiting on steps of the
Legislature for their group Relay For Life 2010 photo.

Below: Lou Beltramini a
his 'shadow' Dionne sha
an emotional hug.

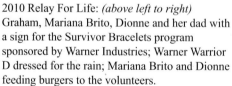

king the Victory Lap with Graham and her dad.
cking one of the many luminaries in her honour.

Hugs were aplenty from supporters, whom Dionne thanked with her own luminary; with Relay friends Tony and Carla Redler.

Left and right: Time to boo the Winnipeg Blue Bombers and show some Rider Pride – all in good fun, of course.

Left: Dionne's hat rack in the wig room of the Allan Blair Cancer Centre, Regina, Saskatchewan.

Right: With Graham's mother Audrey Warner.

For more photos, see slideshow on Accompanying DVD.

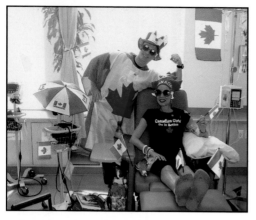

Above and left:
Happy Canada Day!

Left: "Thought we'd take this moment with a little Canada history lesson. The beaver is Canada's national animal."
– Graham

Above: Todd and Leslie Foss, originally from Saskatoon, Saskatchewan, visit from Provo fo the Peace, Love & Happiness theme, July 201

Some of the fu friendly staff o Warner Industr *(left)* and Wasc Flower Shoppe *(below)* dress t support the Pai Canada Pink Week theme.

Pink'd Out In Regina with support from Dionne's cousins *(below left)* and second cousins *(below)* in Ontario.

For more photos, see slideshow on Accompanying DVD.

Left: Coming into treatment in style – on a horse ... er, cowboy ... for the Save A Horse, Ride A Cowboy/Buffalo Days theme.

Right: Nurses Michael Melville *(left)* and Donna Kish join their cowgirl angel.

Below left: Graham does his best Festus impersonation.

Right: Dionne shows her cancer colours on the Relay For Life float in Regina's summer fair parade.

Right: Relay volunteers and survivors *(wearing yellow)* with the float.

Left and below left: Warrior D turned into the Good Fairy, granting wishes to clinic staff during the Make A Wish theme.

Below and right: The pirate wench attempts to take the long dark flowing locks of pharmacist Azure English all for herself!

For more photos, see slideshow on Accompanying DVD.

Right: Dr. Salim uses the pirate's handy blade to try to "cut the cancer out!"

Right: Proudly displaying her cancer colours.

Above and right: Although he's holding the pot of gold, Graham is pure gold in Dionne's eyes.

Below: These motorcycle mamas raise awareness for breast cancer screening.

Left: Dionne with her angel sister-in-law Melissa Warner.

It's 2 p.m. – which means Graham is having a nap.

And now, he's teaching this skill *(right)* to Dionne's dad!

Left: Graham says his prayers before taking Dionne, Linda Rattray, Mariana Brito and Mandy Sauer on a shopping road trip.

Right: And for good reason! Look at that haul!

Time for the 'Banjo Bowl' football game theme.

Right: Mariana doesn't look too sure of Graham's banjo-playing abilities.

Left: Before she can play banjo, Dionne must try to unclog her picc line, September 2010.

Right: While Graham's away (at NASCAR), the girls will play (a little *too* much) – with a Jeff Gordon cut-out and other props.

Deep-fried turkey legs and beer are definitely *not* on Dionne's diet!

Bottom left: Dionne and Kimmie Robulack-Mendes.

Left: Dr. Salim checks under the hood of his Warner Warrior patient.

For more photos, see slideshow on Accompanying DVD.

Left: "Oh, Donny!"

Right: "See, I can be a Bond girl ... or maybe even the next Bond!"

Above: Look at those curves!

Left: "I don't care if it's not on my diet! It's the best french toast in Vegas and I'm eatin' it!"

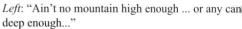

Above left: "What's up?"

Above right: "How ya doin'?"

Left: "Ain't no mountain high enough ... or any canyon deep enough..."

"All this cancer fighting can really make a girl work up a thirst ...

... and an appetite!"

Left: Delivering her 'Message of Hope' at the CIBC Run for the Cure, Regina, October 2010.

For more photos, see slideshow on Accompanying DVD.

October 13, 2010 *My Beautiful Dionne Update* **in Graham's words:**

"In support of Breast Cancer month, may I humbly share the generous, completely unselfish act and efforts made by *moi* towards breast cancer awareness. As you can see, my wife was uninhibitedly supportive! In fact, she kept encouraging everyone with, "Come on, it gives me a night off!"

"Okay, let's see ... Friendly smiling face ... check. Gloves ... check. Examination table ... check. So why does my first customer *(below left)* seem so apprehensive?"

"Nurses Michael and Donna came by *(below right)* . Before they left, of course I offered them my services. Frustratingly, again, not the reaction I was expecting!"

Left: "Come on, Azure, please! ... I think she is considering!"

Right: "Okay, it's one thing to be turned down by all the nurses, pharmacists and admin support staff, but by my good buddy Wes, too? I am *not* happy!"

Left: "Okay, I need to be more specific on my sign. Should have said, "Free *Women* Breast Examinations." But, hey ... *t h a n k   y o u* very much, Wanda and Jen!"

Right: "Perhaps a little too much of a good thing, as they say. Man, those chicks went crazy on their exam! I'm a little sore!"

"So *that* was fun! Have a great week, everyone!"   – Graham

For more photos, see slideshow on Accompanying DVD.

A black widow spider and her devilishly good-looking husband do it up for Halloween 2010.

Above: Go Rid...

Left: Mandy Sa... took Graham's place at chemo, she poked a litt... fun at him whil... she was at it ... ... faking a nap.

Above: There was no joking around on Remembrance Day 2010. The Warners paused to remember those who fought for freedom. November 11th also marked 15 years to the day that Dionne was diagnosed with breast cancer.

Right: Dressing up for Canadian Western Agribition was a pretty tall order, but that mission was accomplished!

Left: Ah, that's nic... Two tired cowpokes having a nap togeth...

Above left and left: On November 11, Dionne asked the clinic staff to cut back on her Benadryl injection so she could go out that night to the Camp Circle of Friends fundraiser with *(top – left to right)* angels Jessica Martorana, Jim and Kelly Greenwood, Lou Beltramini, Mandy Sauer, Linda Rattray, Natasha Kalyniuk and of course, Graham.

Left: Dionne with Linda Rattray, Jayne Clendening, Jess... Martorana and Kelly Greenwood.

For more photos, see slideshow on Accompanying DVD.

In November 2010, it was back to Mexico for dendritic and lymphocyte cell therapy. They reconnected *(left)* with Chef Mariana and met her mother Bessy, cousin Gina and baby cousin Camila.

Right: It was also U.S. Thanksgiving! Look who got the turkey hat! And look who wants to be president!

"A little therapy isn't going to stop me from celebrating the season! Come on, Dr. Garcia, join me!"

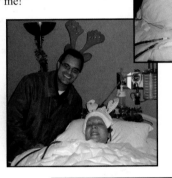

Below: "Let's get this party started! Burn, baby, burn!"

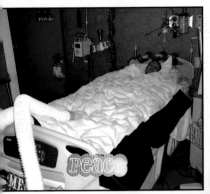

ve: Dionne returned home with quite the ude. Lou wouldn't expect anything less of 'shadow.' And a couple clinic staff showed r attitude with home-made signs *(below)*!

Right: Angel pharmacist Azure shows off her 45's – her records ... Geez!

Left: "Why did those '70s pick-up lines only work on Dionne?"

For more photos, see slideshow on Accompanying DVD.

Left: The Nifty Fifties came to chemo, March 2011.

Right: At the *Look Good ... Feel Bette*r event in Regina with *(left to right)* Michael Melville, Linda Rattray, Kimmie Maki, Mandy Sauer, Bev Holfeld and Donna Kish.

Left: It's time for a pyjama party at chemo. What? It's a hospital – with hospital beds, isn't it?

Left: Rocking it o to AC/DC!

Below: Whoa! Th drugs are making see strange things

Right: Anyone for Twister? Fun and games are guaranteed with Dionne in the room!

"Live! Love! Laugh! No regrets!" – Dionne Warner

For more photos, see slideshow on Accompanying DVD.

huge mountain that is a cancer diagnosis."

In July 2007, Dionne added a new tattoo to the two that she already proudly displayed between her shoulder blades. "I was told that for a brain cancer survivor to make it to 10 years without a relapse in the brain was a pretty big deal. So I waited it out and I won!" she said triumphantly. A tattoo of a grey ribbon for brain cancer was added to Dionne's back to celebrate this wonderful accomplishment.

Dionne became more in demand to share her story of hope and be a public face of cancer. She accepted numerous invitations and was always touched by the encounters she had with the people she met along the way.

Dionne and Yvonne Loustel of Carlyle, Saskatchewan were two of the survivors at the 2007 Regina Pats junior hockey team's Breast Cancer Game. They were given special pink hockey jerseys and were invited to stand at centre ice at the start of the game to be honoured for their breast cancer journeys.

"The whole experience was totally amazing and it was emotional to see all the support," says Loustel. "I helped Dionne sell her Little Shop of Hope items that night. I could not believe the support. I even sold the breast cancer awareness watch off my wrist!"

Loustel had met Dionne four years earlier at the Allan Blair Cancer Centre when, at age 33, Loustel was diagnosed with breast cancer. She was sitting in the recliners with her husband Mike, waiting for chemo. "Dionne was asked by my doctor, Dr. Salim, who is also her doctor, to share her story with me. My husband and I had no clue what to expect from chemo. We had heard about the many bad side-effects. I was so scared. Being diagnosed with cancer is a very scary roller coaster ride. After hearing her story, it gave us the strength and courage to fight this horrible disease. I remember thinking, 'She looks awesome. You would have no idea she has been through so much.'

"Since then, Dionne and I have become good friends. When she started raising funds for cancer, I quickly jumped on board. I could not wait to see the new items Dionne found to sell. Dionne also helped me sell *Breast Friends Cookbooks*. I try to meet up with Dionne whenever I am in Regina. We have had many lunches together. We even had some of our medical tests done at the same time and Mike and I stayed at their house the night before the tests. Dionne and I also went shopping in Moose Jaw one time while my husband was attending meetings there."

Dionne and Graham have flown to Carlyle, about 230 kilometres southeast of Regina, to visit the Loustels. "I have become very good friends with a lot of people I was helping," says Dionne. "We would go out and visit them in their homes. They're friends that we call family."

The Warners and Loustels exchange birthday and Christmas gifts and chat by computer when Dionne is away from Regina, adds Loustel. "Dionne is a true inspiration. She is so strong, courageous, caring, loving, supportive, positive and fun. Dionne has many family and friends who are always there for her. I have shared Dionne's story with many people and they are always asking how she is doing. They continue to be inspired by her."

Dionne was invited to speak at Whitmore Park School in Regina in 2007 and was thrilled when the schoolchildren raised $1,800 in 50 minutes by purchasing $5 silicone wristbands in the various colours of cancer. "Kids were coming with cheques from their parents," says an overwhelmed Dionne. "I was glad I had my girlfriend there to help me."

Dionne was nervous at first in sharing her cancer story with children from kindergarten up. "I didn't want to scare these children," she says, "but they were all great and very sweet. One little girl came up and said, 'Thank you for sharing your story. My grandmother has been sick and I now know what her colour is.' I didn't have that colour wristband with me that day so I told her I would get it and come to the school and bring it to her, and I did that four days later. I wanted to give them as much information as possible so they wouldn't be as scared of cancer."

The following year, Dionne spoke at another elementary school in Regina and educated a few more children about this disease called cancer.

In 2007, Donna Kish, a nurse at the Allan Blair and one of Dionne's Earth Angels, was walking through Wascana Centre in Regina when she heard a promotion for Toyota's Never Quit Award – "Prairie people never quit. Does that sound like someone you know?" The award recognizes individuals 'for their tireless pursuit of their personal goals, their ability to triumph over adversity or their commitment to making the community a better place.' Kish immediately thought of Dionne and filled out a nomination form.

"I just jotted down a few thoughts about Dionne, this wonderful gal I got to meet. I did that on the spot and Dionne was later chosen as one of the top finalists throughout Canada," smiles Kish.

In 2008, Kish asked Dionne if she would speak at the Community Oncology Program of Saskatchewan symposium being held in Saskatoon for physicians, nurses, social workers and pharmacy staff. Dionne readily agreed and shared her cancer battle from a patient's perspective. "There wasn't a dry eye there," says Kish.

It is not in Dionne's nature to ever think of herself as being a superstar personality or a speaker who must be available to her public. She agrees to speaking requests because she has been told that her story gives others hope, and she wants to share that hope as far afield as she can. Besides, it would be difficult to get too caught up in grandiose thinking when one lives with Graham.

"Everybody thinks D's so inspirational and motivated," teases Graham. "Every morning, I look at her and say, 'Good thing you're not a horse.'"

"Yes. You know what they do to sick horses, don't you?" Dionne asks rhetorically.

In early 2009, Graham and Dionne were on Provo when Dionne contacted Carla and Tony Redler in Regina about that year's Relay For Life campaign. "She e-mailed me and said, 'Carla, we need to put a float in the parade. We need to showcase Relay and get survivors involved.' Our committee had talked about it for a few years but it was kind of on a backburner," says Carla. "It was interesting because that winter, I had said to Tony that we should really get serious about putting together a float. Living with someone who has had cancer, every day is a gift. You never know. It could change in one night."

So the Redlers met with another Relay committee member and came up with the theme of 'Hope' for their first parade float in 2009. "It was great. Dionne came over often and checked out what we were doing. She's not often the hands-on girl. She's the everyone-get-up-and-go person. Her presence just gets people motivated. Period," says Carla.

Adds Tony Redler, "She's the thinker, not the doer."

"It was fun doing that float theme and having Graham help with it, too," continues Carla. "If he's doing it, he's doing it all out. Graham provided the tractor and trailer and covered all the costs of all the expenses we couldn't raise with the hot dog sales we were doing. He offered his business place to decorate the float and even provided the pizza and beer while we were decorating! They're just incredible people. Part of the thing Tony and I cherish is that they welcomed us into their circle of friends and we feel so blessed to be even considered in that group."

Through Dionne's volunteering and public speaking, her circle of friends and acquaintances grew to the point where people recognized her in malls and did not know her husband. It was a sharp contrast to what she had experienced in 2001.

"When I first came to Saskatchewan, I was very lonely. Graham and I would go into Home Depot and people would say, 'Hey, Graham!' from way across the store. I remember saying to him, 'I hope someone says, 'Hey D!' to me some day.' And now the joke is that he has to say to people, 'Well, I'm Dionne Warner's husband.'"

December 2009

*"Heaven is freakin' not ready for me! There isn't a disco ball big enough
up there for this sister to rock out to!!" - Dionne*

Graham and Dionne spent Christmas 2007 in Jamaica visiting
Dionne's father and family and then went to Provo for three
months. The following December, they spent a full six months
on the island, returning home to Regina in June 2009.

It was the first time that Dionne had not had a CT scan for an entire
year. "They felt everything was going good. I was doing fine and if I had
any complications or I didn't feel right, it would be time to do it," she
says.

In September 2009, she went on a 60-kilometre two-day walk with a
girlfriend in Toronto as part of the Weekend to End Breast Cancer event.
In hindsight, that trip to Ontario was stressful for Dionne. She had never
walked that far before and she was also working hard to pull together a
surprise bridal shower for her girlfriend while in town.

"I was trying to get to know her new friends who would be part of
this wedding also and I was in tears when I left on the last day." She and
her friend decided to part company after a 12-year friendship. "I realized
this was probably the last time we would see each other," says Dionne.
"Both of our lives were changing. It was time to let go. We decided we
would go our own ways."

Some time in November, Dionne began feeling pain in her back. She
wondered if she'd overworked her back during that long walk. "I'd never
walked that far. Shortly afterwards, I had little twinges here and there. I
would just pop an Aleve but it was getting worse."

For almost three weeks, she went for massage therapy and
chiropractic treatments every other day. Neither helped to relieve her
pain. At one point, the massages hurt so bad that Dionne wanted to cry in
anguish. The massage therapist and chiropractor both became concerned
that Dionne was not getting better and the chiropractor ordered an X-ray
of her back. He thought he saw bone spurs but before Dionne could get

any further with that investigation, she went to the cancer centre on December 8 for her routine follow-up CT scan.

"I went to see Dr. Salim before the scan to tell him what was happening with my back because I wanted him to take a peek. I told him the pain was all across the top of my right shoulder blade. At times when I tried to push myself out of bed, the pain shot down my arm. I think he knew then what was going on, but he said he would make sure they took a look at my back as part of the scan."

Dionne was initially scheduled to see Dr. Salim for the test results on December 10, but his nurse called her a day early, on December 9, and asked her to come see Dr. Salim later that day instead. Dionne knew it could not be good news.

"I called Graham and told him that Dr. Salim wants to see us today at 2 p.m. It was a long drive to the hospital."

When Dr. Salim came into the room, Dionne and Graham could both see that he had been wiping tears from his eyes. He closed the door, sat down and said to Dionne, "Your cancer is back."

He told her that her breast cancer had metastasized to her spine and that there were also multiple spots back in her liver as well as her lungs. "It's not operable. It's Stage IV."

"I figured he was going to tell me the cancer was in my back. I never expected it would be everywhere else, too," says Dionne. "Graham's face went white and he said, 'Oh my God.' I was just trying to absorb this. I was in a daze. It was very scary."

Still, Dionne clung to hope.

"When Dr. Salim said this, he never said in the next breath, 'This is it, there's nothing we can do. You only have this much time to live.' I was waiting for that. I didn't hear that, so I felt, 'Okay, it's not the greatest news – but he's not telling me I'm going to die.' This is what I had to hang on to. This was my thread."

Graham was overcome with emotion. "This was a bigger fight than I thought," he says about that moment. "I always win. I didn't feel like I could win this one."

Dr. Salim left the room for awhile so Graham and Dionne could be alone. "I started to worry a little bit more then and I became more emotional," says Dionne. She held back her tears, though, because she was so concerned for Graham. He was distraught and emotional. Tears poured down his cheeks as he considered the worst.

"When I saw my husband cry that day, it broke my heart," says Dionne sadly. "I thought, 'Oh my goodness, he has to deal with this again.' That broke my heart even more. Looking at him, it was heart-wrenching. One of us had to be the stronger person and, at that time, it was me."

"The ventilation system had just kicked in and put some dust in my eye," says Graham in a half-hearted attempt to make light of those horrible moments.

Dionne still wishes that Graham had not had to bear that pain. "I had been by myself most of the times when I had received my diagnoses, so most things didn't shock me anymore. I was never in denial about this cancer. My life could change again tomorrow, but I'm prepared. I knew when I was diagnosed with this that it could come back. Anything is possible. I live in a reality world."

When Dr. Salim returned to the room, he began telling them the immediate course of action he had arranged to deal with this diagnosis. He changed Dionne's prescriptions and had her scheduled to start on five treatments of radiation the next day to reduce the size of the tumours and thus reduce the pain in her back. She would have an MRI right after her first radiation treatment, a bone scan was scheduled on December 11, she would finish radiation on December 16 and start chemo on December 17 for three-week cycles and then have one week off.

"He said, 'We're going to do this, we're going to do this, we're going to do that. We've got to get on it right away.' And the ball was rolling," says Dionne. "We didn't have time to think about a lot of things. We didn't have a lot of time to sit, which was good."

"There was almost relief in that because they were doing something," adds Graham. "We felt like we were attacking it."

After leaving the hospital, Dionne and Graham drove to the Warner Industries office. Graham went in to see Roger Pettigrew, who is not only Warner Industries' general manager but Graham's friend and second wingman after Dionne. Graham has come to rely heavily on Roger in not only business, but his personal life. When Graham and Dionne are away, Roger looks after their home and checks in on Graham's mom, who is like a second mother to him from their growing-up years. "We could not do what we do or have done, especially with D's cancer battles, without the unfaltering, steadfast and always appreciated support from Roger and his wife Tricia," says Graham with deep emotion.

When Pettigrew heard this new diagnosis, he was upset, sad and even a little bit angry. Cancer is horribly unfair in who it picks on, he said. "Why, when somebody breaks the law, why don't they get cancer? The people who don't respect others, why don't they get cancer? When you see somebody who's a good soul – who lives, loves, laughs – that whole thing Dionne's all about and means it – why do they get sick?"

After Graham spoke with Roger, he and Dionne told Karen Drysdale.

"I'll never forget that day," says Drysdale. "Dionne came and asked if I could find somebody to cover reception because she'd like to talk to me. Graham went into Roger's office and then Roger and I went into Graham's office with Dionne. She told us her cancer was back and where all her cancer was back again. It's the only time I've seen her cry."

A little while later, Graham and Dionne headed home and Graham immediately started researching therapy options on the Internet. "That's Graham," says Dionne with a smile. "Already searching and researching. 'What can we do?' He doesn't waste any time."

Dionne began making phone calls to inform their family and friends. The silence on the other end of the line was painful. "The hardest phone call was to my father to tell him once again that not only was his daughter sick, but she was really, really sick this time. It was Stage IV cancer. It was always Stage II-III before … but I was not told I was going to die," says Dionne with a nervous giggle.

"It was like it was a dream," says Rupert Walford about that phone call. "I thought, 'In no way could this happen to her again,' but then reality clicked in, so I cried and cried some more. I tried to stay strong when I spoke with Dionne, reassuring her that she could overcome it again but no matter how I tried not to, I always ended up crying. Still, my daughter is a fighter and I know she is not going to give in to this disease. She had a seven-year reprieve and I expect her to overcome this bout and live a normal life."

Hearing her father break down was difficult for Dionne, especially knowing his pain at being so far away from her. He offered to come visit her in Regina, but she told him to wait for awhile. "I needed him to come not at the beginning but when I was feeling so good that he could see his daughter was fighting and doing well. I wanted him to see me looking good, looking healthy so it would give him something positive to hang on to."

Dionne had to break the news herself to friends who worked at the cancer centre, including Nadine Desrosiers and her husband Bernie, who also works for the health region. Bernie answered Dionne's phone call to hear Dionne say, "I've been diagnosed again and it's bad." After Dionne explained the diagnosis, Bernie hung up the phone and went to tell Nadine what Dionne had said. "We were a mess," says Bernie. "Then a few minutes later, Dionne and Graham phoned back to make sure we were okay." Bernie and Nadine both shake their heads in wonder at the thoughtfulness of their friends during such a painful time.

Kelly Greenwood received her phone call from Dionne on the evening of December 9 and didn't sleep that night, thinking about her friend's diagnosis. Dionne told Greenwood she was coming to the clinic the next day to plan 'the attack,' and Greenwood wasn't surprised by Dionne's attitude.

"The next morning, when she arrived with Graham, we went for a coffee before her appointment. I was sitting there not saying a whole lot and she pointed at me and said, 'No long faces. I can't have you looking at me with those sad eyes.' I quickly explained that although I was sad, there was no pity – because I knew she wouldn't want that – but I was mad. Really mad. Dionne laughed at me and said, 'I'm not going anywhere, sister! Heaven is freakin' not ready for me! There isn't a disco ball big enough up there for this sister to rock out to!!' "

The three of them laughed at Dionne's comment. "That's Dionne in a nutshell," smiles Greenwood. "No time for feeling sorry for herself – only time for figuring out, 'How are we going to do it this time?' "

Dionne had an MRI (magnetic resonance imaging) test that morning which took a closer look at her soft tissue. Dr. Salim reported that the MRI results showed further cancer on her pelvic bone and her right ribs. Dionne and Graham then met with a female radiologist who said the cancer tumours were squeezing the T-1 through T-8 section of her spine and creating the pain.

She also said that if the cancer had not been caught when it was, Dionne would have been paralyzed or lost the use of her arms within a week to 10 days.

"I'd been fighting it for three weeks not knowing what it was and treating it with massages and chiropractors," says Dionne incredulously.

Dionne had her first radiation treatment that afternoon. A female oncologist spoke to Dionne about the tumour on her spine. "It's palliative," she said. "You're lucky you came this far."

"That worked me up, because we had never had that word used. That's how I got fired up to look elsewhere," says Graham. While most people think of the word 'palliative' in terms of patients who are dying, palliative actually means alleviating pain without eliminating its source – and Graham wanted no part of that. He wanted to get at the source of Dionne's cancer and get rid of the tumours.

He went home and looked up therapy options, including cyberknife technology that had just been approved in Canada in September 2009.

Graham hoped that Dionne's tumours could be shrunken and then cyberknifed out with the non-invasive 360-degree radial surgery. When he mentioned this option to Dr. Salim a few days later, Dr. Salim told Graham that he had already considered that treatment but Dionne was not a candidate because her tumours were too immersed in her system.

Graham did not give up. He asked Dionne if she would consider going to a naturopath to see if any of those therapies would benefit her. Dionne refused, saying she felt she would be 'cheating' on her oncologist.

Graham kept searching.

"From the beginning, Graham was going to Dr. Salim and asking, 'What about this?' I wouldn't even go with him. That's G – investigating. He's leaving no stone unturned. It was like when Graham proposed to me so quickly – this guy doesn't mess around. He was going to snatch me up really fast," smiles Dionne.

"I don't like competition," smiles Graham.

"Yeah, he's in the fight, too. 100%. He is right on it. I just wait for him to come back and tell me the details of what he's found. Then I say, 'How much will this hurt me?'"

"Graham never stops looking," says Dionne.

"I guess it's just a discipline of mine, when you're faced with having to make a decision, ask yourself if you have enough information to make the decision. That's why I instantly started checking everything out. I've spent literally hundreds of hours on the Internet. It's just become part of my life now. I'm still investigating all available options."

Dionne and Graham have looked back on December 9, 2009 many times. They have wondered if the diagnosis would have been different if she had undergone a CT scan in June rather than waiting until December.

Dr. Salim answers that question. "Those six months would not have made any difference. I'll give you an example. You tie two persons to the railway track side by side and give binoculars to one – he will know the train is coming first. The survival will not change."

Hindsight can be a terrible thing some times, but Dionne has never allowed herself to dwell on 'what ifs.' "They say that all my other cancer diagnoses have metastasized from my breast cancer diagnosis. That's why they recommend that women have double mastectomies. The doctor in Ontario didn't mention anything about having a mastectomy when I was 30. I wasn't ready and my doctor wasn't ready. I didn't know then that I also had this mutated gene."

Dr. Salim explained that "a radical mastectomy is not better than a lumpectomy. It depends on the type of the cancer and a lot of other factors such as the size of the cancer." In explaining Dionne's cancer, he added that some cancers have receptors which bind to female hormones and those hormones will then behave like a growth hormone. "With Dionne, it is all breast cancer going places. It's not a brain cancer, it's a breast cancer that went to the brain, it was a breast cancer that went to the liver, bone and all. This is all breast cancer." Family history is the biggest risk factor for breast cancer and in a small number of cases, such as Dionne's, genetics are also a factor, he said.

Although devastated at first by this latest diagnosis, Dionne and Graham soon reacted to the news the same way as they did for her liver cancers. Neither of them panicked. "I panic more when I have a splitting headache because my biggest fear is this cancer could come back in my brain," says Dionne.

Graham feels his pilot training might be the reason he tries to stay calm. "I always think there's no usefulness to panicking, so don't waste energy on it and just deal with what you have to deal with."

Still, in the months following the diagnosis, Dionne occasionally relived that moment right after they heard the news. "I looked at Graham and thought, 'Okay, I can't get upset because then that would be two of us. I always thought I'd be the one who would go down and at that moment, I thought, 'Oh my God, I wonder if he was regretting anything now that I'm sick again.' "

"Oh, geez, I never regret," says Graham quickly, looking at his wife patiently.

This new diagnosis brought a huge roller coaster of emotions with it, more so than any of her other diagnoses, and that feeling of wondering has crept into Dionne's mind a few times since December 9. She and Graham have repeatedly had this conversation:

"Here I am sick again," she says."I offered you that opportunity when I was sick with liver cancer – that you didn't have to marry me and I would go back to Ontario."

"I've said this before – that's like saying to a person, 'You don't have to breathe anymore,' " says Graham.

"I know, and you're a different cat, but I just have to continue to throw it out there. It's tough. It's tough on you."

Graham pauses and smiles, explaining to all who will listen, "You never leave your wingman."

Offering an opening for Graham to leave her is part of Dionne's way of coping with the strain her cancer has caused her husband, even though he willingly accepted that strain in November 2000, in the name of love.

On December 11, 2009 Graham sent an early-morning e-mail to family and friends to explain what had been happening in his and Dionne's lives over the past few days. He called the e-mail, *'My beautiful Dionne.'*

He acknowledged that the e-mail might be "a little bit of a surprise" to some who received it since this was the initial announcement that "after seven years, cancer has returned to once again do battle with our beautiful Dionne." He explained the diagnosis and said that a picc line (peripherally inserted central catheter) would soon be inserted into Dionne's left arm, through her vein and leading up to a spot just above her heart. Through this line, blood samples would be drawn and chemotherapy medications would be injected for the next year, until a new line would replace this one. Dionne had made the "very hard decision" to have a picc line because it was too painful for her to receive treatment with needles through the scar tissue she had built up from other treatments.

Graham told his friends and family, "Dr. Salim says he feels the tumours are totally treatable but will know after the third treatment if they are going to shrink. He is hoping to obtain permission to use a new drug that is being used in the States. This drug has proven quite effective in shrinking tumours but our Canadian government will not pay for it. ($2,600 per dose) A good friend of ours has had excellent experience with it and although it is quite expensive, I have been blessed with having the greatest employees in the world and so we hope to have the opportunity to use it."

Graham went on to say that, "with D's outgoing optimistic personality and volunteering at the hospital, it has truly been overwhelming to see the love and support reciprocated from what seems like every single nurse, doctor, candy striper and janitor who works at the Pasqua Hospital! I actually wondered if all the hugs and well-wishing was interfering in the timeframe of her treatment! (Just kidding.) However, I truly believe that all this love and support explains the absolute rock-star treatment she has received in the last 48 hours with her obtaining all the procedures and treatments in such a timely manner. The outpouring of love and support from all of you who already knew (outside of the hospital) has also been overwhelming and greatly appreciated as well as needed! I promise to keep you updated regularly with D's progress as she once again conquers this mean, nasty thing called cancer. Thank you all for your love and support and keep rubbing those angel wings together!"

Almost immediately, Graham began receiving e-mail responses and phone calls offering support and encouragement. By that evening, he had sent another mass e-mail that showed photos of Dionne with her new picc line dangling from her left arm. He also explained some of their other adventures for that day. Willy Cole, a Regina country radio station host, sent out best wishes that morning "to the girl with a heart the size of Texas" and they had a memorable trip to a local store to find something to cover up Dionne's picc line.

"This picc line must be kept dry, so how could D shower each day?" wrote Graham. "The idea of a calving sleeve was offered, so off to the local farmer/rancher supply store we went. I think this is an absolute hoot that our local Peavey Mart is part of D's recovery process. It is redneck to the core! It's one of our most popular stores and is only three to four blocks from our house. I know all D's friends from the big-city Toronto area will not only be chuckling at this little trivia but also picturing Dionne putting on a calving sleeve all the way up to her shoulder just to have a shower."

Graham continued. "We had to ask one of the store managers for assistance to locate the product and when he expressed disappointment that the boxes of 300 sleeves appeared to have been sold out, while I was simultaneously expressing joy at finding the little bags with 10 sleeves in them, he turned to us and said dryly, 'You're not farmers, are you?' I said, 'No,' and then he replied, 'I don't even want to know what you're going to do with those then!' "

That day, Dionne had a complete skeleton bone scan and a second radiation treatment. She was already beginning to feel relief from back pain, Graham reported, and he again thanked everyone for their support. "We really feel your strength and prayers and look forward to next week as we all travel this road to recovery together." The e-mail ended with a photo of a smiling Dionne and Graham, grinning at the camera and offering hope to all who received the update.

Sometime within that next week, Dionne arrived at the Warner Industries office with gift bags in hand. For the last number of years, Dionne had taken the women who work at Warner Industries out for a Christmas lunch and given them all gifts. "She always finds this different, unique stuff like candles or knick knacks," says Karen Drysdale. "One year, she gave us beautiful breast cancer Christmas tree ornaments. We all had reindeer hats. She calls it 'The Warner Women Lunch.' "

The annual Christmas lunch had been planned for a date during Dionne's first week of chemo treatment, and Dionne apologized to the women for being unable to host the lunch this year. "She came in with a little Santa sack and said how sorry she was she couldn't take us for lunch and she handed out the presents," says Karen Drysdale. "Ruth Patron hadn't seen Dionne since this all happened, so Ruth was very emotional and started to cry. D just shook her finger back and forth and said, 'No tears. We are done with that. It's time to move on and get the healing started.' "

There have been many other people who have been chastised by Dionne over the years for allowing tears to get in the way of a perfectly good visit. "My friends and family, when they come to see me because they know I'm sick and they haven't seen me in awhile, their first reaction is they want to cry and I have to say to them, 'No tears. We're doing fine. No tears.' Graham went to see a friend of ours and she was bawling. 'No, you can't do that anymore. You have to stay positive.' "

Graham sent a *My beautiful Dionne update* e-mail on December 15, showing Dionne sitting patiently as her picc line was injected and cleaned out. There were photos of his 'brave beautiful angel' lying on a table, ready to enter the enormous radiation machine for her third treatment, and a smiling Dionne doing a 'pole dance' with an IV pole that a hospital friend happened to be returning to the cancer clinic.

"Never able to turn down a good pole-dance opportunity, D spontaneously and very enthusiastically warmed up the pole right there in the middle of the clinic," joked Graham in his update. "(You know she believes laughter soothes the soul even in the most challenging times.) Surrounding shocked staff and waiting patients did in fact all enjoy a very good laugh. Although I think that there were a couple old guys who were maybe enjoying the show a little too much, know what I mean??? ... grrrrr."

By December 16, Graham and Dionne had received literally hundreds of phone calls, e-mails and letters of support. Dionne was looking forward to her first day of chemo the next morning and Graham promised everyone he would send an update out the next day "with photos of our Warner Warrior, who I think will be very tired by tomorrow night! (Good thing she got the house cleaned to her standard today!)," he joked.

On December 17, 2009 Dionne showed up at the cancer centre dressed in a bright pink T-shirt emblazoned with the words CANCER SUCKS. She wore a rainbow-coloured headband with matching bangles and had white stripes of 'war paint' on her face to depict the Warner Warrior going in to do battle once again.

Photos included in that evening's update e-mail from Graham showed Dionne in her recliner in the chemo treatment room. She was surrounded by gifts she'd received from friends, including a coffee mug stating 'Cancer ain't for sissies,' a camouflage blanket over her shoulders, and a pink blanket draped over her legs that was emblazoned with the breast cancer ribbon and words such as Live Laughter Life Strength Love Hope Faith. Dionne's girlfriends Crystal Kalyniuk and Nadine Desrosiers were on either side of her for support and Dr. Salim posed for a photo with the Warner Warrior as well.

"Dr. Salim bucked general opinion from the medical community seven and nine years ago to guide D through her survival of her last two liver cancers," wrote Graham in this update. "Yesterday, Dr. Salim obtained permission to use the U.S.-based Avastin chemo drug on Dionne. We were soooo thankful for this, along with all his other efforts. The Avastin was used in her treatment today. On a very personal note, the chemo staff shared with us later that 'Dr. Salim rarely visits the chemo delivery centre.' It really became very clear how much D has influenced him, too."

Treatment regimens change with each cancer patient and depend on factors such as the patient's current health, age, ability to tolerate the treatment, the type of cancer and what treatment the patient had in the past, explained Dr. Salim. "Radiation was used to release some of pain in Dionne's bones. Chemo is almost always used if the patient is fit."

Avastin and Taxol were the two main drugs administered to Dionne during her chemo room treatments. Avastin breaks down the tumour cells and stops tumours from having the ability to form a new blood supply. At that time, Avastin had shown promising results in trials for prostate cancer patients and was covered by Health Canada for first-line breast cancer patients only. Since Dionne's cancer had metastasized, she and Graham would have to pay for the drug themselves.

"Dr. Salim told us of the Avastin option," says Graham. "He said, 'I know you would sell your house if you had to.'" Graham agreed that the doctor knew him very well.

Avastin is commonly used in North America and is on the Canadian formulary for colon cancer, but not breast cancer, explained Dr. Salim.

"Avastin can increase the time period that a patient is free of progression of the disease." If a patient's disease would have progressed at six months, for example, Avastin can increase that time to 10 months on average."

Taxol is used for treatment of ovarian, breast, lung and other cancers and usually causes temporary hair loss starting two to three weeks after treatment. Some of the other drugs Dionne received were designed to reduce nausea and vomiting, stop an allergic reaction to other drugs, treat her specific types of cancer. Dionne is injected with Taxol every week and receives Avastin twice a month out of the three treatments per month. They came to refer to these as single-dose days and double-dose days with the addition of Avastin adding about an hour to the regular three-hour chemo process.

In the *My beautiful Dionne update* after Dionne's first chemo treatment, Graham's generosity and caring nature were shown in a photo of him with some staff of the clinic, who were all enjoying one of the 25 strawberry milkshakes he brought in for them from the local Dairy Queen. Graham wrote that he was trying to "shamelessly bribe and attempt to influence the hospital staff. Hey, you'd all do the same!"

That update ended, as would become common, with a photo of Graham and Dionne together, side by side and smiling. The only difference this time was that Dionne was sitting in her chemo chair and Graham was standing beside her.

Dionne had no idea what she had started by putting on that pink T-shirt that day and painting her face as though she was heading to war. "I just thought, 'This is the T-shirt I'm putting on and we're going to go and I'm going to be the Pink Warrior.' I thought, 'I'm gonna fight back. I have to go get some paint for my face. I'm going in ... I'm going in hard,' " she says as she balls up her fists and thrusts them in the air with a determined look on her face.

Many people who work at the clinic came into the treatment room to see Dionne that day. They wanted to experience first-hand this feisty spirit who was taking on cancer and making a joke of it at the same time.

"I just said, 'I have to have some fun with this.' Doesn't that sound sick?" Dionne laughs. "I thought, 'We can do this! My gosh, I'm a volunteer here. I can't be a wuss. I have to help other people. I have to show some fight.' That's when it was decided that Warner Warrior was born. Little did we know from that day forward that we had created a monster. Oy yoy yoy," she laughs.

Those first few update e-mails were sent "to anybody who was involved with Dionne and I or knew us," says Graham. "I sent the very first one out to family, friends and business colleagues who are friends." The list of recipients quickly grew, though.

Many, many people wanted to know how Dionne was doing, and Graham's e-mails containing explanations as well as amusing commentary and photos became a good way to keep everyone informed while giving Graham a break from answering a multitude of questions and phone calls. "We were getting so many individual requests and phone calls that it was really starting to stress me out," he explains. "I remember getting angrily frustrated. I could easily understand why everybody wanted to know. At the same time, it wasn't giving me any time to look after D or do the things that needed to be done."

By week two of her chemo treatments, Dionne was experiencing the negative side-effects of mouth sores and insomnia. This was explained in *My Beautiful Dionne update # 6* along with a trip made to the hair salon which was requested by Dionne but, to his peril, questioned by Graham. This was related in humourous fashion by Graham, for all to enjoy.

"D's hair has already started to thin/fall. It was blizzardy weather and D asked if I would mind taking her to her hair salon. As you all know, I will do anything for the love of my life and although it was no trouble to take her, I learned something very valuable about being a man yesterday. What could that be, you ask? Apparently, a man ... should never, ever question his wife's desire, intent, or reasoning to attend one's hair appointment. You see, logically (I know that was my first mistake) I questioned why would she need to go when it's just going to be cut off or fall out soon anyway?

"Ten minutes later, after my impromptu tutorial was finished, we were on our way to the hair salon directly, efficiently and silently," he added.

"Within minutes, the salon was full of laughter (this happens wherever our Warner Warrior goes) and a quantity of wigs was pulled out, one after another and properly trimmed and fitted like any true warrior's headpieces should be. Now if she had told me this was the reason for going to the salon in the first place, I wouldn't have questioned it!!!!"

Dionne attended her second chemo treatment on December 23 adorned in a cute little Santa dress accessorized with a Santa hat and elegant black leather boots. She was "smokin' hot," Graham reported, and Dionne joked with the staff that "she put the 'Ho' in Ho Ho Ho!" Plastic reindeer antlers that Dionne and Graham had brought with them were happily worn by their friend Bernie Desrosiers, who took a few minutes off from his work at the hospital to show his support. Photos in the ensuing update showed Dionne napping in her chair during treatment as well as on the couch at their home a few hours later. Graham showed off the 'snow angel' he made for Dionne while she was sleeping, and the happy couple signed off wishing everyone a Merry Christmas.

And thus, the idea of doing themes and updates for each of Dionne's treatment appointments was born.

Themes and Treatments

"You're not going to take everything away that I enjoy. I monitor my food,
but I want to still be happy in the end." - Dionne

Support for Dionne in her new battle with cancer continued to pour in. On December 23, 2009 Keisha Rajnath from Provo posted a Facebook message to Dionne: "What I admire most about you is your strong heart, the will to fight and your wonderful spirit. I pray for you every day that you will get through this ... Your angels are all here! Kick @*! on that stuff! You know you're overdue in getting the tan you love. The hot Caribbean sun and the lounge chairs at the beaches are calling you. Love you!"

On Christmas Day, Graham's mother made a special turkey soup in case Dionne wasn't yet able to eat solid food due to her mouth sores. Dionne was feeling much better by that time, though, and was able to enjoy the turkey dinner with her husband and Mom Warner.

On December 27, four members of the Regina Relay For Life committee arrived unexpectedly at Dionne and Graham's house and erected a huge illuminated 'HOPE' sign in their front yard.

"They were vandals," says Graham. "Angel vandals."

"It was just beautiful," smiles Dionne, who stood on their driveway with Graham, wiping away happy tears as they looked at the glowing message. The 2.5-metre-tall structure, which was part of the Relay's award-winning float in Regina's 2009 summer fair, attracted plenty of picture-taking onlookers over the next few weeks and was a constant reminder of Dionne's motto in facing this disease.

On New Year's Eve, Warner Warrior and her supportive husband rang in the new year in the chemo treatment room wearing Happy New Year hats, bead necklaces and decorated oversized party sunglasses. A disco ball, faux vodka paralyzers (Dionne's favourite alcohol beverage), and party favours completed the scene around Dionne's chemo chair as many clinic friends came by to share in the merriment and be photographed with Dionne.

Two days later, Dionne was having a shower at home when she called Graham to come into the bathroom, 'And bring the camera!'

Graham joked in an update that he was happily taken aback by her request. " 'Hey, she's never suggested anything like *THAT* before! Hmmm, chemo drugs have never acted like an aphrodisiac before! *HEY*, maybe this new chemo drug they've got her on has some great surprise side-effects the hospital staff were just too embarrassed to tell us about?!' These were just a few of the thoughts that raced through my mind in the 3.2 seconds it took me to grab her camera, sprint from the living room to the bedroom, strip naked and make my grand entrance into the ensuite bathroom. Upon my entrance, D rolled the shower door back, shrieked, 'What the heck are you doing?!!!' and then authoritatively ordered me to, 'Put your clothes back on, Tonto.' "

She pointed to the floor of the shower stall, where Graham quickly noticed the piles of black curly hair at Dionne's feet. Graham was surprised and sad but Dionne insisted that he take a photo of this scene and share it in an update. "It's part of the journey," she told him.

That day, they went to a hair salon so that Dionne's head could be shaved.

"After that tingling feeling I had the first time with the breast cancer, I knew it was coming and I was more accepting of losing my hair again," she says. "That's when I started doing the shave off. I was not going to watch it fall out again. It comes back. It's the least of your worries. Hair is not the most important thing. Getting better is the focus."

Dionne also laughs about watching and waiting for her hair to grow back and the exhilarating feeling she gets when her hair is long enough to create a part. "It's tough. The minute you do get that hair coming back and you can actually put one hair over to one side, you enjoy announcing, 'I got a part! Yay!' You feel good. Oh my goodness, my girlfriends laugh with me!

"Watching the hair grow back for the first time was so different. It grew back in patches and the slowest part to grow back was in the centre. At the time it did, I kind of kept going, 'Come on. Come on.' It was fascinating watching my hair grow back. For me, it had to be eight months after the end of treatment that first time before I felt comfortable that I could go out, because my hair is very thick and very curly and it's not a fast-growing head of hair."

After the head shaving, Graham took a photo of the emotional but beautifully bald Dionne. That photo has since replaced the other photo of bald Dionne that was in the wig room at the Allan Blair Cancer Centre.

From December 2009 to early January 2010, Dionne and her cancer struggled back and forth in the battle. She suffered excruciating pain at one point and then rebounded with a camouflage-clad 'I'm Killing Cancer – BACK OFF!' treatment-day theme.

In early January 2010, the cancer clinic staff told Dionne she could not have her chemo treatment that week because her white blood cell count was too low. "They sent us home without even prescribing anything to help, not even an Aspirin. That's when I said we have to do something on our own now," says Graham. "I was pretty far into looking at all the naturopath information. I hadn't made a conclusive decision on it though."

By January 14, 2010, Graham had convinced Dionne, and received Dr. Salim's approval, to pursue alternative therapy options. The only thing Dr. Salim insisted was that they keep him informed of any supplements or therapies that Dionne took to ensure that they did not conflict with the treatment he was providing to her.

Dionne went to see Darwin Stoeber, a doctor of natural medicine at Regina Preventative Therapy Centre. Stoeber explained that conventional chemotherapy attacks all cells equally, which is not the approach favoured by natural medicine therapists. "The trouble with conventional chemotherapy is they're basically dipping you in vats of poison and hoping the cancer cells die first. It's pretty crude. The chemotherapy in situations like that can sort of hold the cancer at bay but it doesn't get rid of the problem, and cancer cells that survive chemotherapy are tougher to deal with," said Stoeber. "Chemotherapy of the future will probably be much more advanced. They'll likely be able to envelope the chemotherapy and it will only be able to open in specific cells."

He explained that "all cells have a fail-safe mechanism called apoptosis in that they will commit suicide if they are too deranged. When those mechanisms are not functioning properly, a potential cancer cell doesn't self-destruct. Then it's up to your immune system to fight if the cancer cell tries to divide and form a tumour. I call the immune system the last line of defence in cancer. The first line would be to repair your genetic integrity, to repair genetic damage, things like that. I gave her a product called MGN-3 which is able to prevent damage to aspects of the immune system that you want to make it through the chemo."

Stoeber believes that conventional cancer treatments "over-focus on neutrophyls," which are white blood cells, but they "are not anti-cancer. It's the macrophages and aspects of lymphocytes, especially certain kinds of lymphocytes like natural killer cells, and dendrites that are more important in the immune system for fighting cancer. Neutrophyls are more for bacterial infections and stuff like that. Right now, going through your tissue are macrophages assessing each cell," said Stoeber. "They can go through the tissue, reading the markers on your cell, and if the markers say, 'Oh, I'm an altered cancer cell' or 'I need to be destroyed,' then the macrophages engulf that cell, send the chemical message to other parts of the immune system and set into motion the killing of that cell. The neutrophyls will mostly go to sites of infection, which is great, too," he added.

"I'm generalizing and that's never a good idea in medicine, because some cancers respond better. It depends what you mean by chemo ... hopefully with advancements in the strategy for killing the cancer cell, they'll just laugh at what is done now 50 years from now. It will be gene therapy because it's a gene disorder, right? It will be fixed genes or altered genes. If you could specifically target the genes that are at fault – whether it's with a drug to kill them or a new gene to make it right again – that would make sense."

Graham and Dionne spent three hours talking with Stoeber that day, learning his explanations of cancer and considering supplements and vitamins that he suggested to boost her immune system as well as to reduce the toxicity and damage to her immune system caused by chemotherapy. "I gave her a couple things that are specific in acting as sort of a natural chemo or a plant chemotherapy – things that can kill cancer cells directly," said Stoeber. "Resveratrol, a uzeveritol flavinoid and courcumin. Also, IP6 kills cancer cells directly even though it saves the immune system, too. The strategy is protecting the genetics and amplifying the detoxification process with Vitamin D and DTX and things that help to lessen the damage to the immune system, especially the immune cells that fight cancer. Vitamin D is known to be supportive for the immune system and helpful for most forms of cancer. I gave her DTX which supports the various enzymatic pathways in the detox factor in the liver and helps to minimize genetic damage, so there are antioxidants in it."

Stoeber recommended that the Warners look into a 21-day program at an integrative hospital just outside of Munich, Germany. Their program has proven effective in shrinking and eliminating tumours without damaging the rest of the body, he said. "While I could still walk, talk and move, this is what I would do," he told Dionne.

Stoeber's recommendation set Graham on a new path of investigation. He contacted the German hospital and reported that information in an update. "As you can imagine, the cost is pretty far out there but we are bound by a life's value that I've upheld my whole life: 'You never say whoa in the middle of a slough!' (For those of you not from Saskatchewan – a slough is a wet, low-lying marshy swamp.) And this cancer battle is definitely a big-ass slough! So hopefully we will be updating you from Germany in the near future."

The plan to go to Germany changed as soon as they heard back from the German doctors. Due to that clinic's distance from its main hospital and concerns over travel if anything untoward happened, the Germans recommended that Dionne instead go to their associated clinic in Mexico. Graham investigated that possibility and on January 31, 2010 he and Dionne left for a hospital in Tijuana so that Dionne could take part in an integrative three-week program there that included not only conventional medicine but complementary therapies including detoxification, nutritional, psychological and spiritual assessment and support.

The cost for the three week-treatment was $35,000 U.S. plus airfare for both Dionne and Graham. It was a price that Graham checked into carefully and was more than willing to pay for his wife's health.

"Naturopathic doctors and conventional doctors are not talking to each other," said Dr. Ariel Perez, leader of the medical team at the hospital. "It's not about choosing sides. It's about using both."

The program takes a holistic approach to each patient as an individual, starting with a head-to-toe assessment of each patient. Patients go through a detoxification process through diet and are then given supplements and vitamins to enhance their immune systems. "In your immune system, you have soldier cells that specialize in the fight against cancer," explained Dr. Perez. "These are dendritic, natural killer cells, and lymphocytes. When somebody has cancer, these cells are blindfolded. Dionne has had this cancer for more than 15 years and maybe more than that. The granulocytes, the general army cells, have been working constantly to fight it. Chronic inflammation appears and it is only supposed to be there for 15 days. We need to calm down that part of the immune system," he said.

He noted their program is not a one-type-fits-all approach and that "a lot of the alternative centres are very aggressive with their detox. Aggressive detoxification is seen by the body as aggressive. The result will be a very serious complication. We modify to the specific needs of the patient. There is no need to run. Things need to be done in the right time frame."

Dionne was placed on a carbohydrate-free (including sugar-free and starch-free), dairy-free and gluten-free diet. Her vitamin D level was measured and found to be low. "It was 38. It should have been between 80 and 100, so they put her on a concentrated dose of Vitamin D intravenously and alternated it with Vitamin C," says Graham. She was given other supplements designed to help her body absorb nutrients as well as to starve the cancer.

Dionne's meals were based on organic food and wheat flour was substituted with rice flour, chickpea flour, quinoa, buckwheat or tapioca. For example, her breakfast could be steel cut oats (oatmeal before it's rolled) that was cooked and served with goat's milk, a little bit of agave nectar or agave syrup and seasonal berries. A few flax seeds were sprinkled on top as well. For lunch, she would be served a lentil soup and a quinoa salad with greens seasoned with olive oil, lemon, salt and pepper. The evening meal could be a broccoli soup and fish or chicken.

Graham wanted to support Dionne during her treatment, so he went on the diet with her. "I fully expected the diet to taste like cardboard but the chef we had there made that food taste like the best I've ever eaten," he said.

Dionne was pleased that her husband was supporting her in the diet but found it difficult to watch other patients who were almost being sabotaged by the people who were there to support them. "I remember the first time I walked down to the dining area, there was a patient and another lady there," says Dionne. "I saw pancakes first and I thought, 'Oh, great!' But then it was, 'No. Not for you.' So it was tough. This woman was eating the pancakes because she couldn't do the diet with the person she came to support." Dionne later found the lady was the patient's sister.

"I was just so thankful that Graham was helping me through this and he was going to be a part of this diet, too, because it makes a difference. When you're looking at pancakes across from you and you have to eat this other stuff, it's tough."

What was even more difficult for Dionne to watch were the many times that the sister went for a cigarette. "Oh my goodness, your sister is here trying to fight cancer and you're going out for a cigarette! It is heart-wrenching at times when you're seeing it in front of you."

Uncharacteristically, Dionne kept quiet and tried to focus on her own healing.

Shortly after arriving at the hospital and tasting the special diet meals, Graham invited Mariana Brito, who was preparing their meals, to come to Canada to stay with them. He and Dionne were sure she would say

'Yes' and were surprised when Brito immediately refused.

"Mariana smiled and said, 'But it is very cold in Canada,' – to which we eagerly and enthusiastically responded that she could come live with us in the Turks and Caicos Islands during the winter," said Graham in an update e-mail. " 'Hey, how could she turn *that* down?' we too confidently thought?

"The reason I said 'too confidently' is because she never even hesitated when she so sweetly responded, 'But I have already been offered a guest house in Costa Rica by another patient.' "

So Dionne and Graham kept gently nudging Brito into their corner as they continued to receive excellent care and food at the Tijuana hospital. It didn't take Brito long to reconsider Graham's offer.

She was working at the hospital while she was taking classes at the local cooking school. She worked with the hospital's nutritionist and experimented to create interesting foods that fit into the specialty diet. Dionne and Graham quickly became two of her favourite patients because of their fun-loving approach to life.

"I used to have patients who were really negative and weren't smiling at all. They were the first couple that was so positive. I just fell in love with them," says Brito. "I remember Valentine's Day. I came in at 7 a.m. and I made breakfast. I came upstairs to let them know it was ready. That was the first time I saw Dionne with a wig. She was wearing this beautiful dress and shoes and Graham was dressed up, too. The room was decorated. I was freaked out – in a good way. They said, 'We'll be downstairs in five minutes.' So I went back downstairs and I downloaded all the Frank Sinatra music I could find. I had to play this for them. They were so cute. They were in the romantic mood. Dionne is always smiling and Graham is always making a joke. They are awesome."

Meanwhile, Dionne's treatments continued.

"The biggest reason we were there was for hyperthermic treatment," says Graham, a process that is being used at UCLA and the universities of Washington and Texas and Dr. Perez believes will soon become routine. "They would pump her blood into a machine and heat it to 43 degrees Celsius. The blood would be passed through ultraviolet light to kill off any bacteria or fungi, then re-introduced to her body. This process ran continuously for two hours. The concept is that cancer cells can't take the stress of the high heat but it doesn't bother the healthy cells, so either the cancer cells atrophy or become severely weakened and she would then receive low doses of chemo that would affect the weakened cancer cells but not harm the healthy cells as much as a full dose of chemo."

The hyperthermic treatment was hot and uncomfortable, but Dionne never complained, says Graham, who was pleased that his wife had agreed to see Stoeber and then to go for treatments in Mexico. "I remember sitting in the Mexico hospital thinking, 'Hmmm, three weeks ago, Dionne wouldn't even fill out an application form for a naturopath.' I'm so proud of her for doing that."

In the last week of their time at the Tijuana hospital, Graham left for Las Vegas to attend a NASCAR trip that he had arranged months earlier for himself with some customers and friends. Before she would even agree to go for treatment to Mexico, Dionne had made him promise that he would keep that engagement, so they arranged for their friend Crystal Kalyniuk to fly down from Regina and stay with Dionne for the last week.

"Crystal was awesome. She was so positive and contagious," says Dionne. They took photos together, as though it was a regular theme week, and they kept each other's spirits lifted during this interesting adventure.

Results from a CAT scan test done when she got home to Regina showed that all of the cancer tumours in Dionne continued to reduce in size and there were no new tumours, Graham informed readers in his update. He admitted being thrilled with this news and somewhat surprised to hear from Dionne that she had been hoping all along that no new tumours had formed since December 2009. It was something that Graham hadn't even considered but he quickly realized how easily that could have actually happened.

"We really are extremely satisfied that the combination of our treatments in both Canada and Mexico contributed to the shrinking of D's tumours and prevented further development of any cancer," wrote Graham.

Dionne came home from Mexico a little underweight and Dr. Salim was concerned about this but otherwise, it was good news all around.

The March 2010 issue of *Prevention Magazine*, a magazine distributed in Canada, the United States and on Provo, contained an article about Dionne's cancer story. Entitled *'Miracles,'* it told readers a synopsis of Dionne's story and shared her unending optimism in her battle to beat cancer for the seventh time.

For Easter that year, Dionne and Graham took a much-needed break from the routine of therapy and cancer to spend some time with friends on Provo. Graham entertained everyone once again by sending photos of the swimsuit-clad 'Easter bunnies' (Dionne and some of her friends) that he found hopping around on the beach and enjoying life.

Cindy Alston, one of those 'bunny' friends, recalls sitting on the beach with Dionne on one of those days when a young boy came up to them and tried to sell them something. "He looked at D's bald head and asked, 'What happened to your hair?' Dionne kindly said that she had cancer and lost her hair from the treatments. He said to her, 'You die from cancer, you know.'

"I wanted to jump up and wring his neck," adds Alston, "however, D got out her finger and wagged it at him and told him, 'Don't ever ask a woman what happened to her hair, but respect her as she is. And never tell someone they are going to die. You don't know that for sure. And no one wants to hear they are going to die!' The young boy walked away saying, 'Yes, ma'am,' and 'Thank you, ma'am.' And D, with her wonderful spirit, turned to me and laughed and said, 'That boy will never approach a bald lady again!'

"Respect," says Alston. "It's very important to Dionne."

Alston also notes that Dionne 'makes fun' wherever she goes. "We've dressed up for St. Patrick's Day with green wigs and flashing necklaces and Dionne has inspired the next generation as well. My 20-year-old daughter was visiting with eight of her university friends. Dionne danced with them and showed them how to shake their booty. She also played the mother hen, keeping an eye on the guys who were eyeing the girls. Later that year, when these girls found out about Dionne's cancer returning, they put their own team together for 'University of Toronto Med Students Walk for Cancer.' A few of the girls stated that Dionne was their inspiration.

"Another time there was a pool-tournament office challenge on the island and D showed up dressed in team colours, carrying cheerleader pompoms and hanging up a 'GO TEAM' sign. Dionne is *fun*!" says Alston.

Graham was pleased that Dionne had been able to realize four of her wishes during their 2010 Easter vacation on Provo. She had wanted to feel the sand between her toes, to feel the hot sun on her face, to dip her feet in the ocean and feel the warm waters of Provo, and to be able to enjoy the view of the crystal-clear turquoise waters from Grace Bay Beach. All those wishes had come true and were brought to friends and family through the marvel of modern-day communication in Graham's *My Beautiful Dionne update*.

One of the activities that Dionne missed the most because of her Stage IV diagnosis was the ability to go into the cancer clinic and volunteer. She cherished the interaction with the patients and staff, and the opportunity to help others while receiving more in return than she had ever imagined.

Although she went into the centre for her weekly bloodwork and treatments, it wasn't the same as volunteering. "I really do miss it but I said to Wilbur, 'Don't you give up my spot! I like my Tuesdays and my Thursdays. I will be back.' "

Dionne's days were a lot quieter and longer without her twice-weekly volunteering stints. She had always been a busy person and now had to stay chained to a routine of being careful where she went so she did not pick up a virus and being careful with what she ate so her body remained stronger. Her daily routine brightened up considerably in late April when Mariana Brito, the spunky 24-year-old chef they had met at the Mexico hospital, arrived in Regina to visit for a few months.

While they were still in Mexico, Dionne had been able to convince Brito that Graham was absolutely serious with his blunt invitation to visit them in Canada. "It was while Graham was away that I said to her, with Crystal there, that Graham was serious. 'I don't know how we are going to do this diet ourselves when we get home,' I told her. She looked into my eyes and knew that I was serious," laughs Dionne, who happily went to the Regina airport with Graham and Kalyniuk to welcome Brito to Regina.

The young chef set about helping Dionne figure out how to live with this new diet. They explored Regina's stores for organic groceries and other specialty food items and Brito then served what Graham and Dionne deemed to be a fabulous meal that next evening. "She received a unanimous vote that she would definitely be staying," teased Graham. A couple days later, the chemo treatment room came alive with the look of Mexico as two senoritas (Dionne and Brito) arrived with a "handsome, barrel-chested, tanned amigo" (Graham) who were all happily pretending to swig tequila while they traded sombreros with the staff for that week's adventure.

Brito stayed with the Warners for five months and, in that time, she helped Dionne re-organize her cupboards to replace plastic storage containers with glass, learn what types of foods to avoid, and shop for and make some of the foods on her new diet. Brito also created a small cookbook that contained some of her recipes and explanations for the healthier diet. With Graham and Dionne's support, a second printing had to be ordered.

"When you put leftovers away in plastic, there is a chemical reaction with heated food," explained Brito while cleaning out Dionne's pantry. "In storage, they're here for so long. The pantry is not cold. The toxins go into food." Brito recommends avoiding canned or processed items and instead eating seasonal fresh and organic food and foods that are close to the source because they provide better taste and nutrition as well as fewer additives and preservatives.

She also dislikes microwaving food, saying "microwaved food contains molecules and energies not present in food cooked in the way humans have been cooking food since the discovery of fire. The introduction of molecules and energies to the body that the body is not used to will likely cause more harm than good. Regardless of all this, my biggest concern is the difference on food's texture, taste and quality of life when cooked or heated in the microwave. We need to heat our food the right way. Even if you can't get rid of the microwave, you should use it as little as possible."

Dionne was told in the Mexican hospital that sugar is the most important ingredient for cancer patients to avoid because cancer feeds on sugar. She should also avoid most fruits because of the sugar content, especially bananas, watermelon and cantaloupe. Berries and green apples, or Gala apples which are a mix of green and red, are the best fruits for her.

Dionne notes that Brito's dressings are all homemade and organic, and she had learned quite a bit about healthier foods from Brito. "I can have slices of green apple or pear, and almonds, pistachio or sunflower seeds between meals as snacks ... and these lovely shakes," laughed Dionne, in reference to shakes made of spinach, celery, lettuce, cucumber and cilantro or parsley – that she definitely did not enjoy. "She made it with love but after about two days, I just couldn't down it."

Brito noted that the ideal protein to eat is fish, three or four times a week. "It's the best fatty acid." Wild-catch salmon is also a favourite of hers, although Dionne prefers bison. "You should have a side of brown rice and maybe some steamed vegetables (asparagus or broccoli or peppers) and a salad," added Brito. "We use whatever vegetables are seasonal. We control the potato to maybe once a week. Potato turns into sugar when it goes into your body, the same as cooked carrots."

"We felt lost before Mariana came," says Dionne. "We learned a lot. Just trying to find the different things was difficult. Mariana taught me to look at the sugar content of everything I pick up. When Mariana came in and looked in our pantry, the amount of stuff that went out was really something. I'm not allowed to have anything by can, no vinegar. She was hard core. I had to beg to keep some Kraft Dinner," smiles Dionne.

"I can't do it all but I can try. I cheat sometimes, usually on the weekend. I don't want people to be afraid to invite us out for dinner because they don't know what I can eat. When that happens, I eat normally. I can taste it if something is really oversweet, though. Then I just leave it or I don't eat all of it.

"When people ask if I want to go for dinner and it's a Wednesday night, I'll say, 'Yeah, I'll go for dinner.' Maybe I won't order a drink this time because on the weekend, we're going somewhere as well or I'll only have one vodka paralyzer when I'd usually have two," she smiles. "You're not going to take everything away that I enjoy. I monitor my food, but I want to still be happy in the end." Dionne laughs about buying a Crunchie bar one day while looking for items at the Dollar Store. "If I'm punished because I ate a Crunchie bar, then I died a happy woman," she giggles.

Although Dionne was underweight when she left the Mexican hospital, the special diet she was on is not for weight loss, says Brito. "You eat everything. You don't eat gluten but you eat enough of the foods you need. If you want to lose weight, you might need to eat less within this diet."

On May 6, 2010 Dionne was honoured with a YWCA's Regina Women of Distinction award, tying with Barbara Hildebrandt of Dress for Success Regina to win the Community Leadership & Enhancement category. The awards committee stated that, "Dionne's achievements demonstrate vision, creativity and initiative. Dionne has volunteered at countless events and given selflessly of herself to raise funds particularly for the benefit of Saskatchewan cancer research efforts. The dedication that she models has helped to recruit many Saskatchewanians to take up the critical role of volunteering and fundraising. As a seven-time major cancer survivor, Dionne has helped literally thousands with her courage, bravery and defiant stand against cancer and the battle it entails. Her enthusiastic and inspiring leadership motivates even the most skeptical or self-pitying to realize, 'If she can do it, then so can I!' She has also helped change a silent culture often found surrounding cancer, by inspiring those battling cancer to allow and encourage their family and friends to join in the front lines of battle. Dionne has been described as a real world hero, serving as a role model for all women."

Heather Choquette and Nadine Desrosiers, two staff members of the Allan Blair Cancer Centre, worked together to nominate Dionne for the award. "As soon as I saw the notice for the award in the newspaper, Dionne was the woman who came to mind," says Choquette. "To me, she is what that means – a woman of distinction. I don't know if I could be doing all these things that she's doing. It would be wonderful if we all could. Dionne continues to give to others. She's volunteering and selling things to raise money for cancer. She's supportive of other patients, and she's an inspiration to me and to a lot of other people. You just feel the warmth coming from her.

"We meet a lot of wonderful people at the cancer centre but she's physically *doing*," adds Choquette. "Whatever she commits herself to, no matter what it is, she is there totally. You don't ever get part of Dionne, you get all of D."

Desrosiers was thrilled to help Choquette put Dionne's name forward. "Who would you nominate for a woman of distinction? Somebody who is a leader," says Desrosiers. "Look at all the people she's encouraged. Look at all the people she's helped. She'll be on her deathbed and she'll still be helping people with their diagnosis. She is someone I'll never be."

In his letter to support the nomination of Dionne for the award, Dr. Salim wrote, "Dionne has an uncanny way of making friends with those patients and helping them find hope and elevating their outlook at life. Over the years, I have been told by a number of patients and families what a great difference she had made in their outlook and especially how easy she has made it for them to go through the treatments and helped them in making the right decisions," he wrote.

"She has become known in the Cancer Clinic as an ideal patient, as a survivor, as a person who you can refer your patient to in the time of need to talk to, and she is always available whenever she is needed. I believe she has shown such character in view of this devastating disease in her personal life and turned it around to make a very significant difference in the lives of women in Saskatchewan with breast cancer in particular, and cancer patients in general."

During the gala awards evening, Dionne was happily visiting with the other people at her table when she thought she heard her name being announced. They called another lady's name first and *then* they called my name, too," she says. "I asked, 'Did you guys just hear my name?' The announcer didn't say it was a tie and I kind of heard, '*And Dionne Warner*.' Another girl at the table said, 'That's you, get up!' Then Crystal – she was at another table – she screamed. Another lady grabbed me and said, 'It's a tie!' I wasn't expecting it. I was there just to enjoy the night and honour these ladies."

Dionne was nervous and a little scared as she walked up to the podium, but she delivered an amazing improvised acceptance speech that earned her a heartfelt standing ovation from the 500 people in the room. The first thing she did was ask the other women who were nominated in that category to please stand "because I thought they were all phenomenal, and I asked everybody to please applaud them and what they did for the city. That was very important to acknowledge them," says Dionne.

She told the audience she was overwhelmed by the honour and then gave them all a bit of information about herself – growing up in Toronto and marrying Graham despite being convinced to come to Regina because 'it never got below minus 10,' and having seven cancers. She thanked the people who nominated her and said she is blessed by her Angel Network.

"My goal at the Allan Blair Cancer Clinic was to give hope, courage and strength to the many patients I have met on my journey and they have inspired me as well. I'm just so grateful that I have so many amazing friends. I had nobody when I moved here and I have to say I was surprised today when my cousin (Yuri Collesso) flew in from Guelph, Ontario to be at this event with me. I'm just thankful he's here. Most importantly, my amazing and wonderful husband Graham – it is his support and love that have kept me strong and I will continue to do everything I can to help raise funds and find a cure for this disease, because we need to save our children. I don't want to hear another child diagnosed with this disease. Thank you, everyone ... very much."

"There was not a dry eye in the house," says Roger Pettigrew about Dionne's speech. "It didn't matter who you were, when you heard her story – oh my God, there was nothing as emotionally charged as that."

After the awards were completed, Dionne had strangers come up to her and thank her for her speech.

"It was just wonderful to be there because she deserved it so much, and to think that they had recognized that," says Choquette. "I think she's amazing. All the volunteering she does and being there for everyone else as well as going through the struggles she is – that's inspiring. She's so upbeat. I've never seen anything else from her. She's lovely and caring and so positive. Because she's so happy, she makes everyone else feel good around her. How can you have a bad day when she comes in and she's laughing and smiling?"

Meanwhile, a photo of Dionne appeared in a tourism magazine for the island of Provo. The magazine highlighted Dionne's wish to go back to the island and soak her toes in the water at Grace Bay Beach and said she was an inspiration to many people in her battle with cancer.

Even when she was not there, Dionne had an impact on the people of Provo.

Atelys Adrian works in a Provo restaurant and has changed her outlook since meeting Dionne and Graham. "Before I knew that Dionne ever had cancer, I used to wonder how she could always be so happy. That is not normal – at least that's what I used to think. 'How can she be so nice and friendly with everybody, all the time?' Every time she was in the restaurant, even the chefs would take a break just to come and say hello to her – just like a celebrity! She will change the mood of everyone around her without even knowing it. Graham is also the same," says Adrian. "They come for dinner and end up making jokes and talking to us like a brother or sister they haven't seen in a long time. Sometimes after they are gone, my friend and I will talk about how nice it is to be around people like them."

Adrian's aunt was recently diagnosed with Stage III breast cancer. "If it wasn't for Dionne's example, I wouldn't be able to encourage my aunt the way I do," says Adrian. "The things I've learned from D and G are priceless. I thank them just for sharing their lives with me and for teaching me it is possible to win if you fight with all you have. Dionne has the best husband. I do not think there could be another man who could love and care for her the way he does. I was telling someone that Graham is a Prince Charming. They do exist. It is just that they are reserved for special ladies like Dionne."

Back in Saskatchewan, Dionne was getting a head start on the annual Relay For Life that was coming up on June 11, 2010. At one of her chemotherapy sessions in May, she showcased the Relay's 'Fight Back' theme. It was also the first theme in which she used music to further add to their big entrance to the chemo room.

"The Relay's theme is the same theme our Warner Warrior has chosen for her seventh cancer battle," wrote Graham in his update after the treatment. "With the perfect fight music theme of *Eye of the Tiger* blaring from her iPod boombox, Dionne sparred, danced and jabbed her way into the hospital's chemo ward. It really was entertaining to observe people's bewildering reactions as to where and why there was music all of a sudden coming into the room. Then on spotting Dionne in her garb, shadow boxing, the reactions quickly turned into pure joy and laughter. With an enthusiastic callisthenics workout completed right in front of her chair, the entire chemo ward broke into applause, which I can tell you I've never heard in that facility ... ever."

Graham also announced that Warner Industries would provide all survivors at Relay For Life with bracelets made up of a yellow bead for every year of survival as well as a bead for their type of cancer. "Yes, D's bracelet will be very colourful indeed."

In late May, Graham dedicated the first part of his update to helping every man who read his words score points with their female partners. "If you are a warm blooded, North American female, you already know that this weekend coming up is the premiere of the much-anticipated second *Sex and the City* movie," he wrote. "If you are a male, and want to score major points, enthusiastically invite your sweetheart out on a date and take her to this movie. Hey guys, no problem ... You are welcome! So please enjoy our tribute to *Sex and the City*."

He went on to describe the two people shown in the update's first photo (Dionne and Graham). "The hot broad happens to combine the personalities of Carrie Bradshaw, Charlotte York, Miranda Hobbes and Samantha Jones. The dude is Big. Not Mr. Big, not Big Boy ... just Big. And yes, those are pyjamas we are wearing, because we're doing the chic pyjama party version of the show for our *Sex and the City* Theme."

Dionne the movie star and her cigar-holding Big enjoyed sharing their fake martinis and some specialty chocolates with their many tiara-wearing fans/clinic staff, but the biggest news of the day came from Dr. Salim. He stopped by to inform them of the results of Dionne's CAT scan from the previous day. "The tumours progressively continue to shrink. I am very happy with the direction things are proceeding," he told them.

"I have to tell you – you never saw two happier campers leave the hospital than us today!" wrote Graham in his update. "Yes, we realize that we still have a long unpleasant battle ahead of us. It just is so refreshing to realize that we are winning and making clear undeniable headway. That all the efforts, energy, expense and prayers that everyone has showered us with are paying dividends and that we really are beating this !@#$#@ cancer disease down into submission. Hoo-ahh!"

A couple of weeks later, in early June, Dr. Salim delivered some other more sobering news to Dionne. "We were informed that D would have to do 10 cycles of chemo," Graham reported. "We are now starting Cycle 3. One cycle equals nine treatments of chemo and this takes three months to complete. This means Dionne could be taking chemo for two and a half years. This was a little surprising to the both of us. Now, anyone who knows D knows she will get through this with flying colours – especially with all of you in her corner. My wife's first concern was, 'Man, that's going to be a lot of themes to come up with!' "

Dr. Salim explained that Dionne will need to be on treatment "until one of the following is met: Either she starts seeing unacceptable toxicity – then the treatment has to be stopped and rethought. If you have too much toxicity, then you have to go back to the drawing board and rethink what we are doing. Secondly, if she for whatever reasons says she doesn't want to continue, she always has that choice. Thirdly, if while on treatment, cancer starts progressing, then the treatment has to be stopped and we have to see what other options we have. She could be on treatment for one year or 2½ years. Nothing is written in stone."

Shortly after the update was sent, people started sending Dionne theme ideas to help her through the next couple of years of treatments. They assumed, of course, that she would continue to fight and to defiantly make it to 2½ years and beyond. Dionne and Graham, meanwhile, were both temporarily stunned by the idea that she could be going through chemo until the summer of 2012.

"We were just going with the motion, not realizing it was going to be this long," says Dionne. "Our weekly routine was bloodwork on Tuesday and my chemo was on Thursday." The closest she'd gotten to a long-term plan was to pack an overnight bag and have it ready at home in case she took ill and had to go to the hospital. "I'm ready to go with all my pyjamas. Graham thinks I'm crazy," she laughed. "I've told him, 'This is the last thing you'll have to worry about.' I will have all the items that make me feel good with me. I've been keeping a photo album of my journey so that if I end up in hospital, I still have my pictures to look at and I can have a few laughs."

One of the pages in that album contains an inspirational cartoon sent by her cousin Peter Ballantine. The caption says 'Don't ever give up.' The cartoon shows a stork trying to swallow a frog while the frog has its little arms clamped firmly around the stork's throat, choking it. "I travel with that every time I go for treatment and I get a giggle," smiles Dionne. "That's the advice I give to people on how to go through this journey. 'Don't ever give up.' "

She has also informed Graham, "If I'm ever sick at home, you'd better drive me to the Allan Blair because that's where my friends are … Princess picks her hospital," she laughs.

In June 2010, Dionne's father arrived in Regina to visit with his daughter, to sit beside her during chemo – for the Jamaica theme, of course – and to walk the Victory Lap with her and Graham at Relay For Life. "This was the first time he had come visiting since I was diagnosed in December 2009," says Dionne. "I said to G it would be nice to have my dad here for the Relay. Graham paid for his airfare."

Dionne was excited that her dad was able to help Graham barbecue burgers for the 150 volunteers setting up for Relay and then he was there to witness the 350 survivors gathered on the steps of the legislature for a group photo. "He got to feel the compassion and the love there," she says.

Dionne had been asked to address the Relay crowd at 10 p.m., moments before all the luminaries were lit. She was proud to do so with her father standing at her side. When she finished speaking, "a soulful, tear-drawing *Amazing Grace* was played by the lone bagpiper," reported Graham. "It was truly the emotional highlight of the evening."

A few weeks earlier, without Dionne's knowledge, Graham had asked readers of the updates to buy a luminary to support Dionne. About 10,000 luminaries are purchased every year by individuals and companies to honour or remember loved ones affected by cancer. The luminaries are made up of individual messages stapled to white bags that have a small candle inside them. On this Relay night, there were more than 250 luminaries dedicated specifically to Dionne, which brought tears of joy and gratitude to her surprised eyes.

"You all came through and blew her away with your love and thoughtfulness," Graham told update readers. "This caused her to openly weep – exactly the reaction I was hoping for. (Mean guy, aren't I?) It was kept as a complete surprise to her and as she walked the course, the never-ending luminaries that were dedicated to her with wonderful messages just kept going on and on and on … and on both sides of the course! Our good friend Crystal (I think we owe her a massage) squatted each time to take more than 250 photos of individual luminaries and, even then, we know we didn't get to them all!"

Despite the challenging rainy weather that evening, "the dedicated people of Regina and of course all of you helped raise more than $505,000 for cancer research through this event," continued Graham. "Now for those of you who don't know Regina well, our city has a population of only 200,000. Obviously, some of the world's most generous people live here!"

Relay's survivor committee chairperson Carla Redler and her survivor husband Tony were again surprised by Dionne's spunk that day. "No matter how sick that girl is, it's important for her to be there. Early in the morning, she was setting up the survivor tent with us," says Carla. "It was a cold, rainy, nasty day. She was there at 10 o'clock in the morning doing some volunteering, then she went home to have a rest and she came back to enjoy the event. If there was an angel on this earth, I think it would be Dionne. She's just so unique. She's very selfless."

"She doesn't take care of herself as much as she takes care of everybody else," adds Tony. "She's looking after everybody to make sure everybody is happy as much as she is taking care of herself."

"She has so much life she still has to live," finishes Carla.

In July 2010, Graham and Dionne ran into the doctor who originally told Dionne in 2001 that Graham might want to leave the room because he might not want to marry her with her liver cancer diagnosis. On this day, that doctor said to Dionne, "You truly are a miracle. You know that, right?"

Dionne was slightly annoyed, but held her tongue. "I wanted to say, 'If I had listened to you, I probably wouldn't be here.'" She knew in her heart that the doctor had only done the best with the information she had at the time, though. Dionne was also pleased to remember again that she was a proud miracle and that she should not waste energy staying angry at this past situation.

At times, Graham keeps Dionne grounded with his quirky jokes and his unique outlook on life. Together, they look at the world from the perspective of appreciating every minute that they have together. While working with Relay For Life volunteers to create the 'Fight Back' parade float for the 2010 summer fair, Graham heard from his mother that one of his favourite aunts had suddenly become ill and fallen into a coma with kidney cancer. "In March, we saw her in the Turks and Caicos and she was just great. She complained and went to the doctor last week. Now she is unconscious and they are giving her two to maybe three weeks," he said.

"How do you go from travelling the world and being fine to all of a sudden you have only a month left to live? It just shocked me, and made me appreciate again how lucky Dionne really is and the reality again of what we're going through. So when we were at this float meeting, we were talking about them needing some help with flowers or whatever and Dionne said, 'Well, on Wednesday I have a double dose of chemo so I might not be able to help then.' So I told her to walk it off. She can do it."

There are some days when Dionne wishes she had been given a timeline for her own cancer. "I'd prefer it if Dr. Salim could look at me and tell me 'maybe a year.' I would rather know that than not know anything at all. There are certain things in life I still want to do and I'd rather do them when I can walk, talk and move around. That's why Dr. Salim said to Graham that if we want to take a month off and go away, maybe we should do it. Maybe that's a bit of a sign when he said, 'We can work around it,' and we could take some time and go away. I don't know. No one knows for sure. I could walk out of here and get hit by one of Graham's Regina school buses," she laughs.

While Dionne was unable to help add flowers and the many colours of cancer ribbons alongside the oversized boxing gloves to the Relay float on that one day, she did her best to contribute to the success of their float entry (which won an award for being 'Too Good Not To Win' by the way). While Graham drove the semi pulling the float, Dionne danced atop the trailer bed and acted as the deejay for the survivors who were walking and dancing alongside the float. Between the honking of the truck's horn and Dionne's cheerleading shouts, the Relay float was heard on the streets of Regina for quite a long time before it was seen.

"Woo Hoo! Shake what your momma gave you!" Dionne called. "It's a great day in Regina! I hope my ribbons are dancing back there!"

"It was a hot, hot day and she was on the back of the trailer bed with the microphone," recalls Carla Redler. "She was singing and she had everyone going. There was no hat on her head and she was giving every bit of what she had out there. We had young people, children, men, women walking beside the float. She had the kids rocking. They were singing. She had everyone engaged. She just makes a party. When she's around, people have fun. By the time we got to the end of the route, she was spent, and apologizing because she couldn't do take-down. She needed to go home to rest."

Meanwhile, Graham had a couple of special passengers inside the semi with him. Two young survivors were not strong enough to be out in the elements for the parade, so Graham told them, "No problem. You can ride with me." Their families were impressed. "They thanked us for inviting them and told Graham, 'You just gave us and our family memories those kids will never forget.' Those children thought it was wonderful to be sitting beside Graham in the cab of the truck," smiles Redler.

"We had a really cool sound system," says Graham excitedly. "Dionne had a mike. I was driving and I could see the crowd ahead just sitting or standing there calmly. As we started driving closer, you could see their feet start to tap. By the time we passed, a lot of times they were up dancing. D would get them pumped up and feeling great. It was a blast."

As a normal part of her day, Dionne continues to keep track of all the dates that are important to her family and friends. She sends notes and small gifts and uses her cellphone and computer to keep in touch and carry on conversations with the people who are important to her as though the physical distance between them doesn't exist.

On weeks when she does not have chemotherapy, she tries to schedule a trip or do something to make that time off special. "I've always lived in a reality world. I say to Graham, 'I would really like to go visit this person or see this person – because you don't know what could happen tomorrow.' If we can go, let's go, let's do it – as long as we can afford to do it and it works out with Graham's schedule."

In 2010, Dionne went on various trips with Graham, with family and friends, or some combination of the above to New York, Las Vegas, the Shuswaps in British Columbia, Arizona and Provo. When Mariana Brito was staying with them, Dionne took Brito to Ontario to see Dionne's family and some of Canada's well-known sights.

"This was amazing to me," says Una Ballantine, Dionne's aunt in Guelph, Ontario. "Dionne was going through all these treatments and she flew to Toronto with Mariana. She rented a car at the airport and drove and she showed Mariana the CN Tower and all the other sites of Toronto. They went out for entertainment at night, then after a day or two in Toronto, Dionne drove to Guelph where we are and we all went out for dinner. They stayed overnight and then from here, they drove to Niagara Falls so Mariana could see it. Then Dionne drove back to Toronto so they could get their flight back to Saskatchewan. Dionne looked frail but she also did not look frail," says Ballantine. "I thought, 'How do you do it, D?' She did this because she wanted to show Mariana this part of Canada."

While most people would concentrate on resting and taking care of only themselves while they are on a cancer treatment regimen, that is not Dionne, explains Ballantine. "She just keeps on keeping on. She always says, 'I've got to live, too.' Living to her means giving it all she's got. She certainly has courage and fight. I wish more of us were blessed with whatever that thing is that she has. At the same time, she's always interested in whatever is going on with the rest of us and is always encouraging the rest of us. If she thinks someone she cares about is being given a raw deal, she's just as feisty as can be.

"She's always been a fighter. She fights her way back to health and enjoyment. Cancer could have taken over her life, but she didn't allow it. She just doesn't let this control her life. She just continues to get as much enjoyment out of life as she can."

Before Brito went back to Mexico in September 2010, she and Dionne visited a tattoo parlour in Regina in August to create some permanent reminders of their time together. Dionne sat in the chair first and added three more cancer ribbons to the tattoos on her back. "The emerald green ribbon represents liver cancer. The yellow ribbon with wings represents survivor to me, with regards to our Relay For Life yellow survivor T-shirts," says Dionne. "The wings on the yellow ribbon are in memory of those angels gone but never forgotten. The lavender ribbon represents all the cancers and was chosen to support my bone cancer and lung cancer. Their colours would have normally been white and pearl but they would not have shown up very well on my back."

In the past, Dionne waited to get her tattoos until after she had been free of cancer for awhile. This time around, she decided she could forgo that rule. "I did not want to wait to add these ribbons because I felt time was of the essence in my fight. Did it hurt? Like a son of a b! Hey, no pain, no gain – or as Graham prefers to say, 'No pain, no pain.'

"I wear my ribbons proudly and they remind me of how far I have come every day on this journey of survival and living life to the fullest with no regrets."

After Dionne was finished getting her tattoos, Brito hopped into the chair to receive her chosen tattoo of a chef's hat and accessories, inscribed on her back shoulder. Brito screamed from the pain of the tattooing and Dionne giggled at Brito's expense.

"Why didn't you tell me it hurt?" Brito asked Dionne.

"I knew if I yelled, you would never have gotten yours done, so I had to be quiet," Dionne laughed.

That same month, Dionne held a surprise birthday party for Graham, with the help of Brito, Crystal Kalyniuk and some other friends. Graham was definitely surprised since the party was held a week or so before his actual 48th birthday, and Dionne was pleased that she and the others had all pulled together to make the evening a success.

She wasn't feeling at the top of her game at about that time and she came home completely exhausted from one chemo treatment in particular. "This was the first chemo where I really felt I was kicked and knocked down. I was really burnt out." She wondered if she had received the medication too fast that day or whether the drugs were just starting to settle into her system after several months and causing some problems.

She knew one thing for sure – she was now losing hair in places where she'd never lost it before.

"My hair is coming back in bits and pieces but I'm losing my eyebrows and eyelashes now. This is the first time in all the treatments I've ever had that my eyebrows and eyelashes are gone." Dionne recalls taking a drug during one of her previous treatment regimens that didn't cause an allergic reaction until after she had taken it for three months. She had also met patients who had encountered other difficulties because of the chemo.

"You'd think my brows and the eyelashes would have dropped when my hair was dropping out," she says. Still, Dionne has her own unique way of looking at things, making light of almost every situation.

"I just wish I didn't have to keep shaving. Just a little help here," she says, laughing and looking up to the sky. "I'm not asking for a Brazilian wax, but just help me out here! Oy yoy yoy!"

Dressing It Up

*"There is life before cancer, during cancer and after cancer.
Live your life to the fullest!" - **Dionne***

D uring their Regina Buffalo Days/*Save A Horse Ride A Cowboy*
theme in August 2010, an older gentleman approached Dionne
while she sat in her recliner in the Allan Blair Cancer Centre's
chemo treatment room and asked her, 'What are you doing here again?'

The man had known Dionne as a volunteer while he was undergoing
treatment and he was surprised to see her getting chemo.

Dionne explained the situation and they chatted for a few minutes.
The man told Dionne what had been happening to him and how his
treatments were going. "But you're doing fine right now, right?" Dionne
asked.

The older man answered her and they chatted for a few more minutes.
Then Dionne said to him again, "But you're fine now."

It was a typical Dionne response to how one should deal with
everyday life. Yes, things might be difficult – but at this very moment, if
you are feeling fine, you should acknowledge that and enjoy this moment
and every moment that comes after it.

By August 2010, Dionne had amassed quite the collection of
costumes and accessories for the themes she had pulled off since being
diagnosed with Stage IV cancer the previous December. Some of the
themes were more unexpected than others.

It wasn't surprising to see Dionne and Graham dressed in *Green Is The
Colour* garb to cheer on the local Saskatchewan Roughriders football team,
for example. Nor were the themes of Valentine's Day, Canada Day,
Halloween and Christmas particularly startling. But there were many other
ideas that completely caught onlookers by surprise and there were always
little pieces of every theme that most people would never have considered
when putting together a costume. These were the Dionne touch – the pieces
that showcased Dionne's style and attention to detail through hats,
sunglasses, jewellery, signs, hanging ornaments and other props.

Although Dionne sometimes decides on a theme topic only a couple hours before she and Graham leave home to go to her chemo treatment, she usually knows what the costumes will be at least a few days in advance. She then makes a list of items that can be used for those themes and scours local stores to find those items. Dollarama and The Dollar Store have become favourite haunts for theme items, as has Value Village, a discount clothing store. When she is on Provo, there is even a favourite shop there that has become a favourite supplier for many unique items including most of her funky glasses. She purchased items for Graham at Cowtown, a country and western store, one day and was met with an enthusiastic response. "I explained to the ladies what I was trying to do and they thought this was the greatest thing."

At Peavey Mart, Dionne found a cowboy-style wind chime, a lasso and the piece needed to finish the theme in style – children's stick horses. "I just feel so exhilarated when I find the one thing that connects," laughs Dionne. "I never thought I'd buy a pair of cowboy boots, but when you've got a theme, you gotta crank it out!" She was disappointed, however, that she couldn't find cowboy-hat earrings.

For the Mexican theme, she went to Value Village to see which items she could find on the shelves. Then she remembered she had some ponchos in storage at home. "You make a list. Okay, check, check, check. So far, Regina's been very good in supporting me to find my themes," she smiles.

"The Dollar Store is just fantastic. I'm in there quite a bit looking at what they've got and then I think of another theme I can do from items they have. It's really been helpful and it's not so expensive. Some of our friends have sent us items to use for our themes as well as their ideas on what themes we could do."

Graham's mother, Audrey Warner, has even been called upon to help set up the perfect gag for a theme. Dionne and Graham grin as they recall the time Mom Warner was helping Graham build a prop for a chemo day theme when her telephone rang in the midst of the construction phase of the project. Mom Warner picked up her phone, listened for a second to find out who was calling and then said, "I can't talk now. I'm making a banjo." She then hung up and continued on with the important work of helping Graham and her "beautiful, talented" daughter-in-law Dionne take a poke at the rival Winnipeg Blue Bombers football team during the upcoming chemo appointment, just before the annual Banjo Bowl in Winnipeg, Manitoba.

Every theme requires items for not only Dionne, but for Graham and all their visitors as well. Since hearing her reason for buying some of their novelty stock during the non-Halloween season, the staff of Bazaar & Novelty, a local trophy and party supplies store, have given her discounts on some of the items she picks up from their store. One morning, after choosing an amusing moustache for Graham to wear for that day's theme, the man behind the counter told Dionne there was no charge. Instead, he said, "You go to chemo and have a fun day."

"You don't hear that very often about chemo," Dionne says with a smile.

Unless you're Dionne Warner of course.

A couple weeks earlier, she had stopped at her favourite hair salon to drop off some cancer awareness merchandise. As Dionne was leaving, her hairdresser called out to her, "Have fun at chemo!" It was a statement that most cancer patients would never hear and would certainly not believe – but not Dionne. Still, it stopped her in her tracks for a second that day. "It was great."

Dionne lives by a motto that she eagerly shares with anyone who will listen: "There is life before cancer, during cancer and after cancer. Live your life to the fullest!"

During one recent treatment session, Graham smiled after making a particularly funny comment and said to those gathered around Dionne's chair, "I don't know if you're supposed to be laughing in the clinic."

Dionne quickly responded, "Then you'd better find somewhere else for me because I broke that rule on December 17, 2009 when I first came in here!"

Dionne and Graham have settled into a pattern for a typical chemo day – kind of. The day begins with Graham rising early and going into work for a while. Dionne then wakes and is dressed in her costume and ready to go by the time Graham comes home. She has gathered all the other theme components in a reusable shopping bag and has her water, camera and iPod at the ready. Graham greets Dionne, then walks into the bedroom and finds his outfit for that day sitting on the bed.

"We have very normal days," smiles Graham in describing a typical week at their house now. "On Wednesday, it's starting to get normal. You wake up, you're going to be dressed in a funny outfit, you go to the hospital," he laughs.

"My husband is the greatest supporter because he just puts on whatever I set out for him to wear," laughs Dionne. "I just say, 'Do you think you can wear it?' He says, 'Yeah,' and he puts it on."

While Dionne has her completed costume on before they leave the house, Graham sometimes adds the finishing touches to his costume – such as a hat, wig or other accessories – in the hospital parking lot after dropping Dionne off at the hospital's front door. "It's great fun just driving to the clinic and watching people looking at us," says Dionne. Graham has attracted more than a few confused looks in the hospital's parking lot and they both turn the heads of Robin's Donuts customers in the hospital lobby area when Dionne's happy husband saunters in wearing his matching themed outfit.

Graham goes along with most of Dionne's theme ideas but he occasionally balks at her concepts. "I'm not totally agreeable. She was going to dress me as a flower. I said, 'No ... I can be the gardener.' "

There are some outfits he has enjoyed wearing more than others, of course. For October's breast cancer month theme, he proudly wore a shirt of a 'very feminine pink colour. It says, 'Don't laugh, this is your girlfriend's shirt,' " smiles Graham. And during another pink breast cancer awareness theme, he was thrilled when Dionne finally allowed him to make a sign that he had wanted to create for months. He walked through the chemo treatment room bringing smiles and laughter to all the patients and staff there. His sign, which he'd attached to a trolley, proudly announced, "Free! Breast Examinations."

"I really felt the blue latex gloves I was wearing added credibility to my presence but, disappointingly, I never received a single taker," he grins.

Outrageous pants, poofy wigs and corny moustaches are no problem for this important businessman. "You gotta dust your cool off," he says. "Who doesn't love to laugh?"

To avoid vomiting on chemo day, Dionne does not eat that morning. "You learn things along the way. With a full stomach, you react differently. When I come home, I will eat something depending on how I feel." During her treatment, she will eat several dry soda crackers and drink carbonated water instead of accepting the cookies or juice offered by the volunteers. The fizzy drink helps her to feel better and gives her the illusion that she is still enjoying a pop, she says. "I never used to drink a lot of water before. One thing they told me in Mexico was I could have orange juice or cranberry juice, but half and half with water in order to dilute the amount of sugar."

When she and Graham first step through the cancer centre doors, they might take off their jackets and make a quick mini-entrance past the main reception desk and over to the chemo room waiting area. They are often stopped immediately by staff or volunteers who walk through this main area and there are many smiles and laughs exchanged within moments of them arriving. If it is the week in which Dionne is to receive Avastin, they go upstairs to a different floor of the cancer centre to pay the $2,600 to get the drug that day. Then they come back and sit in the waiting area, chatting with whoever they see there in those next minutes. Almost every person waiting in that open area either smiles or laughs at the costumes and antics that occur before their eyes. Young or old, Dionne aims to delight.

While waiting to be called into the chemo treatment room, Dionne will inevitably strike up a conversation with whoever is sitting beside her. Sometimes, she will show off a few dance moves and let out a few yells for the staff or the patients she knows and can see who are sitting at the far end of the treatment room. Other times, she and Graham will simply talk between themselves. More often than not, they will become the centre of attention as clinic staff, including doctors, pass through the area and smile, chuckle and comment on the costumes.

"They are not shy of the limelight," says Bernie Desrosiers.

And if you are their friend, you had better not be afraid of it either. "They drag you into the limelight," Nadine Desrosiers smiles.

During a recent visit, a four-year-old boy came shyly over to stand within a few feet of the chemo waiting area to watch the dancing Dionne strut her stuff for the cancer centre staff. After a few minutes of watching, the little boy walked back over to his mother and loudly announced, "This is the best day of my life!"

As soon as there is an open chair for her in the treatment room, Dionne and Graham make their big entrance, coming around the corner of the quiet room with her iPod blaring and attitude definitely on display. Soon, the treatment room is full of laughter and there are even cheers on occasion. "We kind of come in like a tornado," laughs Graham.

While a nurse settles Dionne in to her recliner, Graham begins his job of attaching the ornaments and accessories onto Dionne's IV pole or hanging them on the chair number sign above her head. He then pulls out the props they brought and if there are little treats in the bag, such as a breast cancer awareness lanyard for each staff member, it is Graham's job to hand those out later while Dionne is taking her treatment.

While Dionne is getting settled, other patients often call out to Dionne. They receive a huge smile and a wave from her. Desrosiers teases that Dionne is "waving to her peeps."

On Dionne's treatment days, word spreads quickly through the cancer centre that she is in that day. About 30 nurses and assistants work in the chemo room area and there are numerous staff members as well in other areas of the clinic. Those who visit Dionne are often anxious to tell their colleagues about the theme for that day and some of the staff members have been known to cover their ears and yell, "Don't tell me what she's wearing! I want it to be a surprise!"

"She just lifts this place right up," smiles Jenny Longman, a clinic assistant. "Everybody in the room is quiet, then she comes in and there's music and the laughing. You can hear her voice from a long way off. It's great."

"They just cause such a distraction, but a good distraction," says Lacey Fondrick, a clinic receptionist. "Everyone says, 'Who's that?' Dionne's always laughing. Her attitude is just amazing."

Dionne is often asked questions about the various pieces of her costumes, such as 'Where did you find that?' or 'Where did you get your outfit?' Dionne gladly gives away all her secrets and points out what she bought at which store. When Graham is asked the same questions, he simply replies, "I found it on my bed."

"What's cute is when we go in with the different themes, we usually keep it very top secret," laughs Dionne. "It's the fun part of it – the entrance of walking into the Allan Blair Cancer Clinic and the first reaction from the receptionist. People will ask me, 'What is your theme next week? Are you going to tell me?' I always say, 'No, because then I'd have to kill you,' " she laughs.

"Everybody keeps saying, 'Man, you must have one heck of a tickle trunk from all these themes!' Oh, we work hard. We plan hard. I keep thinking about what we can do. Of course, we work around holidays and what's coming up so we can help support our community and make other people aware of what's going on around the city, like Canadian Western Agribition, Buffalo Days, or Relay For Life. It's all great."

Dionne has so far broken her rule of keeping the theme secret only once, to inform the update readers and others that an upcoming theme was for *Paint Canada Pink* week. "I sent an e-mail out to my angels across the world and said, 'Help us Paint Canada Pink and send me a picture of you or you with your group in pink.' It was cool. I wanted to see the responses I got from everybody. So I let all the nurses know. It was perfect." Dionne's three cousins in Guelph as well as her second cousins and many, many friends from across Canada, the U.S. and Provo donned pink for Dionne, who delighted in every photo they sent to her.

"I'm going to make a little album of all the photos."

There are about 30 chairs in the chemo room area and patients are rarely seated in the same chair two weeks in a row, so many different patients see Dionne and Graham walking by during their entrance. Some patients ask to be seated near Dionne and "one gentleman said to us, 'I'm just excited to see what you guys come up with next week.' It's cool," says Dionne. "We bring smiles. That's what's so nice. With our love/peace theme, there was a lady who came in and was sitting down for treatment. She looked over and she saw me and our friend Leslie Foss dressed in our peace outfits. She didn't know my name or anything and I didn't know her name, but I've seen her there before and she called out to me, 'Hey! Look!' She had peace earrings on that day and she said, 'Ah! Now I'm a part of your theme!' It was cute. I gave her a thumbs-up and yelled, 'You rock!' She was so pumped that she had her peace earrings on. So that was wonderful. Oh my gosh, she was so happy!"

During the first hour that Dionne is in her treatment chair, she is usually visited by up to a dozen cancer clinic staff, a couple volunteers and the occasional patient. She chats, laughs and giggles with them while saline is injected to flush out her picc line. If the picc line becomes clogged, which happens occasionally, Dionne has to move her arm up and down or wait for nurses to find other methods to get the line opened again. This can add up to an hour to her treatment process.

When things go smoothly, which is the majority of the time, her visitors are welcomed and then given the necessary props so that photos can be taken of them alongside Dionne – for the entertainment of everyone there and those who view that week's update. Sometimes, the staff share a few dance moves with Graham and almost every visit ends with words of encouragement and an exchange of hugs.

As the hubbub of their arrival dies down, Dionne settles back in her recliner while the chemo drugs are introduced into her system for the next couple hours. She receives Benadryl to reduce nausea, which she can feel "tingling all the way down to my toes," and is also given an antihistamine to reduce allergic reactions, an anti-inflammatory, a relaxant and an antacid – all to make the chemotherapy process more bearable.

At 2 p.m. every day, Graham takes a quick nap, and Dionne delights in catching this nap on camera, so it can be the brunt of some jokes for the updates. Dionne sometimes naps as well, at which point the now-awake Graham grabs the camera and snaps a photo. This volley of sleeping-beauty photos has played itself out for the amusement of update readers over the course of many themes.

When they return home, Dionne rests for awhile and when she wakes, she forwards Graham the photos from that day. "I have to wait until she kind of comes to because she has the program on her computer for the photos. She selects the photos and resizes them and then sends them to me. I'm not a tech-y guy so I can't do it. She's a control freak," teases Graham.

"It's my life. When you have cancer, you can write your own show," retorts Dionne. She then calmly explains, "It's a group effort. We both work on it together before it goes out."

Graham looks at the photos for that theme and types in captions based on whatever comes to his mind. Dionne then reads what Graham has written and they adjust the final product together.

Karen Drysdale is one of many friends who anxiously wait for the update e-mails. "The idea to do themes didn't surprise me," says Drysdale. "Anything D can do to keep the laughter going and make people smile – that makes her feel good. Graham loves to go overboard. Any time he can take anybody by surprise and do the unexpected, he will do it."

They both note that if they do not send an update within 24 hours of when Dionne was supposed to have received a treatment, Graham starts to get e-mails asking what is happening and whether Dionne is still okay. Once an update has been sent, Graham and Dionne usually spend the next several hours enjoying responses back from people they know and love, as well as from strangers to whom the e-mail has been forwarded.

"We don't know where the updates go," says Dionne. "People are printing them off and putting them in their piles of notices at work so others can take them and read them. We've heard all kinds of different stories. It's incredible."

Graham chuckles about the vastly different responses he receives on the updates. "Her friends all say, 'Oh, you're so nice.' My friends all joke, 'Show me some more skin!'"

On Sunday, October 3, 2010 Dionne addressed the 2,400 people assembled to participate in the CIBC Run for the Cure in Regina. She told them parts of her life story and talked to them about her 'journey of hope.' As she outlined her first few battles with cancer, they listened intently. Many wiped tears from their eyes as she told of her devastating breast cancer diagnosis and her two operations for brain cancer. She spoke of figuring out what was important in her life, of losing her hair and of moving to Saskatchewan to build a new life with her soulmate Graham. She mentioned her two operations for liver cancer and how she thrived with the help of amazing friends and family as well as an excellent oncologist.

"In November 2009, I was cancer-free for seven years," Dionne told the audience.

They spontaneously erupted in applause and cheers.

Standing near the front of the crowd, not too far away from Dionne, Graham said softly, "Too soon. Too soon."

Those who knew Dionne and her story knew that the cheers were premature. They wondered what would happen next.

Dionne was taken aback by the crowd's response. "I thought to myself, 'Oohhh ... you don't know what's coming next. And Graham said the same thing later. I didn't expect anybody to applaud so when it did happen, I thought, 'Oh boy.' But you know what? They were happy for me. I was doing so well. It gave me the kick to go on and say the next piece."

This would be the first time that Dionne had spoken to a group of people about her December 2009 diagnosis of Stage IV cancer. She wasn't sure she could do it – until she heard the crowd's support. It was now or never. She continued with her speech.

"All was fabulous. I was enjoying life with my husband, my family and the friends whom I consider family. Who knew that was all about to change once again? On December 9, 2009 I was diagnosed with liver cancer, lung cancer and bone cancer. Stage IV. All metastasizing from my breast cancer."

There was no sound from the crowd – only shocked looks and sad faces. Many people lowered their heads and silently cried.

"Now these were the hardest phone calls I ever had to make," said Dionne, defiantly continuing on to bring her message home. "Today, I stand in front of you a woman fighting for her life. A woman continuing to believe in hope, faith, medicine and miracles.

"I am a person of great determination to beat the odds and to never give up. I ask all survivors to embrace the disease, own it and fight back with everything you've got and show cancer who's the boss!! I know my cancers are in shock and running scared!!!!" she said.

"I will never say this journey has been easy. I always gave myself 24 hours to say 'Why me?' and then after those 24 hours, I would come to my senses and say, 'Why Not Me?' and 'What am I going to do to beat this??!!'

"The word 'survivor' in the dictionary means 'one who perseveres through life's challenges, hardships, misfortunes and tragedies. One who refuses to give up, give in, or quit trying. One who triumphs over insurmountable challenges and becomes a better person because of them.'

"My message to survivors and their families and friends is this – Does cancer suck? YES! Survivors – never be embarrassed that you have been diagnosed with the disease, or you are already letting it win. Survivors – dig deep into your soul and find the courage, strength and determination to fight back! Survivors – talk to your loved ones. They want to be there for you. Survivors, family and friends – let laughter in. It is the best healing treatment to surround all of you. I have laughed even when it hurt.

"Everyone – believe in hope, faith and miracles. You are looking at one. Today, I am a 13-year breast cancer survivor, a 12-year brain cancer survivor, a nine-year liver cancer survivor, a 10-month bone cancer survivor, and a 10-month lung cancer survivor."

Dionne ended her powerful speech by reading the poem *What Cancer Cannot Do*. She dedicated it to all survivors and in memory of loved ones lost but never forgotten. She gave a special shout-out "to my amazing, incredible and supportive husband Graham Warner, who continues to be my wingman on this journey. Thank you for never giving up on me, babe, and for all your continued love and support. You truly are my lifeline. Thank you again, everyone, for welcoming me and my story into your hearts. With funds raised today at the CIBC Run for the Cure, we are one step closer to helping find a cure to this disease called cancer. I believe we are one step closer to helping save a child. Have a great run or walk, everyone, for we were definitely blessed with a beautiful day today. Thank you."

If the crowd had not already been standing, ready to go on their walk or run, they definitely would have stood to thank this brave survivor for her words of encouragement and inspiration. After her speech, Dionne was surrounded by people who thanked her and wished her well. It took several minutes before the drained Dionne, who was just getting over a bout of pneumonia, could even make her way to Graham's side so the exhausted warrior could go home and rest.

Dionne looks back on that speech as a marker in her journey with cancer. "I'm totally honoured and overwhelmed that anybody wants to hear my story or thinks I have a story worth hearing that will inspire people," she says. "It just blows my mind. When people ask if I can come and do this event, of course I will come. I want to be able to reach out and give as many people, patients and families hope as I can. I have never been embarrassed about any of the diagnoses I've had. To talk about it makes me feel better. Graham said to me that CIBC Run speech was the best he's ever felt I have done in sharing the story. It's the first time I talked about the December 2009 diagnosis. It took everything for me to suck it up and not... cry!!! – but I did it and I'm okay. It was a release for me, too, and I needed to do that."

In her speeches, Dionne usually leaves Graham's name until near the end. "That is when my heart ... Whoa!," she says, stretching out her hands in an enormous reach. "My heart breaks."

Dionne stops to compose herself and then adds, "Mom Warner listened to that speech before I presented it. Every time she heard Graham's name, there was always this smile." Dionne was touched by her mother-in-law's reaction and each time the smile came, Dionne thought to herself, "Yes, Mom. Your boy's a good boy."

A few days after the Run for the Cure, Dr. Salim saw Dionne in his office before her scheduled chemo treatment. "Upon reviewing her recent pneumonia diagnosis, the good doctor immediately and firmly nixed Wednesday's regular planned double-dose chemo treatment," explained Graham in that week's update. "I say *firmly* because he had to defend his decision against Dionne's equally firm belief that she *should* receive her treatment because she 'felt quite fine' and 'she had plans.' All I can say as I watched these two equally strong-willed people vehemently debate each other, (they respect and love each other, so there was never any danger of crossing the line,) I experienced the most wonderful uplifting feeling I have ever experienced since the day I was married. That feeling? For once, I was not in the wrong while Dionne was speaking. Thanks, Doc, for taking the heat and yes, he did win the debate!"

Dr. Salim provided the couple with some very good news at that appointment, however. He had reviewed her latest CAT scan and bone scan results. The CAT scan showed no new tumours, no growth of the existing ones, although there was no shrinkage either, and the report essentially stated a no-change status. "This was considered good news and we'll take that kind of news all day long," said Graham.

"The bone scan, on the other hand, showed definite positive results with a distinct reduction in the number of cancer tumours residing in her bones. Yahoo!!!! We were quite overwhelmed at how such a tiny bit of positive news uplifted our spirits and hopes! The good news continued with her oncologist remarking that Dionne seemed to be handling the toxicity of all the chemo she has been receiving remarkably well. He seemed most pleased over this fact as it means she can continue to receive the aggressive treatment plan he has her on. We attribute D's ability in handling the toxicity so well to her naturopath's program which is concentrated on aggressively getting rid of the toxicity caused by the chemo treatment."

For Dionne, it was one more step in the process of healing. "When having tests done, I can figure out if it's not the best of news by the looks on their faces or their body language. I know my life could change again tomorrow, but I'm prepared. I knew when I was originally diagnosed with cancer that it could come back. Anything is possible. I'm not in denial."

On October 7, 2010 Dionne turned 45 years old. It was a momentous occasion that she and Graham celebrated by having supper with a couple dozen friends and family at a local restaurant. In typical D-and-G style, Graham welcomed everyone and Dionne began her short thank-you speech by asking all the guests to please stand up and do a little dance with her while she turned on a musical toy that a friend had delivered to her earlier that day. When she pressed the button on the toy, an uplifting Dionne-like tune could be heard: *"Celebrate! Good times! Come on!"*

"People say they hate to turn 40," says the smiling 45-year-old. "As survivors, every second, minute, hour is so important to us. We celebrate turning older every year. I sure do, anyway. I look forward to turning 50. I look forward to turning 60. It means I'm still alive and I've continued to beat the odds."

The day after her birthday, Dionne posted a thank-you note on her Facebook page. "I would like to thank all of you who have sent me birthday wishes via Facebook, phone or e-mail. Thank you very much for sending me so much love. My cup truly runneth over today. My love tank is beyond full. I hope you can feel my love back. Happy Thanksgiving to my Canadian families and friends I consider family!"

On November 10, 2010 Dionne and Graham presented the most sombre of all the themes they had done to date. They wore their poppies and khaki in tribute for Remembrance Day. "What also added to the emotion and sensitivity of the theme was that as Dionne sat in her chair receiving the chemotherapy, we realized that it was 15 years ago to the day that she was initially diagnosed with the breast cancer that has challenged her life ever since," wrote Graham in that week's update. "It was a reflective day for us as we remembered all those who fought to ensure our freedom, and we remembered Dionne's personal 15-year fight."

Graham went on to explain that his amazing wife had also on that day convinced the hospital staff to cut her Benadryl injection in half so she could attend their annual Camp Circle of Friends charity event a mere few hours after leaving the chemo ward.

Over the years of their marriage, Dionne has often been brutally honest with Graham and told him whatever was on her mind, no matter the consequences. "As I started getting sick with this illness, I realized life is too short for crap," she says. "Be honest. Get it out in the open. Why would I want to say something three years later? I've said it right now, right here. I've told Graham, 'If you're ever not happy in this marriage any more and you want out, don't prolong it. Just tell me ... so I can pack your things and you can get out,'" she says with the largest of laughs.

Graham nods to their visitor, "She's failing to tell you the seriousness with which I take and keep my wedding vows."

"Yes, and I know that," adds Dionne. "Both of us are coming from a divorce. Don't prolong the agony. I also come from a childhood divorce. I can see how prolonging it can just be horrible. I tell my girlfriends to not just settle for somebody, because then they're really not happy and you can see in their eyes that they're still searching. There's a song I will always remember. It goes, '*It's sad to belong to someone else when the right one comes along*.' I've asked my girlfriends, 'What are you doing? It's okay to be single. Don't be afraid to be single. He'll come when he's supposed to come. My Prince Charming came when I least expected it and I wouldn't just settle for anybody. I'd rather be by myself. I don't lock myself in a room.'"

Dionne freely acknowledges that she is far from perfect and that she has many personality flaws. She is close to perfect in Graham's eyes, however, and her honesty is much appreciated.

"I find it refreshing," he says. "Compared to my first marriage, I always know where I stand. I always know how she's feeling – other than when she's planning surprise birthday parties," he smiles. "It's refreshing to know the difference between honesty and not ... We're both control freaks a little bit, so sometimes it's a bit of a challenge to see who wins," he adds.

Dionne grins and notes that they could never participate in *The Amazing Race* together "because we would kill one another. Only one of us would come out of the race alive." This launches them into a verbal battle about who would be better at navigating, who would be better at physical challenges and who would or would not eat the unusual food that is sometimes provided as a challenge on the TV reality show.

"I'd do some things because it's a race," laughs Dionne. "I just know that I'd be out the door and ready to go, and Graham and I would be arguing about turning left or right for the airport."

For his most recent birthday, Dionne gave Graham a card that said he is allowed "to be right for 24 hours." He appreciated the gesture and commented that "90% of the time, Dionne is right."

Although he and Dionne struggle back and forth for control at times, Graham says he knew shortly after marrying her that he would have to re-think how he interacted with his wife throughout their relationship.

"That was probably the first lesson I learned in this marriage. Coming home from work after leading 180 people, I learned that this person didn't need to be led."

Back to Mexico

"To win the battle, you must win the war. This girl is locked and loaded!!!" - **Dionne**

Since hearing Dionne's Stage IV diagnosis in December 2009, Graham has not stopped looking for other therapies and options. "We still haven't given up hope," he says. "We don't really think about D getting cancer again or about not succeeding. If we would have accepted every diagnosis she received, we wouldn't have made it past 2001."

In the summer and fall of 2010, Graham spent countless hours connecting with specialists at Princess Margaret Hospital in Toronto, the Fred Hutchinson Cancer Research Center in Seattle, doctors at the Mayo Clinic in Rochester, and Dr. Perez in Mexico about the possibility of Dionne undergoing cell therapy treatment.

Dr. Salim gave his approval for Graham to pursue these options and he also listened openly to other ideas that Graham posed to him.

"Dr. Salim told me not to let Graham have any regrets," says Dionne. "He said, 'Graham's going to try everything he can for you.'"

Dionne is thankful that Graham is still looking and she has been happy to listen to explanations of the various treatments he's found. She and Graham then sit down together and consider which options might be the best choices for her cancer.

"We're trying to address the biggest thing, which is the cancer in her bones," explains Graham. "We still think we're going to beat it," he adds, noting that he will gladly pay tens of thousands of dollars more if it will extend the time he has with his wife.

"One of the very first things Dr. Salim said to me was, 'I know you'd sell your house if you had to.' And I would. When we first got engaged, Dionne told me she'd live in a cardboard box with me."

Dionne interrupts Graham to slyly add, "That would be fine, babe. All my stuff comes with me. I don't know where you'll sleep – I don't know how big the cardboard box will be." Then she laughs.

Graham smiles and continues.

We have heard from people who say, 'You're lucky. You can afford all this,' I do feel lucky and I realize how fortunate we've been, being able to do all these treatments. And yet the term 'lucky' can almost come across as a dismissal of the 30 years of hard work, sacrifices and calculated risks I've endured to be 'lucky.' I've heard successful musicians and rock stars talk about this – when somebody says, 'You're an overnight success,' and they say, 'Yeah it only took me 30 years.' I can assure you that finances are still an obstacle that we have to be cautious of regarding how we approach this."

Avastin is not included in his company's medical benefits because it is not approved by Health Canada for metastasized breast cancer, so the money they spend every month on Avastin is not reimbursed. "It is a sad case where you can't afford this drug and this drug could help you," Graham says of other patients who have fewer financial means than he and Dionne. "In fact, 'sad' doesn't even come close to describing the unbearable pain and frustration one would have in not being able to pursue a treatment due to finances. It's just how we're raised in Canada – that we believe all our medical bills are paid for by Medicare. When you find out in real life that it's not the case, it's tough. As Canadians, we're raised to think it's covered, so we also don't prepare for it. Who says I'm going to save a quarter of a million dollars in case I get sick?

"I couldn't look at myself in the mirror if I had to say to Dionne, 'Sorry, we have to stop the Avastin for financial reasons.' "

The year 2011 marks the 30th anniversary of Warner Industries. Since its simple beginnings in an Atco trailer, the company has expanded its product lines to include Thomas school buses, Doepker semi-trailers, numerous products within the fire truck and rescue industry, and driver management services.

In 2007, Warner Transportation Services Ltd. was formed as the enterprise that organizes all of the Regina Public School bus drivers and their routes. "In 2010, we added Warner Leasing Industries and Warner Towing Industries. In 2012, we hope to add Warner Exotic Dancers," jokes Graham.

"He's just lining up his girls now," adds Dionne with a laugh.

In 2009, *Saskatchewan Business Magazine* placed Warner Industries Group of Companies as #84 on its list of Saskatchewan's Top 100 Companies with $43 million in annual sales. In 2010, the *Regina Leader-*

Post named Warner Industries as one of the top 50 companies in Regina and 15th in the top 100 companies in Saskatchewan.

On the snowy winter day that the newspaper highlighted his business with its top-50 designation, Graham was sitting on a Caterpillar loader, removing snow from his company's parking lot. "My mom called and said, 'You made the top 50.'

"I replied, 'Oh. Well, as president and CEO of this wonderful company, I have snow to move. See you later.'

"Yes, I'm lucky to have this great company and these great staff," says Graham. "It's only taken 30 years of hard luck to get it going."

Graham credits his friend and general manager Roger Pettigrew for working so hard and for "making me look good." While Pettigrew handles most of the day-to-day details of Warner Industries, Graham keeps his eyes open for interesting complementary business opportunities and enjoys any chance he can find to jump on a big machine.

"I didn't get into this business to do paperwork. I like using my hands and running machinery and stuff like that. When I bought that big property where the buses are, I loved that time because I kind of went back to my roots. I was using heavy equipment and torches and sledgehammers. I love that. I love building, because of my road building background. There's just something very satisfying about grading or making the commercial yard right. I tore down huge silos. I and a 62-year-old man did probably 80% of the work over there. It was all hard manual labour.

"My main focus now is still building the company in a manner I can handle while still looking after Dionne."

Graham will continue to look for other options and Dionne will continue to try the other therapies they find. 'No regrets' continues to be their motto with this disease.

"We won't know unless we try," says Dionne.

Roger Pettigrew has watched Graham closely since Dionne's December 2009 diagnosis. "The most emotional he's ever been has been this last year," says Pettigrew about his friend. "He's never had a moment when he didn't think that we're going to beat this. He is extremely riddled with the emotion of pure pain. There are not many times that I've seen that man cry. Graham is a strong-willed person, but he's hurting inside. It's hard to watch."

"Graham is a very strong man," says Tricia Pettigrew. "He is doing whatever is humanly possible to ensure Dionne lives for a long, long time. He would spend every last dime he has to have his wife by his side. That is how he is coping – doing whatever is necessary for his love."

"Graham always has a positive outlook on life and he is always ready for the next battle – no matter what it is, where it takes him or how much effort it will require," Sean Westerman says of his friend. "He simply will not give up. I have seen moments of worry from him, but it is soon replaced with the fight to keep D in his life forever."

"When you see those two together, even when they have their little arguments, you still feel all of that love," says Mandy Sauer, who has been a close friend of the couple since 2006. "When I go over there for dinner and we watch our TV shows and we're having a normal conversation, there might be a little pause in the conversation and he's looking at her and you can feel that love. Dionne is one of the luckiest people to have Graham. There are so many men who would just walk away or hide their feelings. Graham sometimes hides his feelings behind his humour and he'll make a joke, but he shows his feelings with people to whom he's close. He's not afraid to cry in front of you. He's not afraid to show his love, his friendship and his support. Some men have the mentality of 'If I don't see it, it will go away,' but he faces everything head on. He doesn't stop."

In November 2010, Graham spoke to Dr. Salim about the possibility of sending Dionne to Edmonton for an MRI-like test that would show more detail in the tumours and lesions within her body. Dionne was all for it. "He's not sure on some things. Is it really scar tissue that he sees? If it's more tumours, tell me. That's what I want to know. Break it down. If I've got 12 tumours in my back, tell me. We've got to know what we're working with," she says.

Dr. Salim said Dionne would have to be off chemo at least eight weeks before that test would be an option and they would have to pay for the test out of their own pocket. Graham and Dionne were willing to try it, but it did not come to pass.

A Seattle doctor responded to Graham's inquiries saying that he could not get Dionne into a clinical trial for cell therapy. A Toronto doctor could not get approval to put her into the same cell therapy program as his pancreatic cancer patients, and the Mayo clinic dismissed Graham's inquiry outright, saying they did not have any cell therapy program.

Dr. Salim told Graham that the mortality rate for stem cell transplants is quite high in the first 30 days because of infection. "He said the treatment Dionne is under right now is far more successful than the risk of the stem cell transplant," says Graham, who then dismissed a stem cell transplant as an option and contacted Dr. Perez in Mexico for more information on an integrative program they offer using killer cell and dendritic cell therapy.

"They take a sample of the tumour and harvest those cells in the lab and make a vaccine out of them," explains Graham. "Then they inject those into your immune system and these killer cells go to the tumour, which is a foreign object, attack it and hopefully get rid of it. I told him I love the concept of it. It's logical. It is using her immune system to fight itself. They said their cell therapy has worked well for pancreatic cancer so why won't it work for bone cancer?"

When Graham told Dr. Perez that the Saskatchewan doctors said the tumours in Dionne's spine are palliative and there's nothing they can do about that, Graham was told that this is because chemotherapy is delivered through the blood system and blood doesn't flow to that area of the spine. "The beauty of these dendritic cells is, and this may sound funny, but they will go through the wall of your blood vessel and they will go to that tumour and try to eliminate it," Graham says. "That gave me a pretty good picture, but I decided to check around some more anyway."

Graham contacted people at two other hospitals in Mexico and made comparisons. Graham then asked Dionne if she wanted to go back to Tijuana under Dr. Perez's care, now in a different hospital. The process would involve treatments of dendritic cell and killer cell therapy as well as more hyperthermic treatments, which stress the cancer cells and make the cell therapy more effective over a three-week period.

"Dendritic therapy is being used in China, India, Germany, Mexico and in the United States at Stanford University," explained Dr. Perez. "Today, stem cell therapy is showing promising results in chronic problems such as cardiovascular disease, neurological disorders and cancer, of course. The linear approach in relation to result doesn't apply to chronic disease in which multiple factors are in place. Dionne doesn't just have cancer any more. She is a combination of her history, the cancer, all the treatments and complications of these last two. You will never find medical evidence under such a scenario. Most of the evidence will come from those who have worked with these therapies under these conditions in these stages. Most importantly, it is not just about the cellular therapy, it is about creating the right environment for the therapy to work, and that's part of the big secret to make them effective. That's where hyperthermia comes into play."

Dionne took a little bit of time to think about going to Mexico again.

The fear of taking the same uncomfortable treatments as she had before, and perhaps even worse, reared its ugly head and caused her to pause. She wasn't sure it was wise to stop Dr. Salim's chemo treatments and she wasn't completely sold on the cell therapy procedures. Dr. Perez and his colleagues had since moved to a different hospital from the first trip down there, but their program was the same. She talked to Graham and some friends and family, who encouraged her to do whatever made her happy. In the end, she decided that she had nothing to lose by trying. "I hope I'm high as a kite three quarters of the time," she joked.

"I don't want to get scared," she said before the trip. "I just want to go there and try it. I'm willing to take a chance. I just don't want any 'what ifs.' I wouldn't do this if I didn't trust the doctors. They seem to really care and want to help."

"The worst case in Mexico is that nothing happens," said Graham confidently, "but the hyperthermic treatment never hurt her before. We think it helps and stresses the cancer cells."

"There's a difference between nervous and scared to me," added Dionne. "Nervous is okay – I guess we're going to see what happens. Scared makes me think maybe I don't want to do this. Nervous is fine with me. I just don't want to get into the mode of scared. That's why a lot of times it's good not to know what's going to happen until you get there."

"We're going to do the cell therapy, whether you want to or not," Graham told her, only half-joking.

Dionne understood the importance of going to Tijuana for treatment again. "This cancer has a mind of its own. I can almost hear it say, 'What do you think, Eddy? Let's go hang out here today! We haven't bothered her here yet!' ... I would be the first person in Mexico to do this dendritic cell therapy for breast cancer. I don't mind being the guinea pig," she said, noting that Dr. Salim told her there was no proof that dendritic therapy worked for breast cancer. "I won't know unless I try. I don't want any regrets. If this works, people will know. If it doesn't work, then it doesn't."

Dionne has been convinced for a number of years that the emotional stresses in her life helped make her sick. "I do believe the different stresses in my life triggered the cancers. I think it was just the planning of my wedding that may have triggered the breast cancer. For the brain cancer, it was the stress of going into a different job where I was not happy.

Liver cancer arrived during her divorce and major relocation to Saskatchewan. In 2009, her Stage IV cancer came after she went to Toronto for the 60-kilometre walk for breast cancer, spent energy planning her friend's bridal shower, then painfully stepped away from that decades-old friendship.

While conventional medicine does not subscribe to the idea of stress causing cancer, both Darwin Stoeber and Dr. Perez believe there is definitely something to that idea. They agree that more and more research is showing that cancer is a "civilization disease. It has to do with artificial and modern lifestyle and everything that keeps us from living the way we should be living," said Stoeber.

"It's related to everything from living inside and not getting enough sunlight to wearing clothes to eating foods that don't have enough protective elements in them, to staying up late, too much stress, all that stuff. And then there's toxic stress. Every day, we face a sea of toxic stress diet-wise and environmental factors such as radiation, all kinds of stuff." Some sources say up to 65% of cancers are caused by diet alone.

"There are a lot of things that are stressful that we don't even think about like using artificial lighting and drinking tap water, taking in a chemical soup of pesticide residues and who knows what. Our poor body then has to fight to deal with some of these chemical residues that it's never met in all its evolution, and that's a tall order. Most bodies won't keep that up forever. Even the natural aging process makes you more susceptible to put all that toxic stress on," says Stoeber.

"The nice thing these days is there's all this toxic stress but there's also more awareness and available organic foods and gyms and our knowledge of how to stay healthy. You get both extremes going at the same time. The onus is on individuals to do what they can."

"Cancer is a multi-factoral disease," adds Dr. Perez. "We cannot just blame it on one thing. With lung cancer, some patients are smokers and some are not, but they have the same type of lung cancers. It's completely untrue that stress is not related. Now more than ever, we can acknowledge that it is related. We cannot talk about a one-on-one relationship. We need to understand what stress does physiologically," he says.

"Stress is a mode that your body has to take to be able to face danger. In the past, it was used only occasionally when one left the home for an unsafe environment to hunt for food, for example. Now we have daily stress – late to work, late to cook, we don't have enough money. This is very different for each of us."

If a person's body is continually under stress, chemical and hormonal changes will occur, he explained. "The adrenal gland on top of your kidneys secretes important hormones for the fight-or-flee response. Now instead of in case of emergency, you are living on this every single day, there comes a point where your body can't maintain this. The sympathetic nervous system predominates when there's a lot of stress and it changes the way your sugar is used, the way your adrenalin is used. We have hormones and substances that are dominating and need to take control. In the case of Dionne, if somebody takes the time to take her history, there are very clear recurrences of cancer that match her emotional problems. We need to determine what the different things are that could help her."

Dr. Perez said because evidence points to the environment as the trigger for cancer, "you cannot treat just cancer. That's impossible. Cancer is more than just the mass. The mass is the physical representation of the problem. It may be nutritional deficiencies or an attempt by the body to reveal problems."

There may also be a genetic predisposition to cancer. "Our genetic blueprint is the way our body works. Some of these genes require 'expression' – something to either be shut down or activated. Let's see your gene as a light switch. I am the environment and I come and turn this gene on or off. The problem is that cultural families come along with the majority of these diseases. There's always that habit in obesity. This person behaves the way the family is behaving. The same thing goes with cancer in some cases. For example, in breast cancer, some BRCA-positive patients don't behave like BRCA-positive. So there are no rules."

A good attitude is essential to a better outcome with all illnesses in general, Dr. Perez added. "The moment we mention cancer, it's like a death sentence. We need to work with the fear the patient has, what they are experiencing and what they are thinking about the disease. The mind is like a filter. We have seen it many, many times. We can have a patient on the right treatment but if the mind is full of fear, the body will fall. We have patients where the biggest thing we can blame this cancer on is emotional problems. We tell them, 'You have every right to be angry but what is the true benefit of being angry? Life is not bad or good. Life is just life.'

"If we don't align mind and body, if there's a negative input from the mind, the body will follow that – and we have seen that very often. The mental part of this is very strong. How strong has yet to be defined. Our program we believe has steps that all patients, regardless of the stage, will benefit from."

Graham and Dionne paid close to $20,000 for the three-week

program which included food and accommodation for Graham as well. "They don't entertain me, though," he added with a smile. Before they left Regina, they received a promise from the hospital that Dionne would receive a high-calorie diet so she would not lose weight like she did during her first visit.

On November 17, 2010 Graham and Dionne left for Mexico, where she was to undergo dendritic and activated lymphocytes cell therapies. The protocol was to do one hyperthermic and three dendritic treatments, but Dionne's body responded so well that the therapy was increased.

"When these cancer cells are stressed, they give off a sort of protein trail and that starts to happen around 24 hours after the hyperthermic treatment," explains Graham. "Then when they inject the cultured dendritic cells, they are attracted to this protein trail even more and follow the trail to the tumours and do their thing," Graham told update readers. To work properly and travel through the entire body, the dendritic cells must be injected between the skin and muscle tissue, which is painful since muscle is not used to being forced apart. Graham's update showed candid photos of Dionne grimacing during this procedure.

"Unfortunately, these dendritic cells have to be injected in between the skin layer and the muscle layer with a verrrrrrrry long and thin needle. Combined with the thick gel-like substance, it spreads these layers that are not used to being spread, which translates into great pain for our brave angel. The pain, which would have had me whimpering like a little schoolgirl, lasts for two to three hours afterwards and leaves her spent for the rest of the day. Our brave Warner Warrior never cried out once."

In the end, Dionne received one hyperthermic treatment, then two dendritic cell injections, then a second hyperthermic treatment the next day, then a third dendritic cell injection. Then she had a three or four-day break. The hospital then tested her blood again and found it could handle a third hyperthermic treatment and a fourth dendritic treatment after that. Then Dionne was sent home to wait to see if the treatment was successful.

"I would do that hyperthermic treatment once a month because you come out of there when it's all done and you feel rejuvenated. Wow!" she said.

Graham noted that the process removes toxins and the heavy metals from one's body, but the hyperthermic procedure is only offered as part of the whole program at the hospital, not as a separate therapy.

One frightening moment occurred during the first hyperthermic treatment, when a new machine unexpectedly heated up Dionne's blood quicker than the old machine at the other hospital had done. This caused Dionne to almost lose consciousness and it put a horrible fear into Graham as he watched his wife's sudden lack of responsiveness. "All of a sudden, D said, 'Something's not right, something's not right,' and she didn't respond when the technician asked her to look her way. "Dionne's eyes had rolled up and locked. Her complexion was the most awful grey. Then her head started to shake and the technician said, 'She's going to seize.'"

Graham was immediately ordered out of the room, some of Dionne's blood was quickly pumped back into her body and a crisis was averted, but Graham did not know this during the two minutes he was sitting outside the room dealing with his own body's reaction to the stress. "In literally seconds, the amount of adrenalin that was dumped into my system was incredible. I had instant panic which I've never had flying airplanes, even with landing gear failures. I felt like, 'What have I done? I'm going to kill my wife.' Because I brought her down here. This was my idea, pushing this."

When Graham returned to the room, Dionne's complexion was back to normal and everything was fine again. She didn't remember anything other than calling out to the technician that something was not right. "The Lord's not ready for me yet," she laughs as she hears Graham tell the story.

"I went from the 'I'm in control' type of thing to 'We're winning and we're pushing forward' to the feeling of 'What have I done?' For the rest of that day, I was physically sick. I didn't eat," adds Graham. "I recognized the feeling. It was from the adrenalin. When you have an adrenalin shot, it almost hurts from the inside out."

This is exactly why Graham does not allow himself to think about anything going wrong with Dionne. The pain would be unbearable.

Still, such an incident will not stop him in seeking out options that will help Dionne. He can't imagine doing anything else.

"I do this in business," he says. "I remember when I went to change my parts display from behind the counter to an open one, my accountant said, 'Do you know how much shoplifting there is going to be?' I said, 'You know what? For the 3% of the population that will do that, why would we cut ourselves off from the 97% who are going to buy more parts because they're open and easily accessible?' I think I use that 97%-

3% rule in a lot of things in life. I think 97% of people are going to do what I do in supporting their partner through cancer. The 3% who walk away, shame on them."

There were many differences in this hospital stay compared to their first trip down to Tijuana for treatment, mostly attributed to the new program beginning at this hospital and this hospital being quite a bit larger. However, Dionne's immediate caregivers were equally excellent, her treatments went well and she and Graham both made the best of their new environment.

Dionne had brought some Christmas decorations from home and she put them up one evening, surprising the staff the next morning when they came into her room. One young staff person said she'd never seen a patient decorate a hospital room before. "When she left, we knew the word was spreading because other people were just coming down to check out the room. We'd never seen some of those people before and they were pretending they were doing something but they were really just checking out our room," laughs Dionne.

"Even the doctors asked where we got all the stuff. I told them I brought it all from home. 'We have themes and people are waiting for us to pull them off even when we're in Mexico. We've gotta come together and do this and a Christmas theme is perfect.' It was just so cute." Hospital staff cheerfully joined Dionne in the theme, wearing the reindeer antlers and posing for photos, of course. When it was time to come home, Dionne left some of the bigger decorations at the nurses' station. "It was so nice to come out the next morning and see they had decorated the whole area with our decorations."

Dionne's regimen was not as intense this time, partly because she was already taking some of the supplements that boosted her immune system, so she and Graham sometimes went out in the evenings for supper – within the guidelines – to a movie or to visit chef Mariana Brito and her family as well as some of the other friends they'd made during their first trip. The nurses couldn't believe their eyes when Dionne and Graham sauntered out for their evening adventures. "I'm sure the nurses were wondering, 'Is this girl really sick? What's up with her and her husband going out every other night and visiting and hanging out? One night, we came home at 12:30 because we had gone to a movie with Mariana and her friend," said Dionne, who happily woke up early the next morning to undergo more tests and treatments.

Graham and Dionne had separate hospital beds in their room. "They're quite far apart because, during the day especially, we had to leave room for the nurses and everybody to have access," says Graham. "Like I always say, I didn't get married to sleep alone, so at night, I would try and put my bed as close to Dionne's as I could – but the way the extension cord was for power, all I could manage was to get the toe of my bed swung over and it would touch her bed. Our friend Vera said she popped in, saw our beds touching and just melted. She said it was so cute. But that's the way we are, right? It was the best I could do to be close to my wife."

Midway through her dendritic cell and hyperthermic treatments in Mexico, Dionne was in good spirits. On December 2, she posted an uplifting comment on her Facebook page: "Take a bite out of life and enjoy every deep and delicious morsel."

The next day, update readers could not believe that they were witnessing update #50. "Well, look at that – #50! For those of you who have been with us from Day One, that's almost a year of weekly updates that you've been subjected to. In fact next week, on Thursday, December 9, it will have been exactly one year since Dionne was diagnosed with Stage IV cancer of both of her lungs, liver, rib, pelvic bone and spine. To see her today as vibrant and beautiful, pain and disability free is remarkable and truly miraculous! (in my humble opinion) I'm also happy to report that Dionne is excelling standard medical protocols they had designed for her and so our hopes remain high for successful results from this leading-edge treatment."

On December 9, 2010 exactly one year after her Stage IV diagnosis, Dionne was in a hospital bed in Tijuana about to undergo her third dendritic cell injection. Graham reported that it definitely was not a pain-free day for Dionne. "This was Dionne's third dendritic injection. They had already done one in each of her arms and hoped that with the leg injection, it wouldn't be as painful. At first, it appeared that the strategy would be effective. However, about five minutes after the injection, we almost had to peel poor D off the ceiling! Fortunately, the doctor was quick with a pain medication injection and she rested the entire day thereafter. There is one more treatment to endure this Friday. The green thing in D's hand is a stress ball that I MacGyver-ed out of surgical latex gloves, tape and air. D loved it ... Patents are pending."

Looking past her pain, Dionne celebrated that night by posting a Facebook message: "On December 9, 2009 I was once again diagnosed with cancer. This time, it was Stage IV liver cancer, lung cancer and bone cancer. Today, I celebrate one year as 'Warner Warrior D' in the fight against this disease and to give 'HOPE' to others. I cannot see or hear the fat lady singing so – Watch out, cancer! I am here to kick your ass!!!!"

One friend responded that Dionne's encouragement "really helped us with my dad and his cancer. Keep up the great work. We love you!!!" Another said, "You are just simply amazing!!! You give so much hope and inspiration to anyone who has had the pleasure of meeting you. Keep up the fight."

Dionne replied to all her angels: "If you guys can 'BELIEVE' in me and miracles, that is all I need to continue to 'FIGHT.' It is the continued love, support and strength that you send me that fills my heart and soul to 'BELIEVE' in myself. Thank you. Now, someone make this girl a vodka paralyzer. Lol. Cheers, Angels!"

On December 10, Dionne's Facebook status said it all: "To win the battle, you must win the war. This girl is locked and loaded!!!"

A few days later, Dionne and Graham returned to Regina and the Warner Warrior looked like she'd just returned from a marvellous sunny vacation. She had rosy cheeks, colour to her skin and no apparent loss of weight. "I went through a lot of pain but I managed to get through it … so no pain, no gain, right? They said my body is reacting very well to the dendritic cell treatments, but they would know more when I do a CT scan eight weeks from my last treatment to see if there are any changes."

Before heading to Provo for New Year's Eve on the beach to enjoy the sand between her toes and watch fireworks with friends, Dionne insisted on delaying their departure so they could attend the annual Christmas ball hosted by Graham's men's business association. "I wanted to go to this party, get dressed up and feel good. I may be sick but it's one of the things I look forward to," she said.

Her comments were relayed by Graham to the club's sergeant at arms, who promptly told the other members, "Gentlemen, that gives you no excuse not to be here with your wives."

Once again, Dionne was being quoted as a role model, "which is kind of cool," she admits with a smile.

That evening, Dionne wore a Diana Ross-styled wig and a retro-styled shift dress that bore sequins in every colour of the rainbow, says Jayne Clendening. "The shift accentuated her slim physique and platform shoes completed her look as the quintessential Queen of Disco. One would never know by looking at her that she had been undergoing continuous treatment for the past year. She was radiant."

At one point during the night, Clendening was on the dance floor with Dionne and another dear friend who had recently had the breast cancer experience. "We had come together on the dance floor at the end of one song when the band struck up an old Bee Gees classic. "So there we were, the three of us, shaking our booty, being in the moment, smiling and laughing, surviving and thriving, singing and dancing to '*Staying Alive*.' Precious moments," adds Clendening.

Christmas 2010 came and went for most people. For Dionne Warner, it was a cause for celebration – again. "Yahoo! I've seen another Christmas! Woo hoo! I've seen another new year. I'm celebrating and still having fun!"

When they reached Provo, she started 2011 with a happy heart and a relaxed spirit. "I love the island and Grace Bay Beach. There is a serenity and tranquility when we are there. That's where I feel most at peace and free."

Epilogue

*"Life is a leap of faith!!! Take it!! You will be amazed
where it can take you." – **Dionne and Graham***

For Dionne and Graham, the beginning of 2011 was spent relaxing, travelling and enjoying life. For update readers, a photo of Dionne posing with a gigantic glass of rum punch in front of the Conch Shack on Provo in January was almost as entertaining as seeing her and Graham standing side by side in February, pretending to run off the edge of the Grand Canyon in a monumental 'leap of faith.'

A CT scan done in early February 2011 showed Dionne's condition as stable and a bone scan conducted a month later showed the same status – 'stable.' No better word could have been uttered, except perhaps for 'gone.'

The Canadian government surprisingly withdrew its coverage of Avastin in December 2010 because the side-effects of kidney and liver damage were proving more harmful than the benefits for the majority of patients who were on the medication. This did not affect Dionne's chemotherapy program, though, because she was already on the drug and was doing well with it, so Dr. Salim was able to keep her on the medication. Dionne and Graham were convinced that her use of supplements from the naturopath had eliminated those side-effect issues for her.

They went to see Darwin Stoeber again in February and were pleased to hear him say that Dionne's blood sample had almost no free radicals – molecules responsible for aging and tissue damage. "He informed us that most cancer patients have a lot of free radicals in their blood and Dionne had almost none," Graham told update readers. "This sounded very encouraging to us indeed!"

On February 22, Dionne was scheduled to undergo her first chemo treatment of the new year, and she was determined to make a statement along the way. Dionne and Graham defiantly showed up at the Allan Blair Cancer Centre wearing army boots, blue jeans and T-shirts that were

emblazoned with, 'F____ CANCER.' Clinic staff and passersby nodded
in agreement when they saw the shirts' bold message and two clinic staff
members even made their own signs and pinned them to the front of their
shirts to support Dionne and give all of that day's patients a little dose of
fighting spirit.

On March 8, Dionne and Graham astounded and delighted everyone
who was anywhere near the Pasqua Hospital that day when they paraded
in for their Disco Days theme. Wearing a metallic silver bell-bottomed
pantsuit, disco-ball earrings and a large black wig that was described by
one nurse as 'Princess Leia gone bad,' Dionne commanded attention even
before she opened her mouth. Graham, meanwhile, was decked out in a
multi-coloured shiny shirt, a long black mullet wig, a moustache that had
a mind of its own, and sunglasses to finish his 'groovin'-Harlequin-
Romance' look.

As they bopped into the cancer centre's main waiting area to the
sound of *Disco Inferno*, all heads turned and every face lit up with a
smile. A small group of people standing near the chemo waiting area
watched Dionne dance around in her typical enthusiastic style.

A female patient commented, "I don't think I'm on the right chemo.
I want what she's on!"

This garnered more laughs throughout the group and a comment was
made that, "I don't think anybody is on what Dionne is on."

Another female patient replied, "Imagine if we all were."

At times, it seems like Dionne Warner is an elixir for cancer patients
and for anyone who is having a bad day, or just an ordinary day. Her
constantly upbeat, positive attitude makes everyone she meets want to
spend more and more time with her. A little dose of Dionne every day can
help almost anyone feel better.

Mandy Sauer, a good friend of Dionne's, comments that Dionne
needs the cancer centre almost as much as its patients and staff need her.
"Her chemo treatment is her medicine to keep her going," suggests Sauer.
"Being an asthmatic person, if I can't have my inhalers or my medication,
I don't feel as well." Dionne strives to keep her blood count up so she can
keep going for treatment, keep making others smile, and keep taking one
more step forward. If Dionne misses a chemo treatment because of low
blood count, everyone's health suffers a bit.

During a summer 2010 houseboat trip in British Columbia's
Shuswaps with the Warners and Crystal Kalyniuk's family, Sauer woke
early one morning to find Graham driving the houseboat and Dionne
sitting in a lawn chair, alone on the top deck. "She was wearing her

sweater, her toque and slippers and she was wrapped in a blanket ...
looking quietly out on the mountains and the water. She looked so
peaceful. I thought to myself, 'She's reflecting, unwinding, relaxing.'
Dionne was sitting there all bundled up, just looking. I wished I'd had a
camera to capture that moment ... because it was so pretty. She was never
angry with cancer. She's at peace with it and she takes it as the day
comes."

Sauer has often asked Dionne to consider slowing down. "Don't you
want to rest and take care of yourself?"

Dionne's response at first surprised her. Then it made sense.

"I don't know if I'm going to be here next year. I'm doing it up
today!"

So Sauer, who is 14 years younger than Dionne, agreed with her
friend, and then tried to keep up.

"That's where I see a difference between Dionne and my other
girlfriend who has cancer. My girlfriend won't travel, she won't do
anything. She's more worried about being sick than about living life.
There are very few people who have Dionne's kind of outlook on cancer
– who are positive, upbeat and know they can beat it. A lot of people have
heartbreak with cancer – it's always a negative ending – where Dionne's
had so many positive times in her journey with this cancer. Hers is a great
story to get the word out there, to give other people the inspiration and the
hope to not sit there with the 'what ifs.' D won't live with the 'what ifs.'
She just lives her life day to day and lives like she isn't even sick."

Dionne has talked with Sauer and a few other close friends about her
own death and what she wants to happen at her funeral. If she is
hospitalized first, she wants people to think it through before they come
to visit her. "She told me, 'I don't want my friends to see me when I'm
gasping for my last breath. It's great if they do come, but I don't want
them to remember me that way.'

"I know so many people who, like my other girlfriend, when they
were diagnosed with cancer, their friends left them," says Sauer. "The day
my other girlfriend dies, those people will be there with so much regret.
What I can heartily say with D is I will never have any regrets."

It is an attitude and a behaviour that Dionne has fostered in all of her
close relationships. 'Live life to the fullest. No regrets.'

On March 27, 2010 Dionne addressed the crowd at the *Look Good ...*
Feel Better Fashion Show and auction charity event for women going

through cancer battles. The *Look Good ... Feel Better* program of the cosmetic, toiletry and fragrance association helped Dionne feel better about herself in 1998 after she went through her breast cancer and two brain cancer surgeries. It was now her turn to give back.

She told the audience about her cancer history and how they can help themselves to feel better by simply putting on a little makeup but mostly by keeping a positive upbeat attitude and keeping hope alive. Her speech took the 500 women and seven men in the room on an emotional journey from laughter to tears to awe within minutes. She was rewarded for her heartfelt message with an emotional standing ovation. It was a treatment that Dionne was starting to see more and more as she shared her story and her spirit of hope.

In April 2011, the Canadian Cancer Society Saskatchewan Division nominated Dionne for the *International Heroes of Hope* award. This was the first time that the American Cancer Society International Relay For Life (IRFL) Heroes of Hope Program would be opened up to Canadian nominees, and the local Cancer Society office was delighted to immediately offer Dionne's name as a worthy recipient.

The award "profiles cancer survivors whose work exemplifies the mission of their cancer organization. The Heroes of Hope program's definition of a survivor is someone who has been told "you have cancer." Heroes of Hope exhibit exemplary behaviour and inspire hope, courage and determination in the fight to eliminate cancer. These cancer survivors display a resilient attitude and inspire others to choose a proactive and positive stance in survivorship."

That is Dionne Warner in a nutshell.

Waking up every morning and greeting each new day is a moment of celebration for Dionne Warner. Her calendar is filling up with speaking engagements, volunteer opportunities, and of course, cancer tests and treatments. At the top of her agenda, though, is the time she takes to appreciate the world around her. She looks out her window every morning and sees the day ahead as a gift. She then might call, e-mail, or text a family member or friend before getting on with her day.

She is not a practising Catholic, but she believes in the power of prayer – any time and anywhere. "I believe God is everywhere and I don't need to be in a church to talk to God. I'm not just praying for myself, I have other people I know who are suffering as well. I always have prayers for anybody I know and I'm always wishing that nobody goes through anything that's horrible. I pray whenever I get the urge and wherever I may be standing. I said a prayer out at the Grand Canyon. I was counting my blessings as well as saying prayers – not just for me but for those I love and care about."

Dionne looks forward to the possibilities of each new day. "I think I'm going to get more into my cancer awareness items," she said recently. "I was making bracelets; I was doing all sorts of things, raising funds for cancer research. I enjoyed that. I also enjoy photography and being at that right place at that right moment to capture something incredible. Taking pictures shows stories and saves memories. That's important."

No one knows what the next day, week, month or year will bring for Dionne Warner and her husband Graham. Stage IV cancer almost never goes away. For now, the goal is to prolong her survival and enjoy the life she and Graham have together during each and every moment they can share.

"I live in a reality world," Dionne has said repeatedly. "Everyone I meet who's a survivor inspires me. I learn something from every person I've met and I've had many people tell me I have a story that needs to be shared. I am happy to do that, to give other patients hope to hang in there, to fight and to not give up.

"Through my journey, people have looked at me and said, 'I wouldn't even know that you've been sick.' That's fine by me," laughs Dionne. "I want to show that there is life during cancer as well as life after cancer. I'm going to walk into that treatment centre and I'm going to have fun with it. If it inspires and touches others, I've done all that I can do."

What Cancer Cannot Do

Cancer is so limited ...
It cannot cripple love
It cannot shatter hope
It cannot silence courage
It cannot destroy confidence
It cannot erode faith
It cannot kill friendship
It cannot destroy peace
It cannot suppress memories
It cannot erode the spirit
It cannot steal eternal life
It cannot conquer the soul.

Author: Unknown

For more information on support items for cancer or the colours of cancer, please visit www.rainbowofhopecanada.ca

Recipes

Courtesy of Chef Mariana Brito

Pear & pumpkin, not pumpkin soup

1 tablespoon coconut oil
½ white onion, sliced
2 red peppers, seeded and sliced
2 pears, peeled and sliced
1 tablespoon cinnamon
3 cups vegetable stock or water
Salt and pepper to taste
In a large pot over medium heat, sauté onion in coconut oil for two minutes. Add peppers, sauté for two more minutes. Add sliced pear and cook for another two minutes or until soft. Add cinnamon and stir. Pour in water or stock; bring to a boil and let cook for 10 minutes in low heat.

In food processor or blender, puree your soup until smooth. Season and enjoy. Serves four.

Quinoa Apple (hot side)

1 teaspoon coconut oil
1 cup quinoa
½ cup onion, diced
1 green apple, peeled and diced
2 cups water or vegetable stock
Rinse quinoa with cold running water. Heat coconut oil in a frying pan over medium-high heat. Add onion. Cook, stirring often, for four minutes or until soft. Add quinoa and vegetable stock and cook until simmering. Season to taste. Once it boils, lower the heat and cook for around 12 minutes. Add the apples and cook for three more minutes. Serves four.

Lemon Garlic Tilapia

4 tilapia fillets
Olive oil, to marinate
Fresh parsley
Zest of 1 lemon (reserve the juice)
4 garlic cloves, sliced
Salt and pepper to taste
Coconut oil

To thaw fish fully, place frozen fillets in a plastic bag and thaw overnight in refrigerator or soak the bag in cold water for about two hours. Mix marinade ingredients except for the lemon juice. Pour marinade over thawed fish and let sit in refrigerator for one hour.

Heat frying pan on high heat for at least three minutes. Add coconut oil to pan and slide in fish fillets. Do not turn the fish until after three minutes, to let the first side cook two-thirds of the way through the fillet. A crust will form and the fillet will release easily when you flip it. Flip the fish once to finish cooking.

What I Have Learned from Dionne and/or Graham

Messages from Some Members of her Angel Network

Atelys Adrian, Providenciales, Turks and Caicos Islands: God allowed them to be together to light up the lives of regular people like me, teaching us that when you have love and strength, you can do just like D & G. I always say to my aunt who is fighting cancer right now, if you dare to fight with all you have and love life, you can make cancer look like it's just a headache. One of the things that I learned from both of them is that positive attitude is everything. We will always have battles in many aspects of life, but only the right attitude determines if we win or lose. D taught me that when we are facing the worst in our lives, it is possible to be happy and enjoy life at the same time. Cancer cannot do much when you are determined to live with a heart full of love and joy for life.

Natalie Akoon, Toronto, Ontario: Live life. Enjoy life. Fight if you have it in you. Giving up is not an option.

Cindy Alston, Providenciales, Turks and Caicos Islands: Whenever D has visitors to the island, she greets them at the airport with a sign welcoming them. Her condo is also decked out to make their arrival feel very special as well, and they leave with a little something special. This is something I learned from D. I now try to make friends and family feel more than welcome and give a little parting gift like a picture frame, etc. That girl can shop but even when I am shopping with her, she comes back with some special 'treat' for me – a bracelet, wing earrings, a small clutch – just something to let you know that she is always thinking of you. She is ever so generous and thoughtful. D makes everyone around her feel special.

David Ballantine, Guelph, Ontario: She's always been a very strong-willed, determined person. 'I'm not going to quit, I'm going to fight.'

She'll use a lot of energy to fight back when she feels something is unjust. That's how she deals with the cancer, too. It isn't right and she's going to fight it. I've learned it's important to find the desire and strength to fight on when others, including the medical profession, are telling you there's not really anything that can be done now. You should never give up is key. You always need to seek a second if not a third opinion and go with what you believe. Her strong belief in the power of love and support of family and friends is something that has certainly carried her through the last 15 years, when a lot of people would not have made it.

Peter Ballantine, Guelph, Ontario: I've learned the amazing strength that can come from an unwillingness to concede. That's always been a part of Dionne's nature. She's always been someone to move forward. A lot of people would hear the big 'C' word and start counting the days until moving on to their next life. Not her. 'I'm not going. What do I have to do to make sure I stick around?' Never say die.

It takes someone with a Graham personality to have a successful relationship with a Dionne personality. He's also got a very strong personality, very successful in his own respect. The two of them connected are just overpowering. The two of them pushing in the same direction is an immovable force. Accolades to him for being the huge support he's been to her. It's over and beyond what a lot of men would have done.

Una Ballantine, Guelph, Ontario: From Dionne, I've learned to keep persevering. She stays strong. She stays positive and it doesn't matter what she's going through, she remembers other people and what's going on in their lives. It's amazing because she has gone through so much and it could totally absorb her but she doesn't allow it to. She's involved with other people and she just continues to live in spite of what's going on, which I'm not sure I could do. She's so tenacious. She's always been very generous, very giving.

They both have that positive personality, that it can be done. Dionne often says about herself and Graham, 'We're both fighters.'

Lou Beltramini, Regina, Saskatchewan: I lost my wife to cancer in 2009. They have been the most supportive in helping me through that. They're very generous people. This reminds me of the saying that 'family doesn't have to be blood in your veins. It's the people who care about you, support you and love you.'

Mariana Brito, Tijuana, Mexico: From Dionne and Graham, I learned: we can't be perfect but we can try; we can't have everything but we are strong enough to believe; FAITH in capital letters; fairy tales do come true; love exists; we must believe in second chances. They changed my life forever and I will always be grateful. The people who surround D and G are truly angels. I know now that there's life through cancer. There's no excuse for giving up ... ever.

Allison Cann, Edmonton, Alberta: When I was diagnosed, I thought I was going to 'drown' in misery and fear from the unknown. Dionne showed me strength I never knew I had. I am a very proud person and I don't like to show others weakness. She has shown me that no one can go through these types of battles alone. I have learned it is okay to lean on others when I am feeling down or overwhelmed. I will forever be grateful for her love, friendship and support.

Shelley and Blair Case, Regina, Saskatchewan: Dionne is an amazing, passionate woman who loves every moment of life. She is a beacon of hope to so many people fighting the cancer battle. No matter what mountain she has to climb or the deep valley she is in, Dionne never gives up. And her co-pilot Graham has always been there by her side to support and encourage her through this long, difficult journey. What incredible role models they are to everyone dealing with cancer or not. A truly inspiring couple!

Heather Choquette, Regina, Saskatchewan: Dionne is an amazing courageous young woman. We should all aspire to be like her and hopefully when we face challenges, we can attack them in the same way.

Jayne Clendening, Regina, Saskatchewan: Facing the greatest of life's challenges, Dionne and Graham epitomize courage – having fear, but going forward anyways, and with smiles on their faces and joy in their hearts.

Yuri Collesso, Guelph, Ontario: Dionne is strong, confident, energetic, vibrant, infectious, addictive, rebellious, free-spirited, unbridled (impossible to bridle), fun to be around and always welcome at our house. Dionne has shown more courage and strength than is imaginable. I have learned from Dionne that the impossible is possible. Mind over body really does work.

From Graham, I have learned to face adversity head on. True love is out there and soulmates do exist. You just have to be lucky enough to find them as Dionne and Graham did.

Nadine Desrosiers, Regina, Saskatchewan: Dionne is always determined to help make everyone happy. I look up to her as a role model. She is so caring and understanding. She makes a special connection with each person in her life, making them feel special. She makes you feel loved and important and she has not changed, no matter what has happened in her life or how many friends she had gained. One of the most important gifts that I received from D is that I believe in hope now more than ever. 'Live, love and laugh lots!'

Karen Drysdale, Regina, Saskatchewan: Dionne has made me a true believer in positive energy and positive thinking and how far it can go for healing. I've taken a lot of inspiration from her in that and I've tried to apply it in my own life. If there are negative people around, I will try and keep my distance. If I have to stand in line for five minutes, I stop and think, 'Is it worth getting upset over?'

Azure English, Regina, Saskatchewan: Dionne and Graham have the ability to inspire others with their kindness and enthusiasm. They are generators of imagination and creativity and always make an effort to make life joyful and exciting. Dionne's dynamic character challenges and encourages everyone she meets to overcome all of life's adversities. Dionne also channels her passion, good humour, optimism and energy by diligently supporting those who are experiencing hardships. I have learned from Dionne and Graham that people can depend upon them at all times for support, encouragement and love. I feel that their love for each other is an excellent example of a marriage that is based on acceptance, forgiveness, passion and truth, and it will last forever.

Marla Fehr-Sinclair, Regina, Saskatchewan: I have learned from Dionne: 1. Always remain positive until you are given a reason not to. 2. Others can benefit from your story and it helps to share your experience if you are able. 3. Laugh! Laugh! Laugh! 4. A Sense of humour can cure most things. 5. We are not invincible!

Fred Foord, Edmonton, Alberta: From Dionne – Never, never say die; dig down deep; reach out to others; keep your game face on. Respect others, smile, laugh, stare adversity in the face and kick it in the 'sesame seeds.'

Graham has shown that he truly believes that 'You never leave your wingman.' He has proven to me that these are not just words but who he is and who D is. The strength that they as a team have shown and continue to show should be a life lesson for all of us – stick together through thick and thin and good things *will* happen.

Leslie Foss, Providenciales, Turks and Caicos Islands: Life does not always give us what we want but we have to do the best we can with what we've been given and fight like hell! Knowing both D and G has made me try to be a better, more kind and thoughtful person. They make you realize how unthoughtful the world can be sometimes.

Kelly Greenwood, Regina, Saskatchewan: From Dionne, I have learned about courage and grace. Also, you must NEVER give up. I have learned that heaven has a disco ball – it's just not a very big one!! And you must love the life you live and live the life you love.

I've learned from Graham that when a pilot says he'll never leave his wingman, he really means it. Graham could have run for the hills before they were even married but he didn't – even though one doctor recommended he do just that. He has taken the 'for better or worse' part of his vows quite literally. He loves Dionne and they have had some spectacular times together but he hasn't faltered through the not-so-great times. For that, he will have my respect and admiration always. Not all men are created equal and he is proof of this.

Petra Janssen, Regina, Saskatchewan: Graham and Dionne are the most inspirational people I have ever met. The love, support and dedication they share with each other has taught me that love can conquer all. Dionne's determination along with Graham's support to not let anything defeat them makes my life challenges look small. They have taught me: to live each day to the fullest, to not sweat the small stuff, and to genuinely smile and care for the next person … because life is wonderful; to cherish the moments we have with family and friends and for me to personally make time to enjoy life; to always remember life is for living; to be strong and determined to not let anything or anyone get you down. Dionne conquers all with a smile and always seems to find the good in everything and everyone. For that, I look up to her and strive to be more like her.

I knew Graham even before he married Dionne. Graham truly was sent to be beside Dionne during all this. He embraces every new challenge with an attitude that defeats the challenge before he even attempts it. He stands by, supports, loves and pushes Dionne to overcome, laugh and love her way through it. I will always love, admire, respect and strive to be a better person because of them.

Crystal Kalyniuk, Regina, Saskatchewan: Dionne lives all the motivation phrases and inspiring quotes that we are inundated with daily ... most of us ignore them or perhaps take them to heart for a moment or a day and then easily forget them while we get wrapped up in the daily grind, but D, she *lives* them. From D, we should learn to step back and truly look at our lives and appreciate them, appreciate who is in them & appreciate the challenges we are faced with, as it is what helps us grow ... this should be done daily and should be enjoyed. From D, we should learn to express our love for one another frequently and vocally – with friends, with family, with our partners. From D, we should learn to find joy in everything – who else can make weekly chemo appointments uplifting? Only D. From D, we should learn to live better lives and be better humans to ourselves and those in our lives. This is what she is teaching me ... but I'm a slow learner, so she's patient. Another thing – experiencing a quarter of what D has been through would crumble most of us, and yet she's succeeded through it all with dignity, grace, energy, love and a ton of laughter! I am in constant awe of her. She teaches patience.

From Graham, I've learned that determination goes a long, long way. That true love does exist and it needs to be nurtured and cherished.

Sylvia Kavanagh, Toronto, Ontario: Never give up; stay positive; sacrifice is part of survival; take a chance; enjoy life and never pay retail.

Donna Kish, Regina, Saskatchewan: Dionne is just an amazing person. She's contagious. Her laugh echoes throughout the clinic. It's unfortunate that we don't have more people like that in the world. She gets her energy from friends and family and I love spending time with her. She's taught me to live in the moment. She loves to say something just to see a person's reaction, such as when we went shopping so she could show off her bald head and watch for reactions. That's just her living her life. What she does as a cancer centre volunteer impacts people in smaller communities and what they do. Those are untold stories outside of Regina and that is a great gift.

Judith Kobin, Portland, Oregon: I have always admired her courage and the way she has coped with her cancer. Graham is so caring and compassionate. This is a marriage made in heaven. It just breaks my heart that she has had to go through so much. In spite of it all, she is still fighting and has the attitude that I hope I would have if I was in that situation.

Yvonne Loustel, Carlyle, Saskatchewan: I have learned from Dionne that a positive attitude can be the best medicine when fighting cancer. I have learned to live each day to its fullest. Stress is toxic so we need to remember not to sweat the small stuff. Remember to live, love, laugh.

Kim Maki, Whitewood, Saskatchewan: From Dionne, I've learned that nothing should ever be able to get you down. Life is what you make of it. Be as strong as you can for as long as you can. Take every day as it comes.

Graham is an amazing man for being by Dionne through all of this, where a lot of people would have said, 'I can't handle this.' He's amazing for supporting her the way he does in everything she wants to do and in his love for life and his giving attitude. Graham is a very down-to-earth person who wants to make friends and be friends. He's just a great guy.

Jessica Martorana, Regina, Saskatchewan: Both of them are so young at heart and full of life, so loving and welcoming to all. Dionne is always so upbeat and so positive and she's such an inspiration. If this had happened to somebody else, it would be over. Dionne is just like, "Yeah, let's go up to bat again and just win this!" She can take something so negative and make something good of it.

Graham is the most amazing, supportive husband. The lengths he'll go to ... he's stuck by her side and plays off her optimism. They're just one of the cutest couples I've ever met. He's just so positive and makes the best of the worst situation.

Michael Melville, Regina, Saskatchewan: Dionne has taught me many life lessons. She gives a whole new perspective to things you may have thought you knew – like to be *positive*. To hear someone battling cancer to save her life and have her say, 'Why not me?' rather than 'Why me?' speaks volumes about staying positive. Dionne lives by example. Each day is a gift to her and a gift not worth wasting. Dionne has been such a huge influence in my life. I appreciate, respect and admire her. I know I am not the only one out there who has been blessed by this Earth Angel. She is a beautiful soul and a cherished friend.

Roger Pettigrew, Moose Jaw, Saskatchewan: Graham is all about commitment. In business, it's about the customers. When he stood on the altar and said, 'I do,' that's what he meant. In sickness and health. His dad was that way, too. In Dionne's life, every single day is a day worth living. If today was your last day, it is a gift, not a given. It's about being honest with yourself, being honest with your partner. I get strength from Graham. We've gotta do whatever we've gotta do. He is absolutely unwavering. He will never stop in trying to find a cure for Dionne. I admire that.

Tricia Pettigrew, Moose Jaw, Saskatchewan: I have learned that any pain or illness I have is nothing compared to what that poor girl has endured. We can all learn to not sweat the small stuff and that there is always someone out there who has more serious stuff in life to deal with than some of the minuscule things we think are catastrophic. Dionne is simply the strongest woman I have ever known. Her passion for life is insurmountable.

From Graham, I have learned to support my spouse in the good times and the bad. We can all learn to 'lighten up' a bit and not take things too seriously.

Cindy Potetz, Lajord, Saskatchewan: My husband Cliff and I met Dionne in 2004 in the cancer clinic waiting room before I went in for my first of 18 months of chemo treatment for breast cancer. Dionne was a volunteer and sat down beside us and was so kind. She helped us relax just by talking with us. I have learned that Dionne truly is an Earth Angel. She is a survivor and a real trooper and lives life to the fullest. I have learned you need to have the right attitude. She is a true blessing and an inspiration to all who meet her.

Graham is a wonderful, caring and funny person – all the right things that Dionne needs right now.

Keisha Rajnath, Providenciales, Turks and Caicos Islands: Dionne has shown me how strong a person can really be and how much power we have that nothing, not even the worst of sickness, can keep us down. She is a huge inspiration to me and I never knew how important living and enjoying life could be. I truly admire her spirit. She has this way of making the grumpy or sad person happy and bringing their laughter back to life. She always has something very knowledgeable and positive to say to me. She is more than who we think she is.

Graham shows me how much and how far we can and will go for love in caring for someone as much as he does for D. He is this very happy person who never shows a bad face to anyone and would always be willing to help in whatever way he can. Their love and relationship is amazing to me. I absolutely adore them and what they have and share with each other. They are made for each other, I've not seen or met a couple like them, ever! God truly made those two for each other and He did an awesome job!

Linda Rattray, Regina, Saskatchewan: Dionne's taught me to live life to the fullest. Her energy just astounds me. She gets more done in a day now than I ever have in my life. When I was getting treatments for breast cancer, she brought me a packaged gift and a really nice card. I barely knew her and she made me feel so special. When we went to Minneapolis one time, she had just completed chemo. We waited a couple hours for her girlfriend to finish work, then we drove all the way to Minot, got there at 10 or 11 p.m. and she wanted to go to Wal-Mart. Graham wisely put the kibosh on that, so we didn't go. She amazes me in so many ways. I'm really proud to call her a friend. She's such a dynamic person.

Kim Robulack-Mendes, Oakville, Ontario: Dionne has taught me that I can face every challenge that comes my way. She inspires me to face challenges. She never backs away from anything. Everything is possible in her mind. Every time I talk to her or read one of Graham's kind e-mails, I have a smile in my heart. I'm proud to call Dionne and Graham my friends. I'm a very lucky lady! Every year, Dionne remembers and acknowledges my wedding anniversary. It was almost 14 years ago. I barely remember it. She's just very generous with her time and her thoughts. We all get caught up in our own lives. We get ticked off, we forget the milk or we're just too busy. D is never like that. She always makes time for people.

Mandy Sauer, Regina, Saskatchewan: I found a different side of myself through Dionne. I'm a more open person, a more loving person. She hugs every time she sees you. I never used to be a hugger. She's brought a different part of me out with her positive energy, her inspiration, her care, her love for her friends and family. And she's fun. I've learned more from both of them because they're so similar but they're so different. It's the weirdest thing, how they feed off of each other. From both of them, I have a different outlook on life, a different understanding. I basically slowed down. I'm not worried anymore about what people think of me or how they might judge me – because D doesn't worry, G doesn't worry. They do their thing. From them, I feel the support, the love, the friendship.

Diane Stein, Guelph, Ontario: We were very sad to see her move far away but more than that we were so happy she had found her knight in shining amour. Recently, we all went out dancing in Toronto. Dionne was glorious is a funky outfit and proudly displayed her bald head with large hoop earrings. She had jaw-dropping reactions! I am sure everyone thought she was a movie star or singer. She was stopped more than once and told how gorgeous she looked. And she danced and danced in the middle of the crowded dance floor … what an amazing spirit!! She has an incredible lust for life and fun. We could all use more of that.

Sean Westerman, Regina, Saskatchewan: I've learned about loyalty and determination. Graham just doesn't give up. He has done some amazingly stupid things that the average human being would not even attempt, and he just keeps plugging away until he completes the job. It doesn't matter if it takes days, weeks, months or even years. If he ever does give up on something, I will know that there was just no humanly way possible for it to get done. His loyalty and commitment to his marriage is fierce. I have learned from him and watched and admired this and have used this in my own marriage. No matter what happens, I don't give up. When the shit hits the fan, put a bag on and wait till it drops. Then wipe yourself off and start again. That is how he lives his life. From Dionne and Graham, I have learned that it could always be worse, so never give up.

Dawn Williams, Mississauga, Ontario: Dionne … she's a trip! She has taught me to love life and to never take anything for granted. She has taught me how to laugh … how to have fun, and how important it is to stay positive. My mom was diagnosed with lung cancer and Dionne has helped us all to cope with this terrible disease. Graham spoils her so much … but she really deserves every bit of it!!

Author Meets Angel

A few years ago, our oldest daughter Lisa began volunteering with the Relay For Life Regina committee. Their annual event celebrates cancer survivors, remembers those lost to the disease, and raises funds to fight back and bring an end to cancer. Lisa often talked about the amazing, inspiring people she met through Relay – survivors and their supporters who have touching stories of overcoming and/or living their lives through cancer.

In April 2010, Lisa told me the committee was planning to write a short biography on Dionne Warner, a seven-time cancer survivor who has an incredible zest for life and walks into her chemo treatments each week dressed in costume. Being a journalist and author, I told Lisa, "I could write that" – but nothing ever came of it.

At the beginning of June 2010, Lisa was gearing up to go to Relay and she was excited that Dionne Warner would be there again to speak and pump up the crowd before the Survivors' Victory Lap that launches Relay. The more Lisa told me about Dionne and her husband Graham – their humour, courage and determination, their themes and updates – the more I was intrigued. Finally, I said, "This woman's a book." I had to go out of town on Relay weekend, so I gave Lisa my business card to hand to Dionne with the message that I would like to talk with her about writing a book about her.

But the story doesn't end there.

Just before Dionne left Relay that Friday night, Lisa begged Relay's Carla Redler to introduce her to Dionne so that Lisa could hand Dionne my card. I am told that when Dionne heard, "My mother wants to write a book about you," Dionne was overcome with emotion and almost fainted in gratitude. The following Tuesday evening, Dionne phoned me and apologized for taking so long to get back to me. I burst out laughing. Four days is hardly a long time in this business.

Dionne was very excited. I quickly learned that she talks fast and is full of energy. I could hear the enthusiasm in her voice with every word she spoke. We arranged to meet at their home the following Monday, on June 21, 2010 to discuss this concept of a book. When I arrived there, I was greeted by Dionne and Graham with wide smiles in a welcome befitting an old friend. I assumed that we would just chat a bit and get to know each other, then revisit this idea over the coming weeks. I was wrong. Within five minutes of my arrival, I felt an open and honest friendship develop that I expect will never disappear. They poured out parts of their story to me, and I was soon overwhelmed by it all.

Due to her Stage IV cancer diagnosis, I felt the need to ask Dionne a tough question. "What happens if you die in the middle of this process?"

She looked me in the eye and said, "I live in a reality world." I actually don't remember what she said next – I was still in shock from her blunt acknowledgement of her illness. Later, I discovered that she had said other people have suggested to her that her story be shared. It has inspired them and would certainly do that for others. A book telling her story would continue her goal of raising cancer awareness, giving people hope and encouraging everyone to live their lives to the fullest – with or without cancer.

After a slight pause in the conversation, Graham said, "If she dies, you'll have to finish this on your own, because I'm climbing in the coffin with her." We all smiled at this comment, but we knew the truth behind his statement.

Graham told me about his parents' reactions to his announcement in 2000 that he was marrying Dionne. When Graham's mother asked, 'What if Dionne gets cancer?' his father asked, 'What if Graham gets cancer?'

Good point. Most of us do not think about the 'C' word in that way.

I spent three hours with Dionne and Graham that first afternoon. On my way out the door, Dionne reached out and gave me a hug instead of a handshake because, she told me, "You are going to be part of our Angel Network." I was touched.

On my drive home, I felt sad that someone so beautiful in spirit should have to go through this pain.

We began to meet regularly and uncover their stories. I interviewed friends and family and laughed like I never thought could happen in a chemo treatment room. It is impossible to leave the Allan Blair Cancer Centre without a smile on your face once you've talked to Dionne and Graham. They have a way of bringing light to even the darkest moments.

For one interview appointment with them, I headed to their house feeling tired and allergy-inflamed. "Dionne will make you feel better," said my husband Al. "She'll pick you up." He was right, of course. With her shaved head and dangly purple earrings, beautiful purple top against her tanned skin, her bright shiny eyes, heart-warming smile, infectious laugh, and her enthusiastic greeting of "HELLO!" as if I was the most important person she had seen that day, how could I not feel better in her presence?

In October 2010, Graham and Dionne came to the book launch for *Running of the Buffalo*, one of our other DriverWorks Ink titles. I was busy welcoming guests, acting as emcee and basically running around as is normal for me at these events. Afterwards, Dionne said to me, "You know, this is the first time we've seen you speaking like this and I was saying to Graham, 'Remember the first time we met and she asked me what happens if I die? I should have asked her what happens if *she* dies!' "

I laughed so hard that I almost fell over. "I guess we're pretty much screwed if that happens, aren't we?" I said. "Well, I don't have any intention of doing that and neither do you, so I guess we just keep going."

Since that first afternoon when Dionne and Graham welcomed me into their lives and trusted me to tell their story, we have shared many laughs, many hugs and a few sombre moments – quickly followed by more laughs. Their unending desire to help others and to share of themselves is fascinating, motivating and inspiring. It has been a privilege and an honour to listen and learn from them, to sit and to dance with them, and to share their incredible story through this book.

A special thank you is in order to my family as they supported me through the creation of *Never Leave Your Wingman* and especially to our daughter Lisa Driver for introducing me to Dionne and Graham's wonderful story in the first place. Thank you to all of you who have given me your glimpse of this amazing couple, and thank you especially to Dionne and Graham for all that you have shown me with your zeal and courage, your love and your hope. May we remain friends forever.

Shortly after that first meeting in June 2010, Dionne lovingly bestowed a special title upon me. I will forever strive to live up to that name –

'Earth Angel Deana'

Acknowledgements from Dionne Warner

First, I would like to acknowledge Lisa Driver, a volunteer with the Relay For Life team who introduced me to her inquisitive mother, journalist and author Deana Driver. After that introduction, Deana first came to our home a year ago to see if there was enough of a story behind my seventh diagnosis of cancer to warrant a book.

A book? I had never ever considered a book!! This came as a total surprise to me and my husband. I honestly expected that once Deana got the facts she would politely inform us that there just wasn't enough there.

After 45 minutes, Deana informed me, "Oh yes, there's a book's worth here. Do you want to carry on?" I still expected her later on to say, "You know, I just don't know about this, maybe not."

Tentatively, we carried on and I am grateful for the tireless dedication and work Deana put into this book during the past year. She logged quite a few miles driving to our home every week and sometimes even twice a week, which is on the opposite side of our city from where she lives, along with many trips to the cancer clinic, Graham's dealership and my speaking events. She recorded hours and hours of stories that were blurted out as they simply came to mind from both our recollections as well as our friends and colleagues that she interviewed. It utterly amazed me that Deana was able to organize all those stories along with the mountain of facts that surround a medical topic like cancer into a chronological story that resulted in an accurate portrayal of our lives.

She sat with us numerous times in the chemo ward just to absorb the atmosphere and take in what words sometimes just cannot convey.

Deana and her husband Al have become a permanent part of our Earth Angels Network that I consider family. Early on in this relationship, it became clear that our husbands Al and Graham shared the identical sense of humour – which has caused me to take great pity on Deana forever more. I know she feels the same for me.

To our Angel Network of family and friends, you will never know how much strength your words of encouragement, love, support and prayers have given both Graham and I. We are where we are today thanks to your cheering us on through the toughest of times.

And through the best of times, we cherish the laughter-filled memories that we continue to create together.

Dr. Salim, your thinking and acting outside the box with my treatments is a tribute to your character and skill for which I also owe my life. You are not only my doctor, you are a true friend to Graham and I. Thank you for not giving in or giving up on me.

To Darwin Stoeber, doctor of natural medicine, Mexico's Dr. Perez and Dr. Garcia, and my dearest Vera – thank you for your patience in explaining everything so thoroughly. The compassionate care and visionary leading-edge medicine you practise have all helped contribute to my survival, no doubt. For this, Graham and I are very grateful.

And of course, I really want to acknowledge all the doctors, surgeons, nurses, technicians, pharmacists, administrators, volunteers and support staff at the Credit Valley Hospital, Princess Margaret Hospital, Royal University Hospital, Regina Pasqua Hospital and the Allan Blair Cancer Centre for doing more than just your job in making me feel safe and comfortable.

It really is important to Graham and I that others may find inspiration and hope from our story that:

Love does conquer all, Everyday is a gift, Never give up, and Always fight back.

Love,
Warner Warrior D

Acknowledgements
from Graham Warner

Yeah......what she said!

About the Author

Deana Driver is a journalist, author, editor and book publisher. She has been a freelance journalist for more than 25 years and has worked on 12 books during the past 10 years as an author, editor, layout designer, self-publisher partner and publisher or some combination of the above. *Never Leave Your Wingman* is her fourth book as an author. She lives in Regina, Saskatchewan and loves to laugh, mostly with, or at, her husband Al.

Graham, Dionne and author Deana Driver

239

Other Saskatchewan and Prairie stories available from DriverWorks Ink:

Letters To Jennifer by Sharon Gray
Maudie is a prima donna Siamese cat. Oliver is her brother, who doesn't get enough love because he lives with the prima donna. When their dear Auntie Jennifer becomes ill, they decide to cheer her up by writing her letters describing their everyday antics, with the help of their LIP (Live-In Person) – author Sharon Gray. You will soon find yourself laughing at and falling for these two precocious pussycats.
ISBN 978-0-9810394-7-3 **Humour $16.95**

This book is due for release September 2011.

Running of the Buffalo by Ron Petrie
Regina Leader-Post Humour Columnist
A hilarious collection of 70 columns written by Ron Petrie, humour columnist for the Regina Leader-Post. Knowing diddly doots about many things, Ron has spent the last 20 years poking fun at relationships, sex, sports, parenthood, aging and all things related to growing up in Saskatchewan. Ron Petrie's unique view of the world will make you giggle and guffaw, chortle and snort – out loud and often.
ISBN 978-0-9810394-5-9 **Humour $19.95**

The Little Coat: The Bob and Sue Elliott Story by Alan J. Buick
Sussie Cretier was only 10 when she met Bob Elliott, a Canadian soldier assigned to help protect her region of the Netherlands from the invading German army. To the Canadian soldiers, brave little Sussie became a glowing example of the innocence of youth and a beacon of hope for the future. On Christmas Day 1944, these battle-weary Canadians honoured their little adopted soldier with a special Army-style coat they ordered from a local seamstress. Sussie held on to that coat for decades, claiming it as the most special gift she had ever received and one she would never forget. Decades later, Bob and Sue reconnected, their relationship flourished, and Sue's little coat became a Canadian treasure.
ISBN 978-0-9810394-3-5 **Non-fiction $19.95**

Prairie Pilot: Lady Luck Was On My Side
The Stories of Walter D. Williams, Compiled and Edited by Deana J. Driver
This collection of 100 true short stories was written by the late Walter Williams, a 'character' and International Harvester dealer in Kerrobert, Saskatchewan, about his flying adventures in the 1950s. *Prairie Pilot* chronicles some of his most helpful and humourous experiences flying a small plane to transport pregnant women, injured children, RCMP, teachers, doctors, criminals and thrill-seekers to more than 75 communities in west central Saskatchewan and beyond. Ignoring bad weather and common sense, Williams tempted fate many times to help others.
ISBN 978-0-9810394-2-8 **Non-fiction $21.95**

DriverWorks Ink
110 McCarthy Blvd. N., Regina, Saskatchewan, Canada S4R 6A4
www.driverworks.ca (306) 545-5293

Other Saskatchewan and Prairie stories available
from DriverWorks Ink: